Turgut Demirel

Thermal Soil Mechanics

By the Same Author

The Frost Penetration Problem in Highway Engineering
Introduction to Soil Mechanics
Soil Mechanics
Mechanics of Soils: Fundamentals for Advanced Study
Active and Passive Earth Pressure Coefficient Tables
Stability Analyses of Soil-Foundation Systems (based on logarithmically-spiralled rupture curves): A Design Manual

THERMAL SOIL MECHANICS

ALFREDS R. JUMIKIS, Dr. Eng. Sc.
Professor of Civil Engineering
Rutgers—The State University
New Brunswick, New Jersey

RUTGERS UNIVERSITY PRESS
New Brunswick · · · New Jersey

Copyright © 1966 by Rutgers, The State University
Library of Congress Catalogue Card Number 66–18873

The cover design symbolizes the Greek letter phi (= ϕ), which is used in soil mechanics to designate the angle of internal friction of soil. The angle of internal friction ϕ is used in soil strength calculations. In the diagram the solid figure below the horizontal line (= ground surface) within the circle indicates the frost penetration depth in soil during a freezing season. The dots represent soil particles.

Scientia cum usu

Preface

The purpose of this book is to present some of the fundamental theories of freezing and thawing soil and the application of these theories to practical thermal problems as they pertain to highway, foundation, and soil engineering.

The subject as here presented is not exactly thermodynamics of soil. Rather, it is thermal soil mechanics, including, however, some aspects of thermodynamics, heat transfer, moisture migration in soil, strength properties of frozen soil, and some aspects of soil mechanics pertaining to the effects of temperature.

Despite the importance to highway, foundation, and soil engineering of problems resulting from freezing and thawing, systematically organized knowledge of this subject in the civilian sector is very meager. It is therefore the object of this book to point out some of these problems in soil and foundation engineering and to try to set down some of the principles underlying certain thermal calculations of heated (fired) and frozen soils as they apply to thermal stabilization of soil in earthworks and foundations.

Particularly stressed are the advantages of stabilizing water-logged soils by artificial freezing preparatory to digging a foundation or shaft. The present method of artificial freezing of soil for foundation engineering purposes has attained a considerable degree of success, and is beginning to be used more extensively. By means of artificial freezing of soil, relatively complex foundation operations can be carried out.

For the convenience of the reader, Chapter 2 presents a summary of the methods of heat transfer, and each problem is accompanied by a brief explanation of the theory involved and the derivation of some of the equations necessary for carrying out practical calculations.

A considerable part of this book is based on the author's lectures on thermal soil mechanics, a graduate course given to civil engineering students at Rutgers – The State University of New Jersey. Some of the text and some illustrations are from the author's published papers.

Acknowledgments

It is a pleasure to acknowledge the assistance received in the writing and preparation of this book. The author expresses his sincere thanks to Dr. E. C. Easton, Dean of the College of Engineering and Director of the Bureau of Engineering Research of Rutgers—The State University, and to Dr. M. L. Granstrom, Chairman of the Department of Civil Engineering, for their help and encouragement.

Dr. R. L. Handy, Professor of Civil Engineering at the Iowa State University of Science and Technology and Director of the Soil Mechanics Research Laboratory there, reviewed the manuscript and made constructive criticisms and many useful suggestions for which the author expresses his respectful appreciation.

The author is also most appreciative of the efficient library service at Rutgers University under the general directorship of Dr. D. F. Cameron, University Librarian, and of the good offices of Mr. H. G. Kelley, Head of the Reference Department, Mrs. Rose E. Czapp and Mr. Warren C. Sledd, Reference Librarians, and Mr. Francis A. Johns, University Bibliographer. Their efforts in procuring new books and many reference sources were valuable in permitting personal examination, checking, and verification of facts.

The author is also glad to acknowledge the following firms, institutions and companies which permitted him to use their material:

Rutgers University Press;
Highway Research Board, Washington, D.C.;
Wilhelm Ernst und Sohn, publishers, Berlin, Germany;
International Business Machines Corporation, New York City;
Reinhold Publishing Corporation, New York City;
Smithsonian Institution, Washington, D.C.;
Blaisdell Publishing Company, New York City; and
Longmans Green & Co., Ltd., London.

The author is also thankful to Mrs. Ruth Ahrens, who edited the first draft of the handwritten manuscript and examined the proofs.

The publication of this book was made possible by a very generous grant from Rutgers University Research Council for which the author expresses his respectful appreciation.

ALFREDS R. JUMIKIS

New Brunswick, New Jersey
June, 1966

Contents

Part IV VARIOUS TOPICS

Part I

The Subject

Chapter 1

Introduction

Frost generally brings about many engineering problems, some of which are described as follows.

1-1. Frost Action on Highways and Airfields. Certain climatic conditions can cause severe damage to highways and airfields not designed to withstand the effects of frost action in soil. By frost action in soil is understood its freezing and thawing. Freezing produces frost heaves, which lift up the surface layers of the soil or pavement. The heaves are caused by the growth of ice lenses between the soil particles.

Thawing produces frost boils. These are caused by softening of the soil and/or base course by saturation from free water when the frozen soil thaws. Thawing, in turn, reduces the bearing capacity, i.e., the shear strength of the soil. Highways are often more adversely affected by thawing than by heaving. These two associated phenomena create uncomfortable driving conditions and affect traffic safety, because every displacement of pavement changes the speed for which a new highway was designed, thus decreasing the safe rate of travel.

Frost action not only causes local heaving and breaks joints in concrete pavements, but also causes loss in load-carrying capacity because of subsequent softening of the soil and localized settlements. This in turn activates heavy damage to rigid and flexible pavements, as well as to unpaved roads. Figure 1-1 illustrates a blacktop road damaged by frost action and by vehicular loads.

In addition, frost dislocates and breaks highway drainage pipes and conduits, and it is responsible for uneven uplifts or differential heaves and settlements of many highway structures such as culverts, trestles, approaches, and bridges. Damage by frost is also associated with improper snow removal from roads and with improper drainage.

Frost troubles are not confined to roads and airfields. On February

FIG. 1-1 A blacktop road damaged by frost action and vehicular loads.

4, 1955, a passenger train derailed near Albany, New York. A news report said that the train, running at high speed, had ripped up 2000 feet of track when it struck a section of roadbed made uneven by frost action and subsequent thawing. A more common occurrence is the dislocation of rails and ties due to frost action.

1-2. Inadequacy of Sheeting and Bracing. A sheeted and braced excavation in winter is illustrated in Fig. 1-2. When the frozen soil thaws, the soil slumps out and the sheeting and bracing collapse.

1-3. Effect of Soil Freezing Upon an Earth-Retaining Structure. If the backfill behind an earth-retaining wall is a cohesive material, or a noncohesive material with no drainage provisions, i.e., with no "weep-holes" for drainage, then ice pressure may force the wall out of position or crack it.

1-4. Depth of Foundations, Frost Heave, and Damage to Superstructures. The base of a foundation footing must be below the frost penetration depth in order to avoid heaving and settlement of foundations during freezing and thawing periods, respectively, and subsequent damage to superstructures. This requirement is frequently made in building codes.

In foundation engineering, the significance of frost action in soil lies in the capacity of the freezing soil under certain conditions to lift foundations several inches above their original positions.

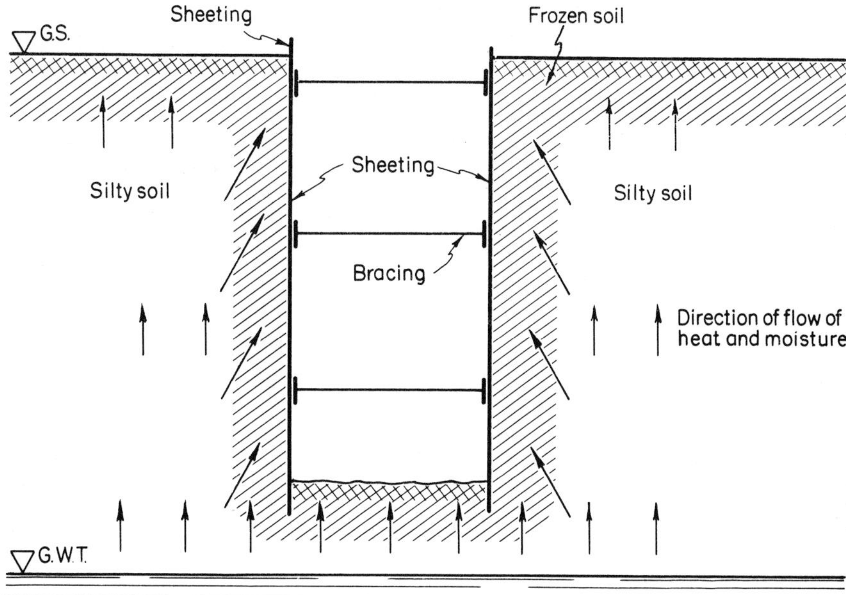

FIG. 1-2 Freezing of soil around a sheeted excavation. Upon thawing of the frozen soil, the soil slumps out and the sheeting and bracing collapse.

Wickoff,[(2)] in a discussion of Taber's article on ice pressure, cited the case of a brick wall weighing 2000 lb/ft² which was raised $\frac{3}{4}$ in. and another instance in which several piers, supporting columns and roof trusses, were raised $\frac{1}{2}$ to $2\frac{3}{4}$ in.

Frost action in soil may also bring about differential heaving of foundations, accompanied by the inducement of secondary stresses in the superstructure.

Figure 1-3c shows an overstressed wooden diagonal member of a framework of a cooling tower. The central part of the framework of the tower was lifted up, bringing about a displacement at the upper end of the diagonal and a permanent failure at the lower end of the diagonal. The lifting up of the diagonal could have been brought about by the upward displacement of the timber column which rests on the top surface of the slab. When frost action in soil underneath caused the slab to heave, the column was lifted up, which in its turn may have added to the upper end of the diagonal an additional force component perpendicular to the diagonal and possibly one axial tensile force component. As evidenced by Fig. 1-3, the split of the diagonal timber occurred tangentially to the bolt-hole, thus indicating the possibility of a bending moment.

Another effect of freezing is seen on piles driven into soil at the bottom of calm bodies of water. When ice forms, sheets of it adhere tenaciously to the piles, and when the water level rises, the ice sheet is lifted up and tends to pull out the piles.

Similarly, when cultivated land freezes, fragments of rock in the soil below are lifted up by frost action and may appear on the ground surface. This is explained by settling of the thawed, saturated soil around the rock fragments, the latter being supported by soil that is still frozen.

1-5. Damage to Structures from Ice and Frost. Frost may affect adversely the functioning of dam intakes, crests, grates, and gates. Ice may exert an undesirable pressure on water-impounding structures and intake gratings. Chellis [(3)] writes that Swedish observations have indicated that the magnitude of the ice pressure on a dam may approach 10,000 lb per linear foot. The ice pressure can be relieved by heating the intake gratings electrically. The rim of an ice sheet in contact with hydraulic structures may be cut loose along the structures to relieve the ice pressure on the structures.

Frost can interrupt the operation of hydroelectric power stations and break power transmission lines. Water supply may be interrupted by frozen pipelines. The cold weather bursting of water mains laid in soil within the frost penetration depth and at a certain frost intensity is another familiar occurrence.

(a)

FIG. 1-3 Damage to superstructure by frost action in soil. (a) Cooling tower. (b) Slab heave. (c) Structural damage.

(b)

(c)

Masonry and concrete are also liable to frost damage. Frost is also one of the disintegrating agents of rocks.

In tunnels, frost, depending upon its intensity and the size of the cross section and length of the tunnel, may penetrate into the ends of the tunnel up to about 3000 feet and thus, during the course of years, may change the temperature regimen of the soil or rock behind the tunnel walls. Tunnels can thus become leaky and icy.

Unfinished buildings should be closed up and adequately heated to prevent soil beneath the building from freezing and causing a floor placed directly on the soil from heaving.

Frozen soil is frequently used to advantage in foundation engineering. The hardness of the soil prevents shafts and foundation pits from caving in during excavation. The freezing can be brought about by cold weather or by artificial methods.

The storage of liquefied natural gas incurs some insulation problems: tanks must be constructed of carefully chosen material, and the ground into which they are sunk must be kept within certain temperature limits. The temperature of liquefied gas may be as low as −160°C.

1-6. Damage to Refrigerated Buildings and Cold-Storage Plants. The soil beneath refrigerated buildings and cold storage plants should be protected from frost penetration. The frost in the ground resulting from prolonged freezing temperatures in the structure above penetrates to a great depth over a prolonged period. This causes the soil moisture to migrate towards the frozen zone of the soil (underneath the structure), to freeze, heave, and crack the superimposed structure. A prolonged interruption of refrigeration, on the other hand, can thaw the soil and result in intolerable settlement of the structure.

1-7. Soil Sampling in Cold Weather. When soil is sampled at freezing temperatures, the tubes containing undisturbed soil samples should be stored and shipped to the laboratory insulated in such a manner that they do not become frozen. If the frozen samples thaw, they transform into a soupy mass of no value for testing.

1-8. Construction Operations in Winter. The significance of frost in construction operations is illustrated by the following example. A contracting company excavates at from 35°F to 45°F, producing a given amount of work per day per crew. As winter progresses and temperatures go below freezing, the amount of work performed per day per crew drops progressively. The lowered production indicates the progressive decrease in effectiveness of equipment in frozen ground.

1-9. Damage to Structures and Highways in Warm Climates. Damage to structures and highways can occur not only by the freezing and thawing of soils in cold climates, but also by changes in soil properties in regions where freezing temperatures almost never occur. The cause of damage here is attributable to swelling of certain types of clays. Swelling is caused by the accumulation and concentration of soil moisture in the upper layers by the natural process of thermo-osmosis. The damage to light structures can be pronounced, resulting in heaved floors and cracked walls. Soil moisture tends to move from unshaded places (warm regions, exposed to sun) to cool places (underneath structures and pavement slabs).

Chapter 2

Concepts and Definitions

The contents of this chapter are intended primarily as a guide to the various physical concepts in thermal soil mechanics in connection with heating, or firing, of soil and frost action in soil. It is hoped that this chapter may help also to consolidate the information pertaining to thermal soil mechanics and present the subject as a scientific and technological discipline. As the amount of theoretical and experimental data pertaining to frost action in soils accumulates, the need for generalization and consolidation increases, and a review here is appropriate. Such a review will be made by providing definitions and presenting a brief description of some of the fundamental concepts pertaining to the freezing soil system. It may be assumed that, although picturing an ideal condition, the generalization will differ but little from existing conditions.

2-1. Some Physical Concepts

i) *Density.* Density ρ of a substance is defined as its mass m per unit volume:

$$\rho = \frac{m}{V} \qquad (m/L^3), \tag{2-1}$$

where V = volume and
L = linear dimension, or length.

ii) *Mass.* Mass is the absolute quantity of matter in a body and is calculated as

$$m = W/g \qquad (FT^2/L), \tag{2-2}$$

where m = mass,
g = acceleration of gravity, in L/T^2,
W = weight of body,
F = force, and
T = time.

iii) *Specific Gravity.* Specific gravity G is the dimensionless ratio of the specific weight (or density) of the substance to the specific weight (or density) of pure water at 4°C. At this standard temperature, the specific gravity of water is 1.00000.

iv) *Specific Volume.* Specific volume v is volume per unit mass of the substance:

$$v = \frac{V}{m} = \frac{1}{\rho} \qquad \left(\frac{L^3}{W/g}\right). \tag{2-3}$$

v) *Specific Weight, or Unit Weight.* Unit weight is the weight of the substance per unit volume:

$$\gamma = W/V = \rho g \qquad (F/L^3), \tag{2-4}$$

where γ = unit weight.

vi) *Weight.* The weight W of a body is the total gravitational force, or earth pull, acting on the body.

2-2. Force, Work, Energy, and System

i) *Driving Force.* By driving force is here understood a source of motion. Whenever and wherever there exists a difference of temperature, motive power can be produced.

ii) *Electrokinetics.* Electrokinetics is the discipline which treats the laws of distribution of electric current.

iii) *Electro-osmosis.* Electro-osmosis is the phenomenon of moisture migration through a porous system such as soil, brought about by an electric potential.

iv) *Energy.* Energy is the capacity of a body to perform work. Because the work done is a measure of the energy expended, both energy and work are measured in terms of the same unit, such as the erg.

v) *Field.* The gradient of the potential along its path is called its field.

vi) *Force.* The cause of the acceleration of the movement of material bodies is termed force.

vii) *Gradient.* Gradient is the rate of increase or decrease of a variable quantity, such as temperature.

viii) *Heat.* Heat is a form of energy and cannot of itself pass from a lower to a higher potential, nor from a colder to a hotter system.

ix) *Potential.* Potential is the energy necessary to transfer the unit mass of soil moisture through a porous medium from a given position in reference to another particular point within the system.

"Potential" is used in several other senses in engineering. For example, in physics and engineering this term, commonly used as an adjective, means "available." One speaks of potential energy or energy of state or position. In contradistinction, in soil science dealing with moisture migration in soil, and in thermal soil mechanics dealing with frost action in soils, "potential" is traditionally used as a noun—for example, thermal potential, capillary potential, electric potential, concentration potentials (solvent, density, moisture potentials), and gravity potentials. In this sense, the potential at a point or the potential difference between two points of a freezing soil system would have the meaning given in the definition—the energy necessary to transfer soil moisture through the soil, as from the groundwater table to the downward penetrating cold front, or to any other coordinate point within the system. The potential is the energy or driving pressure for the moisture movement in soil; it must therefore be capable of being expressed by a function from which the intensity of the driving pressure and/or the velocity and amount of the upward-migrating soil moisture passing a horizontal cross section of a system at any point can be mathematically described and calculated.

Energy potential is a simple concept and easily applied in studying freezing soil systems.

Classification of Potentials. For convenience and simplicity, the various potentials that can occur under varying conditions in a freezing soil system are classified here into two broad groups [4,5]

1. Primary potentials.
2. Secondary, or induced, potentials.

A *primary potential* is one applied to the system externally. For instance, a primary potential may be a thermal potential (heat energy, causing in soil the phenomenon known as thermo-osmosis), an electrical potential (causing in the soil the phenomenon of electro-osmosis), and a gravity potential (important in permeability problems where water permeates through a porous soil medium by gravity).

A *secondary potential* is one which is induced within the soil by an externally applied primary potential. Any primary potential can cause one or several secondary potentials, which are new processes or mechanisms for the translocation of soil moisture, such as new heat potential, electric potentials, and concentration potentials (moisture, soluble salts). For example, a primary thermal potential may bring about a change in soil moisture densities, which in turn may induce hydrodynamic pressure differences. Or a concentration gradient may cause an energy flow, which in turn causes a temperature difference. Thermal potentials in a freezing soil system induce electric (galvanic) potentials. The magnitude of the induced electromotive force depends largely upon the strength of the concentration of the electrolyte (i.e., soil moisture containing soluble salts) in the soil. Induced electromotive forces in freezing soil systems may contribute to moisture flow in the same direction as the flow caused by a primary potential, or they may act in the opposite direction, depending upon the properties of the porous material and other factors still not clearly understood.[6]

Potential difference (driving force) is measured by the work done.

x) *Process.* A process is here defined as any event in nature or in a soil freezing experiment in which a redistribution or transformation of energy (heat) and moisture takes place. The processes of moisture and heat flow within a freezing soil system are the essence of soil mechanics, fluid mechanics, heat transfer, and thermodynamics. This implies the complexity of the freezing processes in soil. However, one important factor must be kept in mind in the study of the processes of moisture translocation: in order to transfer or transport moisture within the soil system, or to cause the flow of moisture, there must be a driving pressure, or more generally, a potential difference between these two points, such as the entrance and exit of the system.

xi) *Property.* A property is any observable characteristic of a system (e.g., pressure, temperature, volume, and dynamic viscosity), or any combination of observable characteristics (e.g., the product of pressure and temperature).

xii) *Streaming Potential.* Streaming potential may be classed as a secondary potential induced by a primary potential, such as a heat potential. It is the cation flow in a porous system in the direction of the temperature drop in the system. Streaming potential is the converse of electro-osmosis.

xiii) *Surface Tension.* Surface tension may be defined as that property, resulting from molecular (tangential) forces, by which the surface film of all liquids, including water, tends to take a form having the least superficial area.

xiv) *System and Surroundings.* A *system* is a part of external reality. The material with which a system is in contact forms the surroundings of the system. The soil system which we subject to freezing for technical and study purposes is a separated, free, finite part of matter (free body), such as a soil sample separated from its surroundings by its insulated container. Thus, the system is clearly defined by spatial boundaries (Fig. 2-1). It is possible to study changes in the state of matter (for instance, water) in the system and the transfer of energy and mass (for example, heat and water, respectively) upon freezing.

A *homogeneous system* is one in which the properties of its components are either uniform or vary uniformly throughout the system.

A *heterogeneous system* consists of two or more homogeneous systems.

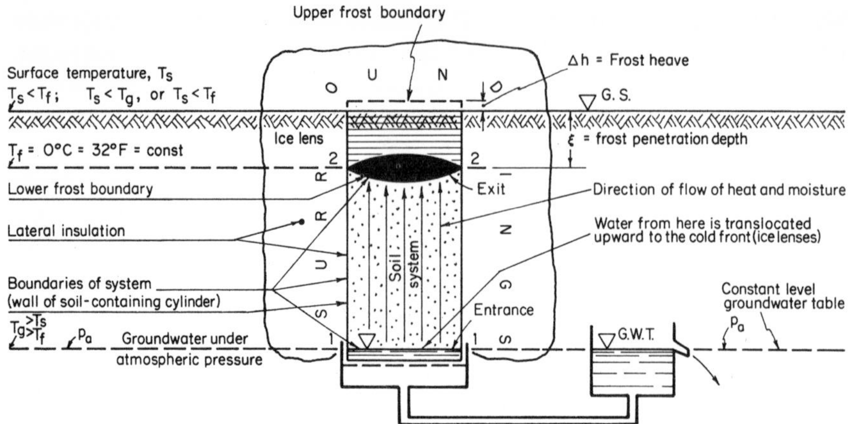

FIG. 2-1 System, boundaries, and surroundings.

An *open system* is one which can exchange matter as well as heat and energy and work with its surroundings.

A *closed system* is one which cannot exchange matter, but can exchange heat, energy and work.

An *open soil system* is one in which free water in excess of that contained before freezing in the voids of the soil is available to be a source of translocated water (groundwater, for example) to the cold front. A closed system, on the other hand, is one in which no source of free water above the soil moisture content before freezing is available during the freezing process.

A special case of a closed system is an *isolated system,* a system which in no way interacts with its surroundings.

Unlike the conditions in a soil freezing experiment in which the samples are insulated laterally, conditions in nature do not have absolute boundaries. All uncontrolled systems "diffuse" more or less with their surroundings. Because no boundary in nature is absolute, a system cannot be isolated and insulated completely. Hence, open systems transferring some heat energy laterally are more or less "incomplete."

xv) *Thermo-osmosis* is the process of moisture migration, i.e., translocation through a porous system (such as soil) brought about by a thermal potential, i.e., temperature gradient.

xvi) *Work.* Work is energy in transition, an interaction between a system (or two systems) and its surroundings by virtue of a force acting through a distance at the system's boundary. Work is done by a system on its surroundings—if, for instance, the sole external effect of the interaction could be the lifting of a body. The magnitude of work is the product of the weight of the body lifted and the distance it could be lifted if the lifting of the body were the sole external effect of the interaction.

2-3. Temperature. Temperature is the measure of the intensity of heat energy. The temperature of a body may be defined as the property or parameter of its thermal state from the viewpoint of its ability to transfer heat to other bodies. When two bodies are placed in thermal communication, the one which loses heat to the other is said to be at the higher temperature.

Equality of temperature is a condition for thermal equilibrium between two systems or between two parts of a single system.

Temperature Scales. By convention, temperature scales are based on the melting point of ice and the boiling point of water at a standard pressure of 1 atmosphere.

The Centigrade Scale. The centigrade scale, introduced by Celsius in Sweden and known as the Celsius scale, has the two fixed points divided into one hundred divisions. Each division is called a *degree.* The melting point of pure ice is assigned the value of 0°C. The boiling point of water in the centigrade system is at 100°C.

Fahrenheit Scale. On the Fahrenheit scale, at standard atmospheric pressure of 760 millimeters of mercury, the melting point of ice is 32°F above the zero of its scale, and the boiling of water is 212°F above zero. Fahrenheit's reasons for calling the two points 32°F and 212°F on his scale, however, have never been clearly explained.

Conversion of Temperature Readings. To convert a temperature reading from the Fahrenheit to the centigrade scale, subtract 32 from the Fahrenheit reading and multiply the result by $\frac{5}{9}$:

$$C = (\tfrac{5}{9})(F - 32). \qquad (2\text{-}5)$$

To convert from degrees centigrade to degrees Fahrenheit, multiply the centigrade reading by 1.8 and add 32:

$$F = (1.8)C + 32. \qquad (2\text{-}6)$$

Also,

$$1C = (1.8)F. \qquad (2\text{-}7)$$

The relationship between the centigrade and Fahrenheit scales is shown graphically in Fig. 2-2.

2-4. Heat. Heat is a form of energy transferred by a thermal process. Heat is energy in transition between a system (or between two systems) and its surroundings and it is caused by a difference in temperature between the system and its surroundings. Consequently, heat can be added to a body or taken away from it. Cold cannot. Cold, it

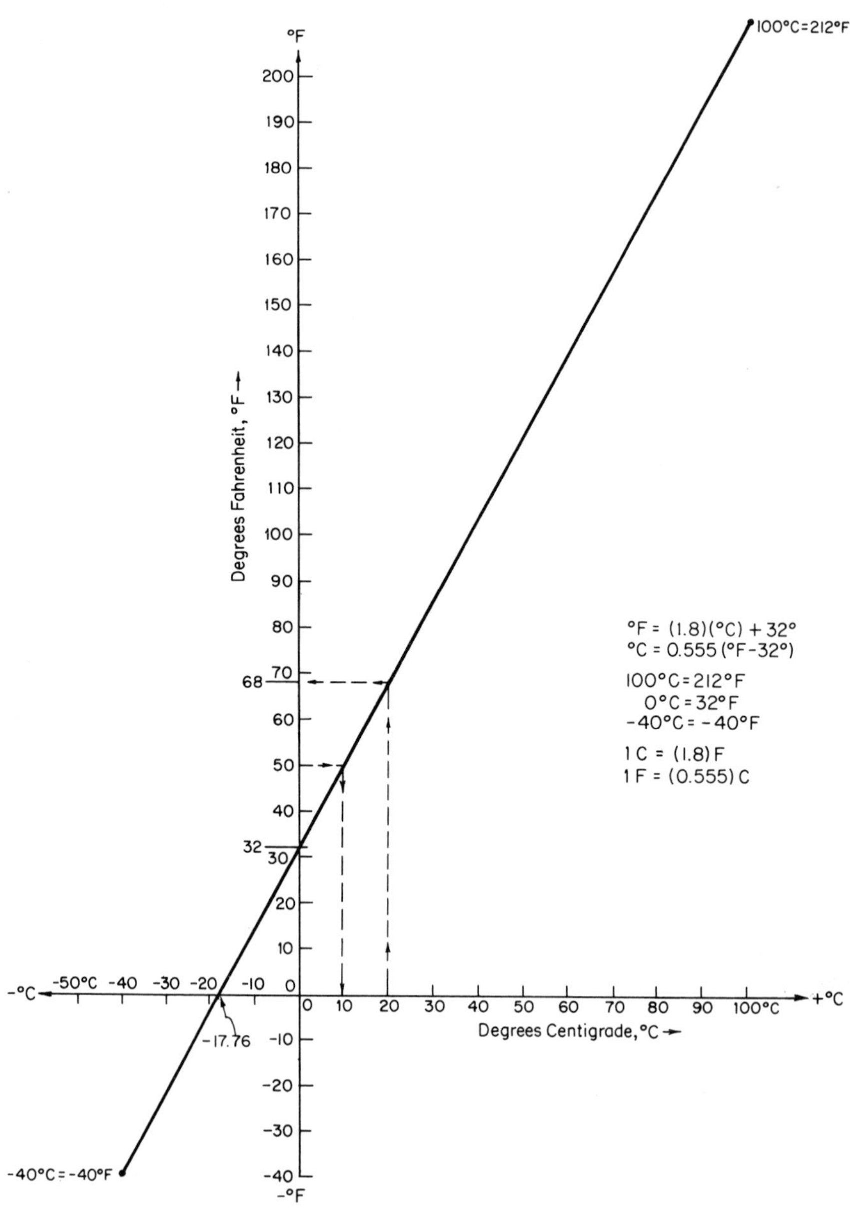

FIG. 2-2 Relationship between centigrade and Fahrenheit temperature scales.

may be said, is the absence of heat. A body becomes colder only because it loses heat. A body becomes warmer only because it gains heat (i.e., its temperature rises).

Heat cannot be measured directly or as simply as some of the other quantities in the physical world such as length, mass, or time. Like mechanical energy, heat is intangible, and a unit of heat cannot be preserved in a standards laboratory. A quantity of heat can be measured by the effect it produces.

One of the striking characteristics of heat is its tendency to move. It is continuously moving from points of higher temperature to points of lower temperature.

Heat can be measured in terms of dynamic units of energy, such as the erg and joule, or in terms of the amount of energy required to produce a definite thermal change in some substance, or a system.

Three heat units are in common use:

> the gram-calorie (g-cal, or simply *cal*),
> the kilogram-calorie (*Cal*), and
> the British thermal unit, designated by BTU, or

btu, or simply B. Henceforth the British thermal unit will be designated by the symbol B, as recommended in "American Standard Abbreviations for Scientific and Engineering Terms" (American Society of Mechanical Engineers, Sectional Committee on Letter Symbols and Abbreviations for Science and Engineering, 1941).

One gram-calorie is the quantity of heat which must be supplied to one gram of water to raise its temperature through one degree centigrade. One kilocalorie = 1000 gram-calories.

One British thermal unit is the quantity of heat which must be supplied to one pound of water to raise its temperature through one Fahrenheit degree.

Because 454 g = 1 lb, and $1°F = \frac{5}{9}°C$, the British thermal unit may be defined as the quantity of heat which must be supplied to 454 g (0.454 kg) of water to raise its temperature through $(\frac{5}{9})°C$, which is $454 \times \frac{5}{9} = 252$ g-cal or 0.252 kg-cal. Hence, 1 B = 252 g-cal.

Mechanical equivalents of heat:

$$778 \text{ ft-lb} = 1 \text{ B} = 107.5 \text{ kg-m}$$
$$4.186 \text{ joules} = 1 \text{ g-cal}$$
$$4186 \text{ joules} = 1 \text{ kg-cal.}$$

2-5. Isotherm. The word "isotherm" can be defined as a line connecting all points (in soil, for example) at the same temperature. An isothermal surface is one that has the same temperature over its area.

2-6. Thermal Properties. Determination of the depth and rate of freezing penetration or the depth and rate of thaw of frozen soils requires knowledge of the thermal properties of water and soils, properties which influence freezing and thawing. These are

- the latent heat of fusion of soil moisture, designated by the symbol L;
- heat capacity of water in soil, c_v or c_m (volumetric and mass heat capacity, respectively), and
- thermal conductivity K.

Other related properties important to thermal calculations are

- specific heat, c_{sp}, and
- thermal diffusivity, α.

2-7. Latent Heat of Fusion. The quantity called latent heat of fusion of soil moisture, L, is of critical importance in thermal calculations relative to frost penetration depth and thawing problems in soils, as well as in treating icing problems on pavements and the heating and firing of soils.

Latent heat depends upon the percentage of soil water that actually freezes. Unfortunately, in the case of fine-particled soils, there exists a considerable uncertainty as to the exact quantity of soil water frozen at any given "sub-freezing" temperature.

When an amount of water is cooled, it means, physically, that heat is removed from it. When heat is removed, the temperature of water decreases by one degree centigrade for every calorie removed per gram of water, down to 0°C (at atmospheric pressure). At this temperature of 0°C, theoretically, the removal of heat causes a transformation in the phase of the water, namely, from a liquid to a solid (= ice). The amount of heat energy required to make this change with no temperature change (= isothermally) is 79.7 small, or gram, calories per gram of water at 0°C, or approximately 80 cal/g, and is termed the *latent heat of fusion, L* (cal/g).

In the British system of units, the conversion of one pound of ice to water at 32°F requires $L = 144$ B. Thus, 80 (cal/g) = 144 (B/lb). Note that the magnitude of latent heat of fusion in the British system of units is $\frac{9}{5}$ of the corresponding value (80) in the metric system. This heat energy is necessary to tear down the structure of the ice.

The principle to remember is that before ice melts, latent heat of $L = 80$ cal/g first has to dissipate. When the ice melts, it absorbs heat from the air in contact with it.

The latent heat of fusion contributes to the chilling effect of large quantities of melting snow and ice on the temperature of the surrounding air and soil. The same amount of heat must be added to ice to transform it to water without a change in temperature.

It is significant that ice has a relatively large value of latent heat of fusion as compared with other common substances.

If the unit weight of dry soil is γ_s g/cm³, and contains, in addition to the soil content, $w\%$ of water by dry weight, then the amount of latent heat of fusion of water in this case is calculated in the metric system as

$$L = (\gamma_s)(w/100)(80) \qquad \left[(\text{g/cm}^3)\left(\frac{\text{g-cal}}{\text{g}}\right) = \left(\frac{\text{g-cal}}{\text{cm}^3}\right)\right], \tag{2-8}$$

or in the British system of units as

$$L = (\gamma_s)(w/100)(144) \qquad [(\text{lb/ft}^3)(\text{B/lb}) = (\text{B/ft}^3)]. \tag{2-9}$$

2-8. Heat Capacity. Among the important thermal properties of water is its heat capacity. Heat, or thermal capacity c_m of a substance, is the actual amount of heat energy Q necessary to change the temperature of a unit mass, say 1 gram, of the substance by one degree:

$$c_m = Q/\Delta T, \tag{2-10}$$

where Q = the capacity of heat absorbed by a substance corresponding to the rise in temperature by $T_1 - T_0 = \Delta T$;
T_0 = initial temperature, and
T_1 = final temperature ($T_1 > T_0$).

The units of heat capacity depend upon whether a unit mass or a unit volume of substance is used in thermal calculations.

Mass Heat Capacity. The units of heat capacity c_m for the mass m of a substance are

$$\frac{\text{cal}}{(\text{mass-gram})(°\text{C})}.$$

The mass heat capacity of water is relatively very high and serves as a unit of comparison with other substances. It is set equal to unity, i.e., the c_m for water is 1.000 (cal)/(g)(°C) = 1.000 (B)/(lb)(F).

The numerical values of mass heat capacity in the British system of units are the same as those in the metric system, namely:

$$1\ \text{cal/(g)(°C)} = 1\ \text{(B)/(lb)(°F)}.$$

Volumetric Heat Capacity. In heat transfer problems in soil engineering—e.g., in analyzing thermal conditions in highway and airfield runway soils and pavements—the concept of volumetric heat capacity is very useful. The volumetric heat capacity c_v of a substance —e.g., frozen soil—is defined as the amount of heat necessary to change the temperature of a unit volume of the substance by one degree. With soils, a unit of calories per cubic centimeter per degree centigrade is generally used:

$$\frac{\text{cal}}{(\text{cm}^3)(^\circ\text{C})}.$$

Between the heat capacity by mass c_m and by volume c_v the following relationship exists:

$$c_v = c_m \cdot \gamma \frac{(\text{cal})(\text{gram})}{(\text{gram})(\text{C})(\text{cm}^3)} = \frac{\text{cal}}{(\text{cm}^3)(\text{C})}, \tag{2-11}$$

where γ = unit weight of the material in g/cm³.

Thus, the volumetric heat capacity may be expressed as the product of the gravimetric heat capacity and the density of the material.

The volumetric heat capacity of a soil depends principally upon its unit weight, its moisture content, and its temperature (whether the soil is frozen or unfrozen).

The relationships between the volumetric heat capacity and density for various soil moisture contents are as follows:

1. for unfrozen soil:

$$c_{vu} = \gamma_s \left[c_{ms} + \frac{(c_{mw})(w)}{100} \right]; \tag{2-12}$$

2. for frozen soil:

$$c_{vf} = \gamma_s \left[c_{ms} + \frac{(c_{mi})(w)}{100} \right], \tag{2-13}$$

where γ_s = dry unit weight of soil,
c_{ms} = mass heat capacity of dry soil,
c_{mw} = mass heat capacity of water,
w = moisture content of soil by dry weight, and
c_{mi} = mass heat capacity of ice.

With $c_{ms} = 0.20$ B/(lb)(F) for dry soil (soil mineral matter),
$c_{mw} = 1.00$ B/(lb)(F) for water, and
$c_{mi} = 0.50$ B/(lb)(F) for ice,

the volumetric heat capacity c_v for unfrozen (u) and frozen (f) soils for the above conditions may be written as

$$c_{vu} = \gamma_s \left[0.20 + \frac{(1.00)(w)}{100} \right], \tag{2-14}$$

and

$$c_{vf} = \gamma_s \left[0.20 + \frac{(0.50)(w)}{100} \right]. \tag{2-15}$$

2-9. Specific Heat. When two different substances of equal mass absorb equal quantities of heat energy, then the increase in temperature of one of the two substances is not necessarily the same as that of the other. The difference of temperature of the two substances is attributed to the different molecular structures, which require varying quantities of heat to increase their temperature by one degree centigrade or Fahrenheit.

The ratio of the amount of heat necessary to change the temperature of a unit of mass of a substance by one degree to the amount of heat necessary to raise a unit of mass of water through the same change in temperature is defined as the specific heat c_{sp} of a substance; or, in other words, the specific heat of a substance is the ratio of the heat capacity of a substance to the heat capacity of water.

The specific heat of a substance is *dimensionless*, being just a ratio. The specific heat of water is 1.000. Numerically, specific heat is the same as the heat capacity of the substance because the numerical value of heat capacity of water is unity.

Sometimes specific heat c_{sp} is stated as the quantity of heat necessary to bring about a unit change in temperature in a unit mass of the substance with the units of cal/(g)(°C). The confusion as to terms is unfortunate. Because of the dimensional logic, the term "specific heat" should be understood as a dimensionless ratio, but the term "heat capacity" should be used with the units of cal/(g)(°C) or cal/(cm^3)(°C), whichever the case.

The values of specific heats, c_{sp}, of water at various temperatures are compiled from the Smithsonian Physical Tables [7] in Table 2-1.

The variation of the specific heat of water with temperature is illustrated in Fig. 2-3. The specific heat of water has a minimum at 37.5°C of $c_{sp} = 0.99865$.

The numerical values of the heat capacity of water, as well as of other substances, are the same as those for specific heats; the units of heat capacity corresponding to the numerical values of specific heat are those of cal/(g)(°C).

The numerical values of specific heat of various substances other than water are listed in the Appendix of this book.

Table 2-1
Specific Heat of Water[7]

Temperature (°C)	Values (c_{sp})	Temperature (°C)	Values (c_{sp})
0	1.0080	29	0.9987
5	1.0043	30	0.9987
10	1.0019	35	0.9987
15	1.0004	40	0.9987
16	1.0002	45	0.9989
17	1.0000	50	0.9992
18	0.9998	55	0.9996
19	0.9996	60	1.0001
20	0.9995	65	1.0006
21	0.9993	70	1.0013
22	0.9992	75	1.0021
23	0.9991	80	1.0029
24	0.9990	85	1.0039
25	0.9989	90	1.0050
26	0.9989	95	1.0063
27	0.9988	100	1.0076
28	0.9987	120	1.0162

2-10. Thermal Conductivity. Thermal conductivity K is the quantity of heat Q which flows normally across a surface of unit area per unit of time and per unit of temperature gradient normal to the surface. It is usually expressed in calories transmitted per second through one square centimeter of material (soil, for example) one centimeter thick per degree centigrade between the two surfaces, or in British thermal units (B) per hour through one square foot of material one foot (sometimes one inch) thick per degree Fahrenheit between the two surfaces. For coefficients of thermal conductivity of various substances and materials see the Appendix.

Heat conduction of the solid phase of soil varies from about 0.001 to about 0.006 cal/(cm)(sec)(°C). The coefficient of heat conduction of water is about 0.00124, and that of air is only 0.00005 cal/(cm)(sec)(°C). Therefore soil moisture content appears to have a great influence upon the thermal conductivity of soil.

2-11. Thermal Diffusivity. Thermal diffusivity (in the German technical literature known as the temperature conductivity) is an index of the facility with which a material will undergo temperature change, and is expressed as the quotient of thermal conductivity K and the volumetric heat capacity, $c_v = c_m \cdot \gamma$, i.e.,

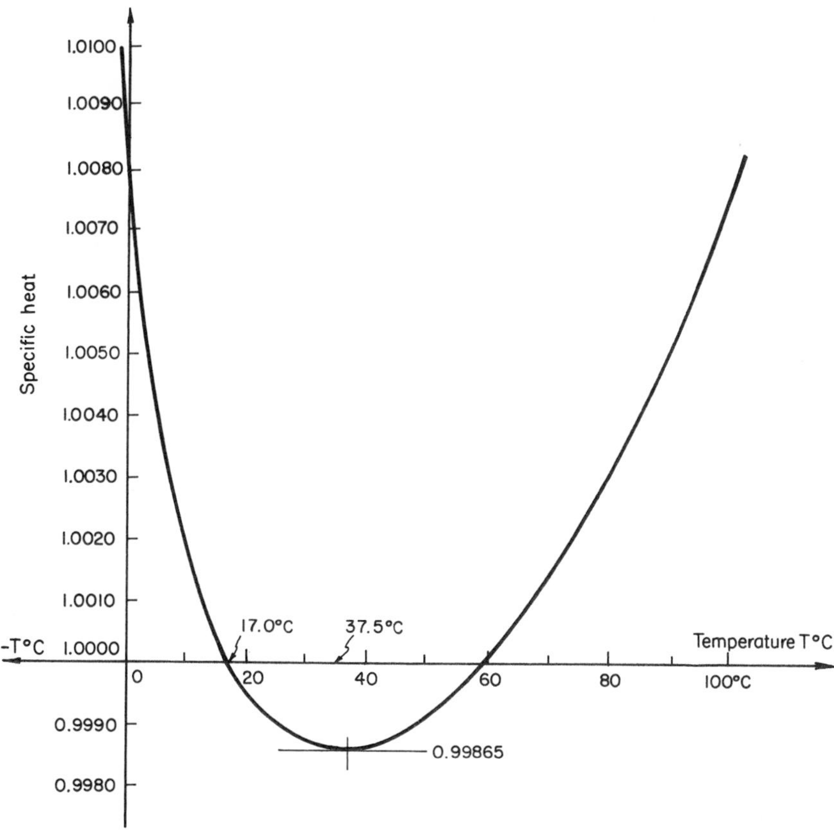

FIG. 2-3 Specific heat of water as a function of temperature.

$$\alpha = K/(c_m\gamma) \qquad (\text{cm}^2)/(\text{sec}), \tag{2-16}$$

where α = coefficient of thermal diffusivity (in cm^2/sec, m^2/hr, or ft^2/hr, depending upon the system of units used),

ρ = density of material (g/cm^3 or lb/ft^3).

SOME PROPERTIES OF ICE AND WATER

A knowledge of ice properties is essential for understanding the freezing process in soil. Let us now, therefore, apply ourselves to some definitions, basic concepts, and descriptions pertaining to some of the properties of ice.

2-12. State and Phase. According to thermodynamic concepts, the expression "change of state" of a matter is a broad one and denotes a change of pressure, temperature, or volume.

A phase is any homogeneous part of a soil system different from other parts of the system and separated from these by *abrupt* transition. Thus we distinguish a gaseous and a liquid phase in a colloid. We obtain a solid and liquid phase when we shake up quartz dust in water.

The expression "change in phase" denotes a more fundamental change than change in state. Ordinarily, a substance has at least three phases: liquid, solid and gaseous. Water, for example, may be in a liquid, solid or gaseous phase. Here by phase is understood the state of aggregation. When water freezes, it changes from its liquid phase into its solid phase. When water evaporates, it changes from its liquid phase into its vapor phase. The possible number of states for matter is infinite. The number of phases, however, is few.

2-13. Some Anomalies of Water. Water is noted for several anomalies it displays in its physical properties. It has a high value of specific heat, of latent heat of fusion, and heat of vaporization. One such property is its increase by 1/11, or 9%, in volume upon freezing. The density of water at +4°C is approximately 1.000, but the density of ice at 0°C is 0.917. Now, upon freezing, 1 unit of volume of water increases in volume by $(1/0.917 - 1/1.000) \approx 0.09$, or by 9%.

The expansion of ice is due to its rather loosely packed hexagonal crystal structure, which relates to the directed nature of the hydrogen bonding between water molecules. Because of this increase in volume, ice crystals in soil form thin, horizontal ice lenses and tend to push the soil particles apart (provided there is enough groundwater to fill all of the voids in the soil).

The forces exerted by freezing water are very large, as evidenced from the bursting of the strongest water pipes in freezing periods. The expansion of freezing water in the joints, crevices and cracks of rocks and masonry breaks off small and large fragments from them, thus wearing them down. Also, pressure lowers the freezing point of water.

2-14. Freezing Point. The freezing point of a liquid is the temperature at which it solidifies. The theoretical freezing point of water at normal atmospheric pressure is $T_f = 0°C = 32°F$, when water transforms into ice. This is the *normal freezing point.*

2-15. Melting Point. The melting point is the temperature at which a solid substance begins to melt and change to liquid. The melting point of ice under standard pressure of one atmosphere is $T_m = 0°C = 32°F$. Thus, the freezing point or melting point, T_m, is the temperature at which the liquid and solid are in equilibrium with one another, i.e., at a higher temperature the solid will gradually melt and at a lower temperature the liquid will solidify. Crystalline substances have definite melting points. Amorphous substances do not have any definite melting points.

2-16. Freezing Laws. The laws of freezing for ordinary water may be summarized as follows:

1. Under standard temperature conditions of 1 atmosphere a pure, normal ice has definite freezing and melting temperatures.
2. The melting point of ice is the same as the normal freezing point of water. However, under special conditions water may be undercooled, or, as some say, supercooled, or subcooled.
3. A unit of mass of ice requires at its melting point a definite amount of thermal energy or heat to transform it into the liquid state in the form of water. Upon freezing, water releases the same quantity of heat as does ice upon melting. This definite amount of heat is termed the latent heat of fusion of ice (water).
4. Upon freezing, water undergoes a change in volume: it expands.
5. The freezing point of water changes with pressure.

2-17. Undercooling. Undercooling of water is the formation of a metastable condition when water is cooled below its normal freezing point, i.e., below the temperature at which its state of aggregation normally changes without a change of phase occurring (without solidification). It is a transient condition in the process of formation of the solid phase (= ice) of water. The formation of ice crystals depends upon the existence of nuclei in the water as distinct starting points from which crystallization of ice can start. Pure water ordinarily can be undercooled to about −22°C or lower without crystallizing into ice. When it is disturbed, as by a shock, or by dropping into the undercooled water a small fragment of ice or any other object on which ice crystals can be formed, the change of phase takes place, i.e., the undercooled water solidifies almost instantaneously. With this change of phase, heat is evolved and the temperature in the system rises to the normal freezing temperature.

2-18. Sublimation of Ice. The direct evaporation of snow and ice at temperatures below their freezing points directly from the solid phase into the gaseous phase without going through the liquid phase is termed *sublimation.* Much of the snow on the ground in the winter sublimes rather than melts. The same phenomenon is also observed in the evaporation of dry ice, frozen carbon dioxide, which evaporates without melting at atmospheric pressure, even at temperatures far below its melting point (which is $T_m = -55.65°C$ at 5.1 atm).

2-19. Various Types of Ice. Experiments have shown that at high pressures there exist several crystal forms of ice.[8] According to Bernatzik[9] at least ten types of ice are known, five of which are in a stable form, with differing properties. Some of them, unlike common ice, decrease in volume upon freezing. Such ices can form under special pressure conditions, for example, at about 2200 atmospheres.

"Ice I" (*Density:* 0.88–0.92 g/cm^3, 54.8–57.3 lb/ft^3). Ice I (α-ice) crystallizes into the hexagonal crystals system. The ice crystal is formed so that its principal axis is oriented perpendicularly to the cooling surface, or parallel to the direction of flow of heat. Thus the growth of an ice sheet takes place principally in the direction of heat loss. Ice I has a vitreous luster. In large masses pure ice appears light green to blue in color. The blue color is attributed to the scattering of light by the ice molecules. When water is supercooled a few degrees, ice I crystallizes into a rhombohedral system (β-ice).[10]

2-20. Volume Change of Ice. Most substances expand when they change from the solid phase to the liquid phase and contract upon freezing. However, ice expands during freezing. The course of volume changes upon melting is shown graphically in Figs. 2-4a and 2-4b, where T_m is the melting point. Note the oppositely directed abrupt changes in volume at the melting points of the various substances and water.

It is significant that ice has a relatively great value of latent heat of fusion as compared with other common substances.

The transformation of liquid to solid, vapor to solid, and vapor to liquid involves release of heat. Conversely, the transformation of solid to liquid, solid to vapor and liquid to vapor involves absorption of

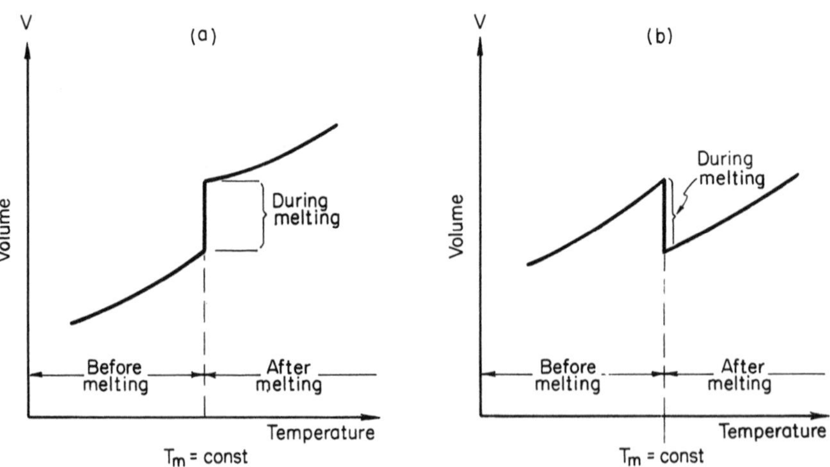

FIG. 2-4 Volume changes upon melting. (a) Course of volume change of the more usual substances before, during, and after melting. (b) Course of volume change of water before, during, and after melting.

heat. In the transformation from solid to liquid, the absorbed heat is termed the latent heat of fusion, i.e.,

solid → liquid (melting)—latent heat of fusion,
solid → vapor (sublimation)—latent heat of sublimation,
liquid → vapor (boiling)—latent heat of vaporization.

The values of the aforementioned three kinds of latent heats for a water system are:

fusion: $L = 80$ cal/g,
sublimation: $L = 137.9$ cal/g (at 1 atm pressure for dry ice),
vaporization: $L = 540$ cal/g (970 B/lb).

2-21. Cooling Curves. When a constant amount of pure water is subjected to a gradual cooling-freezing process, so that heat is abstracted at a constant rate, and when the temperature T of water during this process is measured over certain time intervals, then the cooling-freezing process can be represented graphically as in Fig. 2-5. The arrows on the graph indicate the course of the process under discussion.

Figure 2-5 pertains to freezing without undercooling of the water, and Fig. 2-6 pertains to undercooled water. The temperature is plotted against time. Point 1 in Fig. 2-5 corresponds to the start of cooling

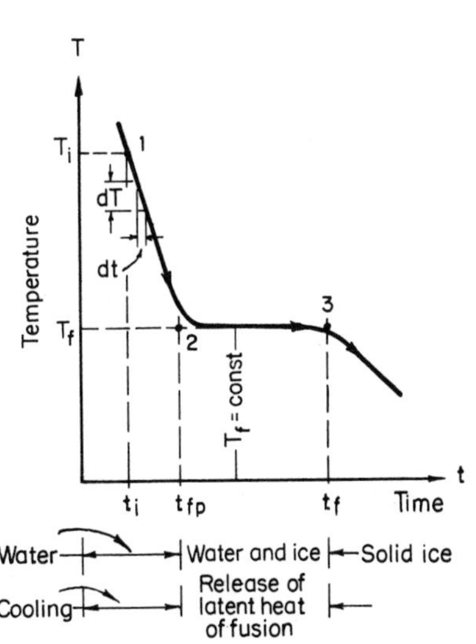

FIG. 2-5 Cooling-freezing curve of pure water when not undercooled.

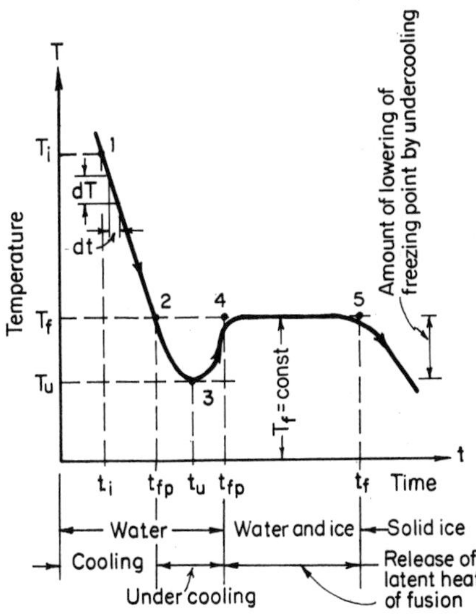

FIG. 2-6 Cooling-freezing curve of undercooled pure water.

at time t_i. Cooling continues till time t_{fp} at point 2. Part 1-2 of the curve indicates cooling where temperature is gradually lowered. The rate at which the temperature is gradually falling is characterized by the slope of the cooling curve.

At point 2 (and time t_{fp}), there is a break in the curve. Here the cooling of water has stopped. Because, practically, the temperature of the entire mass of ice is not quite uniform, and because it is physically difficult to keep a small quantity of liquid in thermal equilibrium with the forming ice and the apparatus used in performing the cooling experiment, there is a slight rounding between the end of the cooling curve and the horizontal part 2-3 of the curve. Thus during the cooling time, $t_c = t_{fp} - t_i$, the temperature of the water dropped from T_i (before cooling) to T_f (freezing point) at a rate of

$$\frac{dT}{dt} = -\frac{T}{t} = -\frac{T_i - T_f}{t_{fp} - t_i} \qquad \text{(degrees/sec)}.$$

The minus sign is a geometric requirement because the tangent (= slope of 1-2) is here in the second and fourth quarters, where it is negative.

Point 2, at time t_{fp} and temperature T_f, is the beginning of the process of solidification, i.e., ice crystals begin to form. Here t_{fp} means time at freezing point, and T_f = temperature of freezing point of water. If the cooling system is well insulated, then the temperature will remain constant, as shown by the horizontal part 2-3 of the curve, until all water has changed to ice. This part, from time t_{fp} to time t_f, indicates that upon solidification latent heat of fusion of ice is set free or released. As seen from the graph, the length of the solidification time is $t_{sol} = t_f - f_{fp}$. During this time the release of latent heat of fusion arrests the drop of temperature.

The horizontal part 2-3 of the curve continues until all latent heat is released (or, as long as any water is left) and a new phase of water appears. This happens at point 3, or at time t_f, when freezing of water begins, which means the beginning of the process of crystallization of ice. The new phase begins at point 3 with a break, and part 3-4 of the curve below the freezing point indicates that the substance is in the solid phase.

The slopes of parts 1-2 and 3-4 of the curve are not necessarily equal. The slopes depend upon the rate of cooling and the rate of freezing. At uniform cooling and freezing, save for experimental and observation errors, both slope rates of chilling can be made equal.

Gradual cooling of water brings about a relatively small nuclear formation and therefore large crystals of ice. Rapid cooling, on the other hand, creates a large number of fine crystals.

Figure 2-7, which is an exaggerated sketch of Fig. 2-4b, shows diagrammatically (not to scale) the volume change of water with temperature during cooling and freezing.

If water is undercooled below its freezing point T_f, the horizontal part 4-5 is usually preceded by a dip, part 2-3, Fig. 2-6. The cooling curve first sinks below the temperature of the freezing point T_f (until point 3), and when crystallization starts, it rises again to the temperature of the freezing point (point 4) and remains there for a time t_{sol}. This dip is caused by undercooling of the water before the start of solidification. From this figure it can be seen that water undercools before it freezes. At the instant when solidification of water starts (point 3), at the temperature of undercooling T_u, the temperature of the water rises (3-4) to the freezing point (4), the temperature of which is T_f. The rise takes place because in the freezing process latent

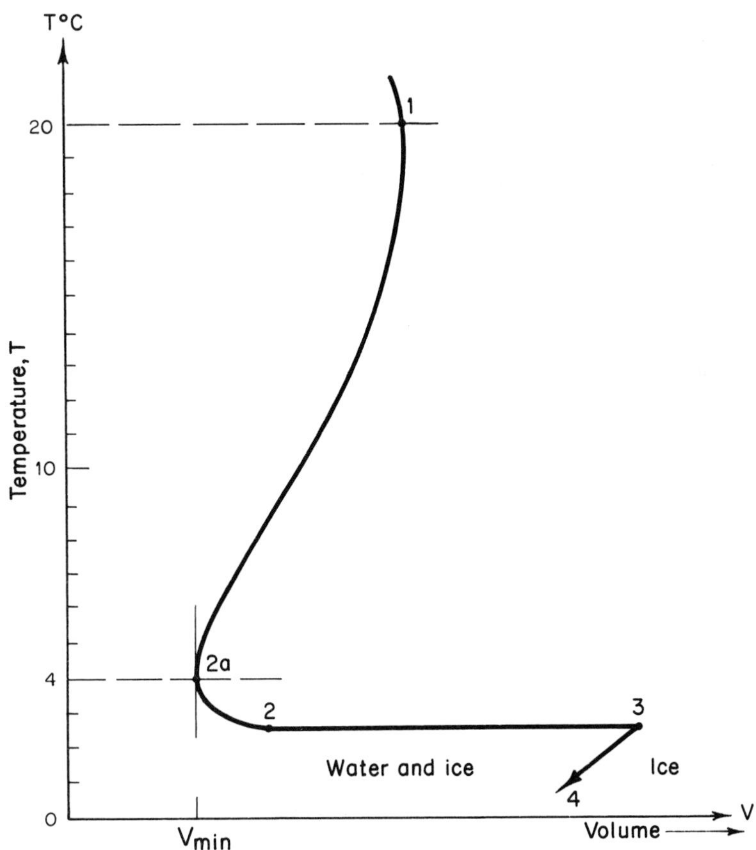

FIG. 2-7 Volume change of water with temperature.

heat of fusion is evolved. The difference between the two freezing temperatures, $T_f - T_u$, gives the lowering of the freezing point by undercooling.

2-22. Effect of Pressure on Freezing Water. Upon freezing, water increases in volume by 9%. If pressure is applied to the freezing water, the pressure tends to keep the water from expanding, and its transformation into ice is somewhat delayed. In this way the freezing and melting point of a substance which expands upon solidification is lowered below the normal freezing point before solidification takes place. The greater the pressure, the greater is the lowering of the freezing point, and a temperature lower than the normal freezing point of water would therefore be required. An increase of pressure of one atmosphere lowers the freezing point from 0°C to −0.0075°C. The freezing point is lowered by pressure up to about 2200 kg/cm^2.

If the freezing of water takes place in a confined space, say in a closed container or pipe or under a paved road, then the lower the temperature the greater the pressure of the freezing ice. The confined pressure developed by freezing depends upon the strength of the confining material to resist the expansion. This explains the great bursting energy of ice in breaking pipes and damaging pavements. The maximum pressure developed by freezing of water in a confined space is 2200 kg/cm^2, which occurs at −22°C. At this point ($p = 2200$ kg/cm^2 and $T = -22$°C) another type of ice forms—the so-called ice III. This ice is denser than water. For a description of the "other ices" see Ref. 8.

The effect of pressure on freezing of water can be followed from the figures as compiled in Table 2-2 after the Smithsonian Physical Tables[7] and Bridgeman.[11]

2-23. Phase Diagram of Water System. Water can exist in equilibrium in each of its three phases simultaneously if the pressure and the temperature are properly adjusted. By plotting the two physical factors—temperature and pressure—in a graph, the phase diagram, representing the water system, is obtained (Fig. 2-8, not to scale). The phase diagram consists of a combination of three separate graphs:

1. the vapor-pressure graph for ice,
2. the melting point graph for ice, and
3. the sublimation point graph for ice.

On this diagram, the regions of the three phases are indicated by the solid-liquid, liquid-vapor, and solid-vapor curves, which are the equilibrium curves. These regions are where ice, water, and aqueous vapor exist. The equilibrium curve between liquid and vapor is the

Table 2-2
Effect of Pressure on Freezing of Water after Forsythe † and Bridgeman ‡

Pressure (kg/cm^2)	Freezing Point (T_f)	Phases in Equilibrium
1	2	3
1	0.0	Ice I – liquid
1,000	−8.8	Ice I – liquid
2,000	−20.15	Ice I – liquid
2,115	−22.0	Ice I – ice III – liquid (triple point)
3,000	−18.4	Ice III – liquid
3,530	−17.0	Ice III – ice V – liquid (triple point)
4,000	−13.7	Ice V – liquid
6,000	−1.6	Ice V – liquid
6,380	+0.16	Ice V – ice VI – liquid (triple point)
8,000	12.8	Ice VI – liquid
12,000	37.9	Ice VI – liquid
16,000	57.2	Ice VI – liquid
20,000	73.6	Ice VI – liquid

† *Smithsonian Physical Tables*, The Smithsonian Institution, Washington, D.C., 1951, p. 119.

‡ P. W. Bridgeman, *Proceedings, American Academy of Arts and Sciences*, **70**, 1935, p. 25.

vaporization curve, that between the solid and liquid is the fusion curve, and that between solid and vapor is the sublimation curve.

2-24. Triple Point. For water, these three curves intersect at a point P, whose coordinates are $p = 4.58$ mm of mercury column and $T = 0.0075°C$. This point of intersection is termed the *triple point of water.* The triple point of water is the temperature and pressure at which ice, water and its vapor can theoretically coexist simultaneously in equilibrium with one another without one of them gaining in mass at the expense of the others. Practically, however, such fine values of pressure and temperature are very difficult to achieve.

There is only one such triple point for a substance like water. Within the single-phase regions the water system is bivariant. Here

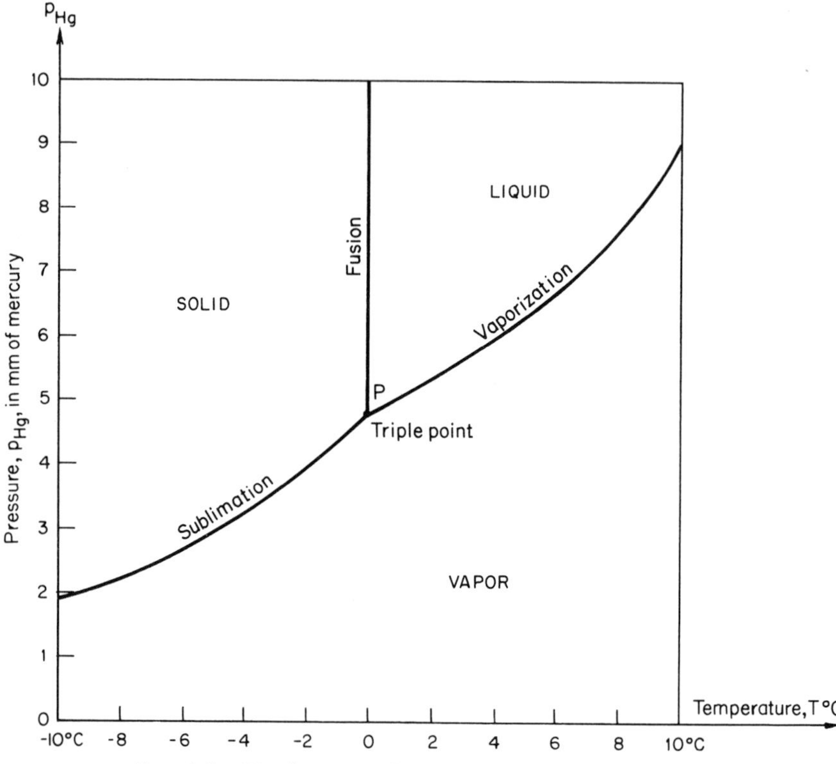

FIG. 2-8 Triple-point diagram for the water system.

temperature and pressure may be independently varied. At the triple point the water system is invariant, i.e., neither pressure nor temperature can be changed here. The slightest change in these two factors will cause one of the three phases of water to disappear.

Note that the triple point is not the ordinary melting point of ice designated in Fig. 2-9 by *M*. The melting point *M* $(0°/1_{atm})$ of water is the temperature (0°C) at the standard pressure of one atmosphere at which ice and water are in equilibrium.

Substances having more than one crystalline form will display one or more additional triple points.

2-25. Vaporization Curve. The curve *PC* which separates the region of liquid from the region of aqueous vapor is the vapor-pressure curve of liquid water, called simply the vaporization curve. The significance of the vaporization curve is that at any given temperature there is one and only one pressure at which the vapor of water is in equilibrium with liquid water. Along the vapor-pressure curve the liquid is in equilibrium with its own vapor.

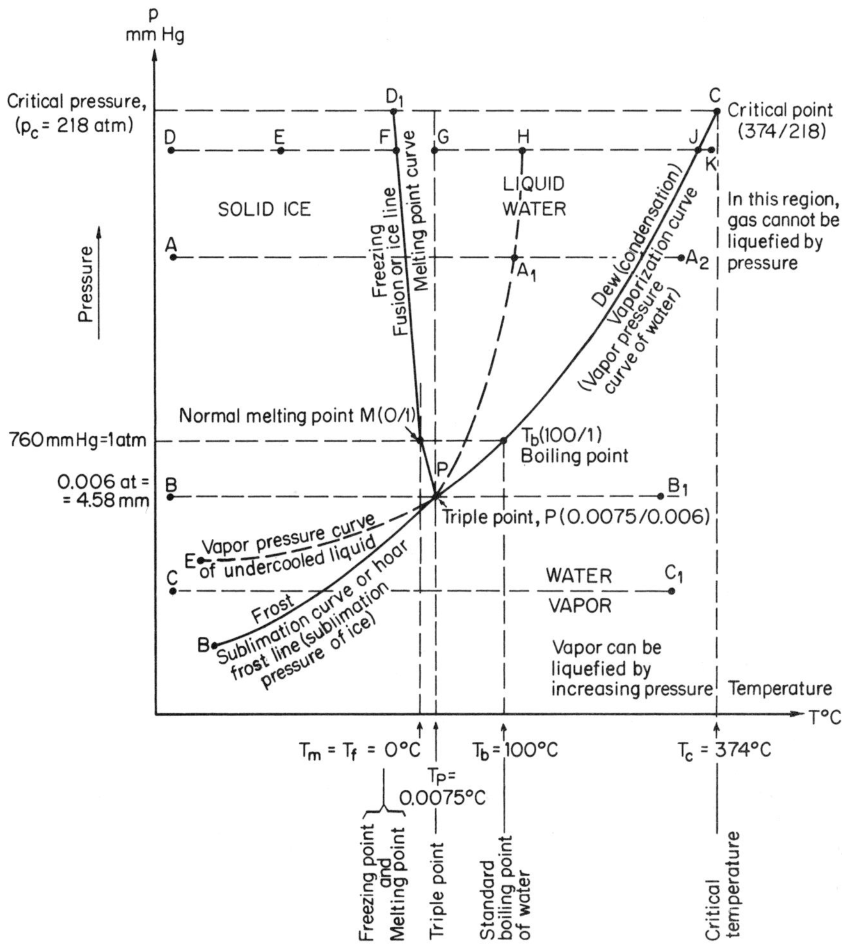

FIG. 2-9 Ordinary phase diagram of the water system.

At 100°C the evaporation pressure is 760 mm Hg, or 1 atmosphere. This is the boiling point T_b of water. At temperatures lower than 100°C the pressure drops, and at 0.0075°C it is 4.58 mm Hg or 0.006 atm (the triple point). At 0°C temperature and 760 mm Hg pressure water freezes.

The upper end of the vaporization curve ends on the high temperature side at point C, its upper limit, termed the *critical point,* whose coordinates are $T_c = 374$°C and $p_c = 218$ atm. The critical temperature is the highest temperature at which it is possible to liquefy a vapor by the application of pressure alone. Above the critical temperature, no liquid phase can exist and the substance is entirely gaseous. The distinction between a vapor and a gas is that vapor refers to the fluid below and gas above the critical temperature.

Table 2-3 contains data on freezing point, boiling point, and critical temperature of some of the common gases.

Table 2-3
Critical Data of Some of the Common Gases

Gas	Freezing Point T_f (°C)	Boiling Point T_b (°C)	Critical Temperature T_c (°C)
1	2	3	4
Helium	−272.0	−268.8	−268.0
Hydrogen	−259.0	−252.7	−234.5
Argon	−188.0	−186.0	−117.4
Nitrogen	−210.0	−195.7	−146.0
Oxygen	−219.0	−182.9	−118.0

On the low side, below the triple point, the vaporization curve continues to the left of the triple point into the solid region, making a branch *PE* (see dotted curve).

Liquid water can be cooled below its normal freezing point without solidifying to ice. The dotted curve *PE* represents the metastable vapor pressure curve of undercooled water, which is a continuous prolongation of the ordinary vaporization curve *PC* through the triple point. It can be observed from the phase diagram that the metastable vapor pressure of the undercooled water is greater at the same temperature than the vapor pressure of ice (compare the ordinates of the dotted curve with the sublimation curve), and the tendency is for the liquid to solidify.

2-26. Sublimation Curve. Below the triple point, the curve *PB*, continuing with a slightly different slope, is called the *sublimation pressure curve of ice.* The sublimation curve *PB* is not the continuation of the vaporization curve *PC*; the continuation of *PC* is *PE*! The sublimation curve *PB* intersects the vaporization curve at the triple point *P* at a very small angle. This sublimation curve separates the ice region from the vapor region and along this curve the solid ice may be in equilibrium with its own vapor.

2-27. Fusion Curve. Curve PD_1, drawn from the triple point *P*, separates the solid-ice region from the liquid-water region, and thus shows, in general, the relation between temperatures and pressures at which a substance in its solid state is in equilibrium with its liquid phase, e.g., ice and water. The fusion curve is also called the *melting point curve*. The direction of the very gently curved fusion curve appears almost vertical, and for water it is oriented through the second/fourth quarter of the coordinate system at an angle of >90°, i.e., it slopes slightly to the left above the triple point. For other substances the fusion curve generally leans in the direction opposite to that shown.

The fusion curve of the water system indicates specifically that with increase in pressure the freezing temperature of the water is lowered. It also shows that the melting point of ice or the freezing temperature of water decreases with increase in pressure. Whether the fusion curve has an upper limit, and at what pressure, is not known.

2-28. Effect of Varying Pressure and Temperature on Phase. If a substance such as ice is characterized by temperature and pressure coordinates corresponding to point A in the phase diagram (Fig. 2-9), and the substance is continuously heated at constant pressure (line $A - A_2$), then ice gradually transforms into water (point A_1) and then into the vapor phase (point A_2). Thus, with increasing temperature at constant pressure the solid gradually vaporizes, whereas a decrease in temperature, say from point A_2, gradually transfers the vapor back to the solid phase. If the ice is heated at a constant pressure of 0.006 atm = 4.58 mm Hg (point B), it goes through the triple point P and transforms into vapor (point B_1). If the ice is characterized at a constant pressure by point C, then, when the temperature is increased, ice crosses the frost line and transforms directly into vapor (point C_1).

2-29. Vapor Pressure of Ice. Definition. Vapor pressure of a liquid (or a solid, or a solution) is that pressure which is exerted by a vapor when a state of equilibrium has been attained between a liquid (or a solid, or a solution, respectively) and its vapor. When the vapor pressure of a liquid exceeds the pressure of the confining atmosphere the liquid is said to be boiling.

Table 2-4 and Fig. 2-10 show some values of vapor pressure of ice in contact with its own vapor, and for temperatures between −40° and 0°C. If the ice is in contact with the atmosphere at a certain temperature, say T°C, then the corresponding vapor pressures are a little greater than those indicated in Table 2-4 and Fig. 2-10. Therefore to the vapor pressure values in Table 2-4 a correction Δp must be added. This pressure correction, in millimeters of mercury, for ice

Table 2-4
Vapor Pressure of Ice and Water Below 0°C

Temperature (°C)	Vapor Pressure (mm Hg) *Ordinary Ice*	*Water*
1	2	3
−40	0.0966 †	–
−35	0.1681 †	–
−30	0.2859	–
−25	0.476	–
−20	0.776	–
−15	1.241	1.436
−12	1.632	1.834
−10	1.950	2.149
−8	2.326	2.514
−5	3.013	3.163
−4	3.280	3.410
−3	3.568	3.673
−2	3.880	3.956
−1	4.217	4.258
0	4.579	4.579

† International Critical Tables, Vol. 3, published by McGraw-Hill Book Company, Inc., New York, in 1928, for the National Research Council of the U.S.A., pp. 210–211.

and water below 0°C is calculated by the following equation [12]:

$$\Delta p = \frac{20p}{100(T + 273)},$$

where p is the uncorrected pressure in mm Hg at temperature T. One cm (= 10mm) Hg of pressure equals 13.5954 g/cm^2. For comparison, vapor pressures of water from 0°C to −15°C are included in Table 2-5, and a graph for these two substances is given in Fig. 2-10. At 0°C the vapor pressures of ice and water are equal. Below 0°C, the vapor pressure of ice is less than the vapor pressure of water at the same temperature. Both vapor pressures decrease with a decrease in temperature, but the vapor pressure of ice decreases faster than that of water.

2-30. Dry Ice. Dry ice is solidified carbon dioxide. It is odorless and in blocks has a snow-white color.

Carbon Dioxide Gas, CO_2. Carbon dioxide gas is colorless, considered odorless, and is tasteless at low concentrations. At 20°C it is one

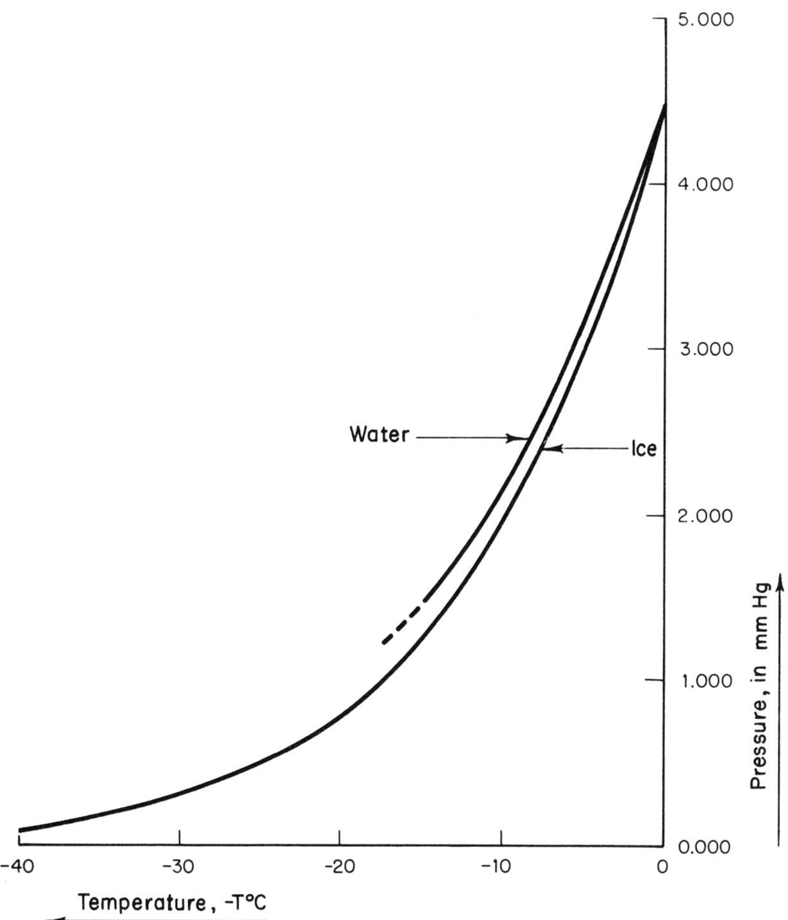

FIG. 2-10 Vapor pressure of ice and water.

and one-half times as heavy as air, does not support burning, and will put out a flame. The gas has a density of 1.977 g/liter. Its critical temperature is 31°C at a critical pressure of 73 atm.

Liquid Carbon Dioxide. At +20°C and $p = 58.5$ kg/cm^2, the unit weight of liquid CO_2 is about 710 kg/m^3, but at $T = -40$°C and $p = 10.25$ gk/cm^2 the weight is 1115 kg/m^3. At the triple point the unit weight of liquid CO_2 is 1178 kg/m^3.

Manufacture of Dry Ice. Dry ice is made by compressing and cooling high purity natural and/or industrial carbon dioxide gas to a liquid. The compression of the carbon dioxide takes place at 5 atm and −57°C. (At +20°C a pressure of 52 atm would be required.) Then the high pressure is reduced to atmospheric pressure, whereupon some of the cold liquid carbon dioxide expands rapidly in the confined space and returns immediately to vapor. This evaporation brings about the lowering of the temperature of the remaining liquid carbon dioxide, which freezes to a snow-like solid. The carbon dioxide snow is then compressed into dense blocks of solid ice. The size of the blocks is usually 10 in. × 10 in. (25 cm × 25 cm), and such a block weighs about 45 lb. Sublimation of dry ice takes place at −78.5°C at atmospheric pressure.

Some Properties of Dry Ice. The specific gravity of dry ice is $G =$ 1.56 at −79°C.(13) One unit volume of dry ice is equivalent to 450 units of carbon dioxide gas. Upon vaporization, dry ice absorbs a little less than twice as much heat from its surroundings as does the same amount of water ice in melting. When liquid CO_2 solidifies, its volume decreases. The unit weight of dry ice at atmospheric pressure and ordinary temperatures varies from 1505 kg/m³ to 1560 kg/m³ (94 to 97.5 lb/ft³).

The latent heat of fusion of carbon dioxide is $L = 45.2$ cal/g at −56.7°C and at 5.1 atm pressure. At this temperature the liquid CO_2 starts to freeze. At −78.5°C the solid CO_2 sublimes. The latent heat of sublimation of the dry ice is $L_s = 137.9$ cal/g ≈ 246.3 B/lb. The specific heat of carbon dioxide gas at $T = 20$°C and constant pressure is $c_{sp} =$ 0.1988, and at $T = 20$°C and constant volume, $c_{sp} = 0.1525$.

The addition of powdered carbon dioxide to acetone and ether permits one to prepare cooling mixtures that maintain constant temperatures down to −110°C.

Phase Diagram of Carbon Dioxide. The phase diagram of carbon dioxide is shown in Fig. 2-11. The data for plotting the phase diagram are as follows (8):

Sublimation point, S: −78.5°C at 1 atm pressure.
Triple point, P: −56.7°C at 5.1 atm pressure (3885 mm Hg).
Critical point, C: 31.0°C at 73 atm pressure.
Liquefaction of gas at 0.0°C requires 35 atm pressure.
Liquefaction of gas at 20.0°C requires 56 atm pressure.

The fusion temperature of carbon dioxide increases by 0.02°C/atm. This helps to plot the fusion curve. From the carbon dioxide phase diagram it can be seen that under atmospheric pressure liquid CO_2 is unstable at any temperature, but dry ice evaporates directly without melting or liquefying unless the pressure exceeds 5.1 atm. Hence, solid carbon dioxide does not melt upon warming at atmospheric pressure because its triple point lies at $T = -56.7$°C and a pressure of 5.1 atm.(8)

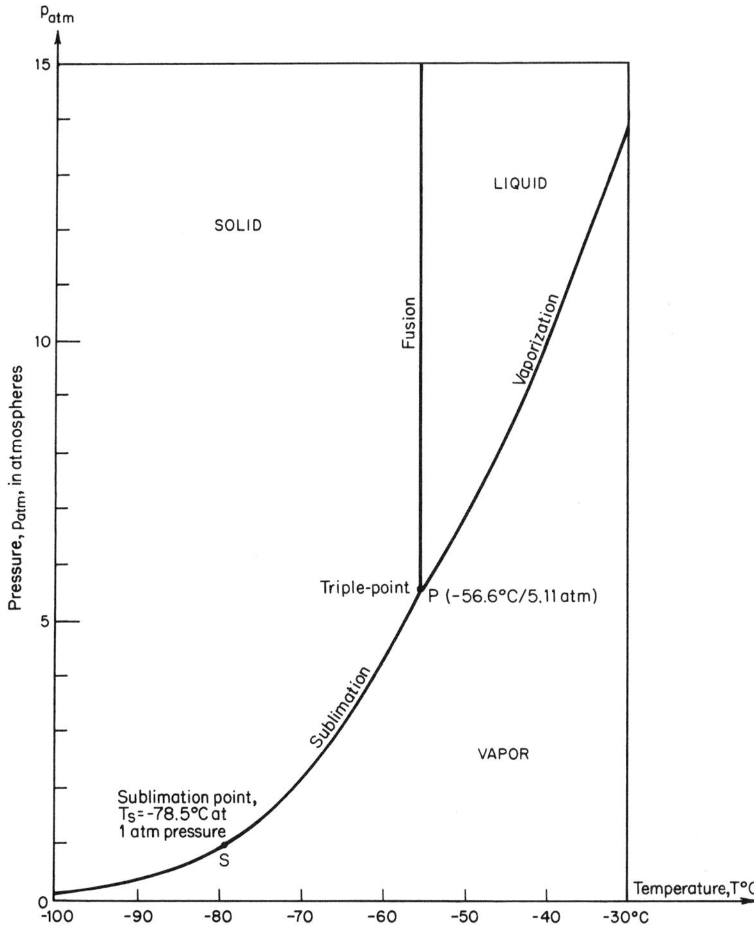

FIG. 2-11 Phase diagram for carbon dioxide.

If dry ice is placed in a container which is subsequently closed and heated, the pressure on the carbon dioxide increases according to the vapor pressure curve. When the temperature of the triple point is attained, dry ice begins to melt.

Use of Dry Ice. Dry ice is used in scientific work for creating inert atmosphere. The dry ice is usually enveloped by a cloud of very cold carbon dioxide gas, which makes its cooling power far greater than that of water ice. This property, and the fact that it sublimates with no residue, makes it an excellent refrigerant. The temperature of dry ice is −80°C, and thus it has a cooling effect equivalent to about ten times that of melting water ice.

2-31. Some Concepts Pertaining to Frozen Soil

i) *Soil.* Soil is geologically unconsolidated rock material by means of which (earth structures) and upon which (support of foundations) engineers build structures.

ii) *Frost.* The term "frost" usually has two connotations in soil engineering:

1) temperatures below 0°C which cause freezing, also termed "climatologic frost," and
2) the action of freezing temperatures upon the soil, i.e., the freezing ofwater in the voids of the soil.

iii) *Frozen Soil.* When the temperature in soil drops below freezing, soil moisture is transformed from the liquid into the solid state in the form of ice crystals, grains, lenses or ice layers located between the soil particles. Thus, a frozen soil is one whose temperature is below freezing and which contains voids partly or completely filled with individual layers of segregated ice (see Fig. 2-12).

iv) *Frost Action in Soil.* Frost action in soil is the result of the freezing and thawing of soil moisture.

v) *Frost Damage.* The term "frost damage" is understood to mean damage to streets, highways, foundations, and structures in the widest sense of the word.

vi) *Frost Heave.* The raising of the ground surface, a highway

FIG. 2-12 Rhythmic banding of ice in a frozen soil sample. Author's study.

pavement slab, or a foundation by ice in the underlying soil is frost heave.

vii) *Frost-Susceptible Soil.* A frost-susceptible soil is one in which significant and detrimental ice segregation will occur when the requisite moisture and freezing conditions are present. A non-frost-susceptible soil is one which under freezing conditions will not bring about damage to roads and/or foundations.

viii) *Ice Banding.* Ice banding is the rhythmic formation of parallel or almost parallel ice layers in soil upon slow freezing (see Fig. 2-12).

ix) *Ice Lenses.* Ice lenses are distinct layers of ice in a frozen soil.

x) *Degree-Day.* A degree-day is defined here as the difference between the daily average temperature below 0°C (32°F) and 0°C (32°F).

xi) *Thermal Resistance.* Thermal resistance R is the reciprocal of thermal conductivity K: $R = 1/K$.

Chapter 3

Modes of Heat Transfer

Some of the heat problems in thermal soil mechanics may be satisfactorily solved by the application of the various heat transfer theories. Heat transfer between bodies takes place by conduction, convection, and radiation, and by various combinations of these.

3-1. Description of Modes of Heat Transfer. Heat transfer by *conduction* takes place principally in solid bodies when different parts of a body are at different temperatures. Heat flows from the warmer part of the body or system to the cooler one. The nature of this kind of heat transfer is that the warmer molecules of the body, having a greater velocity of motion (i.e., greater kinetic energy) than the cooler ones, collide with the neighboring molecules – cooler ones (having a smaller velocity) – and transfer to them some of the kinetic energy, causing the cooler ones to move faster than before. In this manner heat is distributed throughout the entire mass of the body. Heat passes through the substance of the body itself (see Fig. 3-1).

Heat transfer by *convection* takes place by means of the motion of matter. Here heat transfers between the surface of a solid body and a liquid or gas in contact with its surface. The nature of convection lies in the molecules of the liquid or gas being in contact with the solid surface and warming up by conductivity (Fig. 3-2). Then cooler molecules take the place of the warmer ones. Thus, distribution of heat in a liquid or gas takes place by way of mutual displacement and mixing up of the molecules.

Free convection is a slow process of heat transfer. A much faster convectional heat transfer may be achieved by forced convection – by pumps, blowers, fans, and ventilators.

Heat transfer by *radiation.* Whereas heat transfer by conductivity and convection requires in each case a medium, fixed (solid) or mobile (liquid, or gas), radiation does not require any medium. Here heat

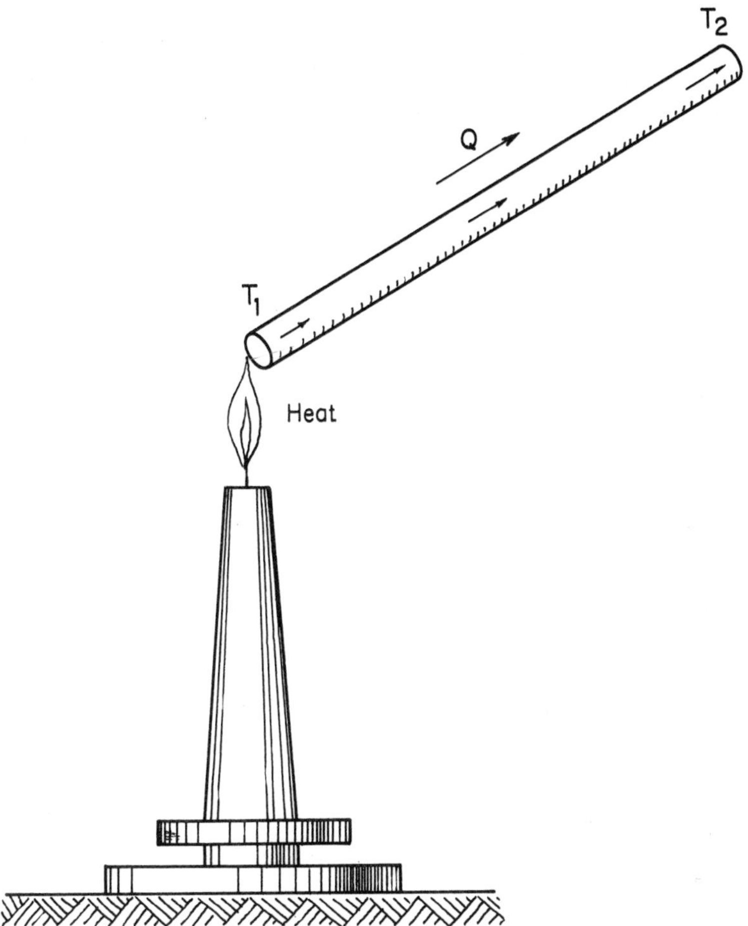

FIG. 3-1 Conduction of heat.

transfer between bodies takes place through space (through air and through space devoid of air) by electromagnetic radiation. The nature of radiation of heat lies in the phenomenon that part of the heat energy of each of the bodies is transformed into a radiant energy. The latter, in the form of electromagnetic waves (similar to light energy) propagates radially in all directions. Upon meeting other bodies in their paths, radiant energy may be partly absorbed by them and transformed again into heat energy, thereby increasing the temperature of the absorbing body. The farther away the interfering body *B* (see Fig. 3-3), the less energy it receives, that is, the less it warms up, because *B* then receives fewer rays from the radiating source *H*.

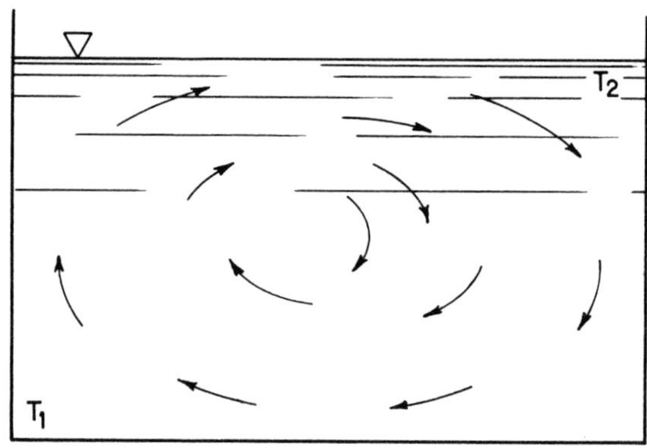

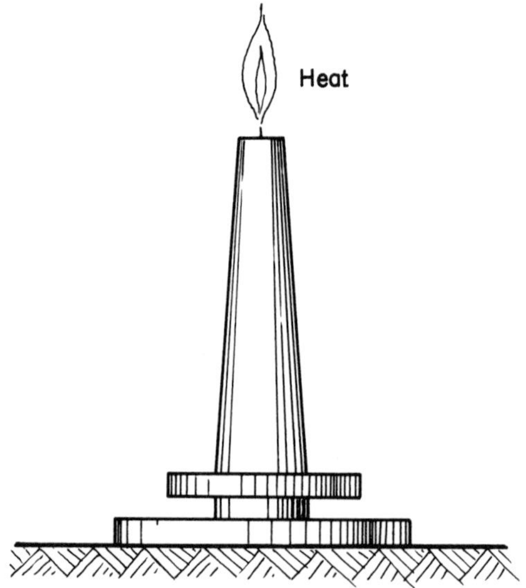

FIG. 3-2 Free convection. Circulation of water molecules from a warmer region to a cooler one; $T_1 > T_2$.

HEAT CONDUCTION

3-2. Methods and Theories. For the analytical treatment of the various heat problems, below or above freezing, the following well-known methods and theories are among those generally applicable:

1. the steady-state flow of heat,
2. the unsteady-state heat conduction,
3. F. Neumann's theory, and
4. J. Stefan's theory.

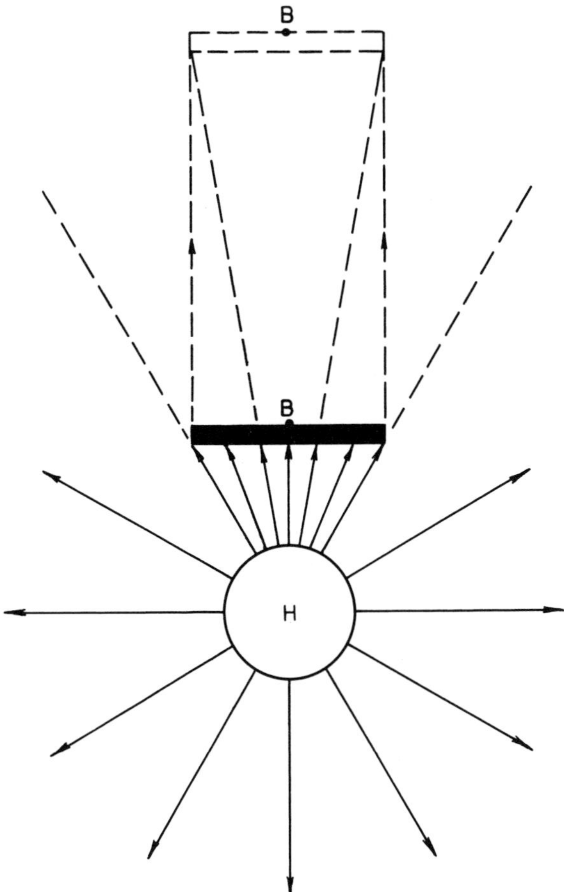

FIG. 3-3 Radiation.

All these theories are based on the natural laws that

a) heat flows from regions of higher temperature to regions of lower temperature;
b) the amount of heat in a differential element of soil or other material is proportional to its mass and its temperature, and
c) the rate of heat flow across an area is proportional to its size and to the temperature gradient.

In this book, only the unidirectional heat flow is considered. For a discussion of heat conduction in the unsteady state the reader is referred to Ref. (1) and Appendix 16 of this book.

3-3. Steady-State Flow of Heat. The theory of stabilized, steady-state heat conduction is given by Fourier[(14–19)] as

$$\frac{dQ}{dt} = K \cdot A \cdot \frac{dT}{dx}, \qquad (3\text{-}1)$$

where Q = amount of heat (in calories),[1]
t = time (in seconds, for example),
dQ/dt = rate of heat flow (in calories per second),
K = coefficient of thermal conductivity of a material [in cal/(cm)(sec)(°C)],
A = cross-sectional area through which heat flows, normal to the direction of heat flow (in cm^2), and
dT/dx = change in temperature T over a distance (thickness) x of wall or slab through which heat flows, called the temperature gradient.

Referring specifically to finite quantities, the amount Q of heat transferred may be written as

$$Q = KAt(T_1 - T_2)/x \qquad \text{(cal)}, \qquad (3\text{-}2)$$

where t = time (in seconds or hours),
$T_1 - T_2$ = temperature difference (in °C) between two points in the material x distance apart, and
$(T_1 - T_2)/x$ = temperature gradient (in °C/cm).

Equation 3-2 reads: "The amount of heat Q transferred through a body x units thick through an area A during time t is proportional (K) to the cross-sectional area, time and temperature difference $(T_1 - T_2)$, and inversely proportional to the thickness (or distance) x."

Dividing Eq. (3-2) by At, obtain unit flow q of heat, or rate:

$$q = K(T_1 - T_2)/x \qquad [\text{cal}/(\text{cm}^2)(\text{sec})], \qquad (3\text{-}3)$$

flowing in one unit of time through one unit of area.

The coefficient of thermal conductivity K depends upon the physical properties of the material.

Equation (3-3) may be rewritten as

$$q = \frac{T_1 - T_2}{x/K} = \frac{T_1 - T_2}{R} \qquad \left[\frac{\text{cal}}{(\text{cm}^2)(\text{sec})}\right], \qquad (3\text{-}4)$$

where $x/K = R$ = thermal resistance in $(\text{cm}^2)(\text{sec})(°\text{C})/\text{cal}$.

The unit heat flow through a compound layer system, by analogy to Eq. (3-4), is

$$q = \frac{T_s - T_n}{x_1/K_1 + x_2/K_2 + x_3/K_3 + \cdots + x_n/K_n} \qquad \left[\frac{\text{cal}}{(\text{cm}^2)(\text{sec})}\right], \qquad (3\text{-}5)$$

where T_s = surface temperature (in °C),
T_n = temperature at exit of the nth layer (in °C)(see Fig. 3-4); the indexes at x and K mean the consecutive numbers of layers in the compound system, and the denominator x/K (Eq. 3-4), or x_1/K_1, x_2/K_2, x_3/K_3, . . . , x_n/K_n, is the thermal resistance to heat conduction.

Or else, Equation (3-5) may be written as

$$q = \frac{T_s - T_n}{\sum_1^n R}, \tag{3-5a}$$

where $\sum_1^n R$ is the total thermal resistance consisting of the sum of the individual thermal resistances of the compound layer.

Equation (3-4), or (3-5a), reads as follows: "The amount of heat conducted is equal to the ratio of the temperature head to thermal resistance."

If the surface temperature is freezing, i.e., $T_s < 0°C$, as in winter (Fig. 3-5), then Eqs. (3-4) and (3-5a) are written

$$q = \frac{T_2 - T_1}{R}, \tag{3-4a}$$

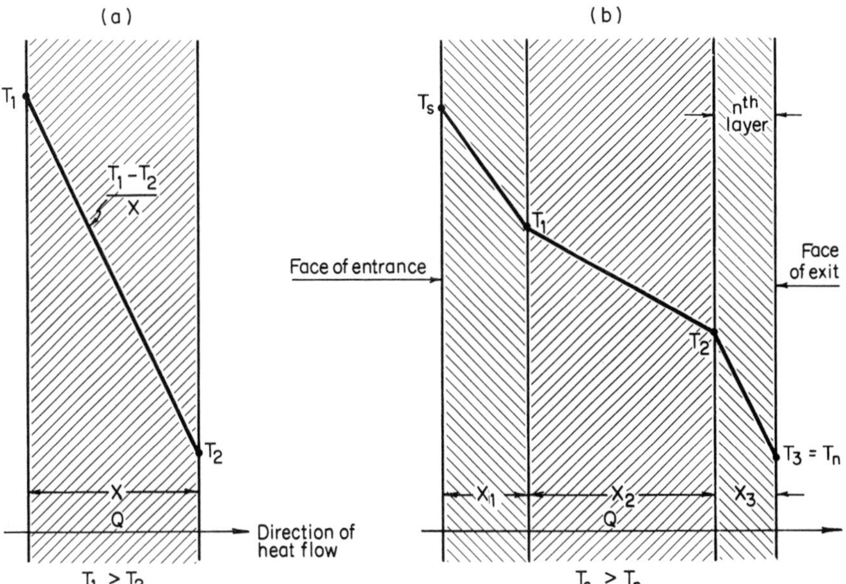

FIG. 3-4 System of (a) single and (b) compound layers.

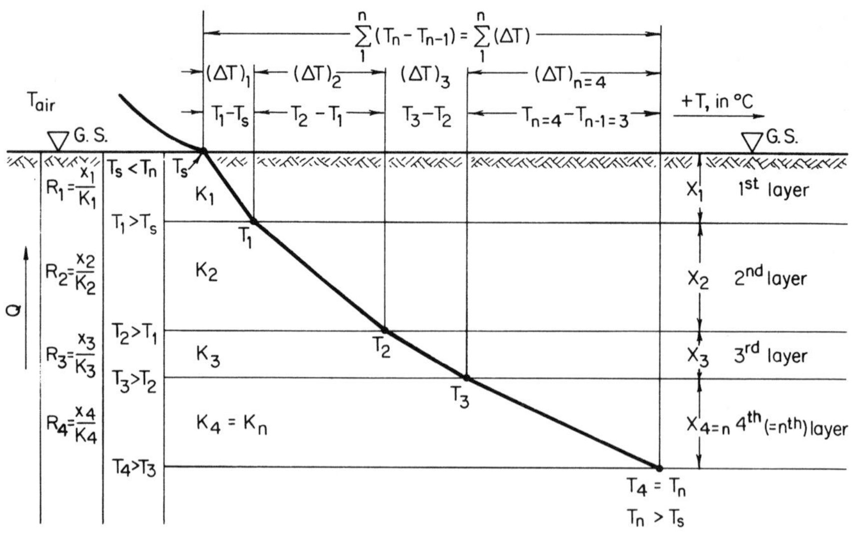

FIG. 3-5 Temperature drop in a system of compound layers. Thermal resistances in series.

and

$$q = \frac{T_n - T_s}{\sum_1^n R}, \tag{3-5a}$$

respectively, because $T_n > T_s$, and mainly because the direction of heat flow is from points of high temperature to points of low temperature.

For example, with a freezing surface temperature, where $T_s < 0°C$ (Fig. 3-5), each layer possesses a different coefficient of thermal conductivity K. It is assumed that each of the four layers is in perfect contact. By the principle of continuity of flow, the amount of heat q flowing through an area $A = 1\ cm^2$ is the same for each single layer:

$$\left.\begin{aligned}
q &= \frac{K_1}{x_1}(T_1 - T_s) && \text{for the first layer,}\\
q &= \frac{K_2}{x_2}(T_2 - T_1) && \text{for the second layer,}\\
q &= \frac{K_3}{x_3}(T_3 - T_2) && \text{for the third layer,}\\
q &= \frac{K_4}{x_4}(T_4 - T_3) && \text{for the fourth layer.}
\end{aligned}\right\} \tag{3-6}$$

From these equations, the temperature differences, or temperature heads, are

$$\left.\begin{aligned} T_1 - T_s &= q\,\frac{x_1}{K_1} \\ T_2 - T_1 &= q\,\frac{x_2}{K_2} \\ T_3 - T_2 &= q\,\frac{x_3}{K_3} \\ T_4 - T_3 &= q\,\frac{x_4}{K_4}. \end{aligned}\right\} \qquad (3\text{-}7)$$

Here $T_4 = T_n$. The summation of these temperature differences gives the total drop in temperature from $T_n = T_4$ to T_s:

$$T_n - T_s = q\left(\frac{x_1}{K_1} + \frac{x_2}{K_2} + \frac{x_3}{K_3} + \cdots + \frac{x_n}{K_n}\right). \qquad (3\text{-}8)$$

Then the rate q of heat flow through a unit area $A = 1\ \text{cm}^2$ across the compound layer system is

$$q\uparrow = \frac{T_n - T_s}{x_1/K_1 + x_2/K_2 + x_3/K_3 + \cdots + x_n/K_n} = \frac{T_n - T_s}{\sum_1^n \left(\frac{x}{K}\right)} = \frac{T_n - T_s}{\sum_1^n (R)}. \qquad (3\text{-}9)$$

When $T_s > T_n$, then the temperature T at any isothermal surface between the individual layers in contact in the compound system can be calculated as follows. The temperature T between the first and second layer is, by Eq. (3-7),

$$T_1 = T_s - q\,\frac{x_1}{K_1} = T_s - qR_1 \qquad (^\circ\text{C}), \qquad (3\text{-}10)$$

(heat flows down, ↓). Further,

$$T_2 = T_1 - q(x_2/K_2) = T_s - q(R_1 + R_2) \qquad (3\text{-}11)$$

$$T_3 = T_s - q(R_1 + R_2 + R_3) \qquad (3\text{-}12)$$

$$T_{n=4} = T_s - q(R_1 + R_2 + R_3 + \cdots + R_{n=4}) =$$

$$= T_s - q\sum_1^{n=4} (R). \qquad (3\text{-}13)$$

When $T_s < T_n$, heat flows up, and (see Eq. 3-7)

$$T_1 = T_s + q(x_1/K_1) = T_s + qR_1 \quad (3\text{-}10a)$$

$$T_2 = T_s + q(R_1 + R_2) \quad (3\text{-}11a)$$

$$T_3 = T_s + q(R_1 + R_2 + R_3), \quad (3\text{-}12a)$$

and

$$T_{n=4} = T_s + q \sum_{1}^{n=4} (R). \quad (3\text{-}13a)$$

Equations (3-10) through (3-13a) read that the temperature at one isothermal surface is equal to the temperature at the previous isothermal surface plus or minus the product of unit heat flow and the thermal resistance between these two isothermal surfaces.

Example. Given a brick wall 3 m long, 2.0 m high, and 25 cm thick. The outside temperature of the surface of the wall is $T_1 = T_s = -20$°C, and the inside temperature is $T_2 = T_n = +10$°C. The coefficient of thermal conductivity of the brick is given as 0.5 Cal/(m)(hr)(°C). Calculate the amount of heat flow Q through the entire wall per hour.

Solution. Rate of flow per 1 m², by Eq. (3-3):

$$q = K\frac{T_2 - T_1}{x} = (0.50)\frac{10-(-20)}{0.25} = 60 \quad \left[\frac{\text{Cal}}{(\text{m}^2)(\text{hr})}\right].$$

Rate of heat flow through an $A = 6.0$ m² surface area of wall is, by Eq. (3-2):

$$Q/t = qA = (60)(6.0) = \underline{360} \quad \left(\frac{\text{Cal}}{\text{hr}}\right). \qquad (Answer).$$

Example. Calculate the rate of heat flow through the wall of a cooler. The cross-section of the wall is shown in Fig. 3-6.

For brick: $K_1 = 0.6 \quad \left[\frac{\text{Cal}}{(\text{m})(\text{hr})(°\text{C})}\right];$

For dry cork: $K_2 = 0.06 \quad \left[\frac{\text{Cal}}{(\text{m})(\text{hr})(°\text{C})}\right].$

Neglect the thermal resistance of the waterproofing. Calculate also the magnitude of the contact temperature T_1.

Solution. By Eq. (3-5):

a) *Rate of heat flow:*

$$q = \frac{T_s - T_n}{x_1/K_1 + x_2/K_2} = \frac{25-(-2)}{(0.25/0.60)+(0.20/0.06)} = \frac{27}{(0.41)+(3.33)} =$$

$$= \frac{27}{3.74} = \underline{7.2 \quad \left[\frac{\text{Cal}}{(\text{m}^2)(\text{hr})}\right]}.$$

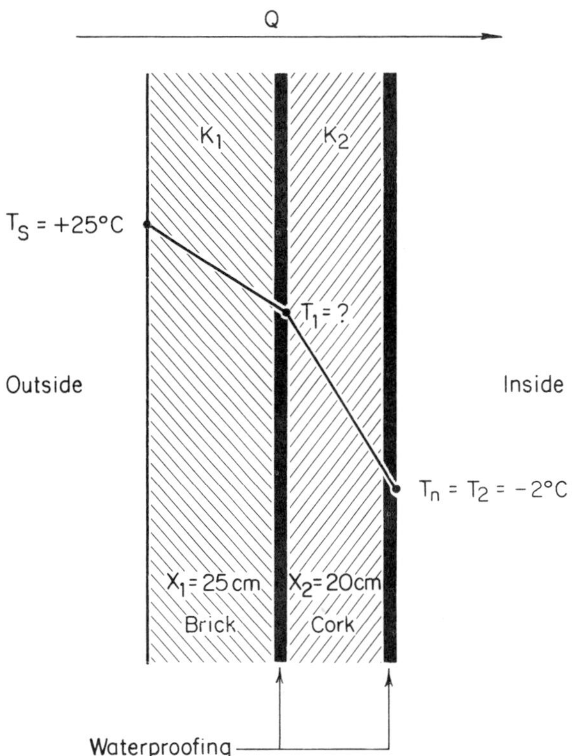

FIG. 3-6 Heat flow through a brick wall.

b) *Contact temperature:*
By Eq. (3-7):

$$T_s - T_1 = q(x_1/K_1),$$

and

$$T_1 = T_s - q\,\frac{x_1}{K_1} = 25.0 - (7.2)(0.41) = \underline{22.1\ (^\circ\mathrm{C}).}$$

3-4. Frost Penetration Depth. A compound layer example of practical interest concerns a soil profile with the upper part frozen and the lower part unfrozen. The question in this simplified problem relative to the thickness of the layer of the frozen soil may be asked in this manner: How deep, $x = \xi$, will frost penetrate through a cover of snow into the soil? Refer to Fig. 3-7.

The coefficients of thermal conductivity are
K_{sn} — for snow,
K_f — for frozen soil, assumed here to be constant,
K_u — for unfrozen soil.

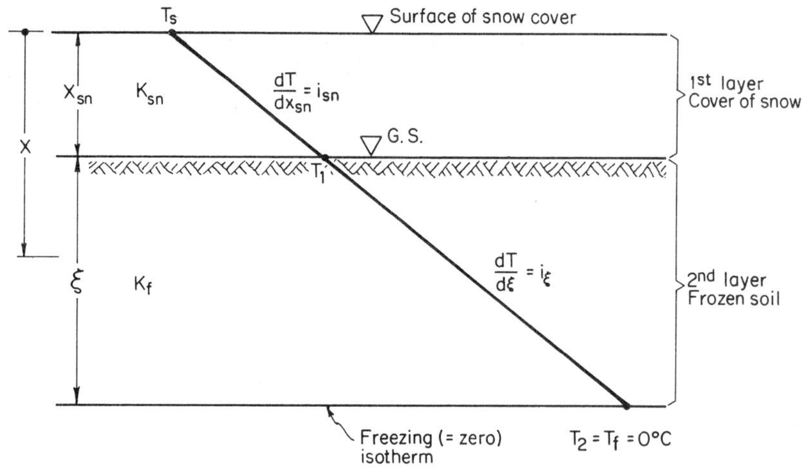

FIG. 3-7 A compound layer of snow and soil.

Here ξ = frost penetration depth (in meters),
$T_f = 0°C$ = assumed freezing temperature,
i_{sn} = temperature gradient in snow,
i_ξ = temperature gradient in frozen soil.

Assume that the thermal gradients in snow and in frozen soil are the same, i.e., $dT/dx_{sn} = dT/d\xi$.

By the principle of continuity of flow, and setting $K_u = K_f$, the frost penetration depth ξ may be solved by Eq. (3-13a):

$$T_n = T_2 = T_f = T_s + q \sum_1^2 (R) \tag{3-13a}$$

$$K_f \frac{T_f - T_1}{\xi} = K_u i_u, \tag{3-14}$$

and

$$\xi = \frac{K_f}{K_u} \frac{T_f - T_1}{i_u}. \tag{3-15}$$

Or, with $K_f = K_u$, the frost penetration depth ξ is

$$\xi = \frac{T_f - T_1}{i_\xi}. \tag{3-16}$$

The frost penetration depth may also be calculated by means of the simplified Stefan's formula.[1]

3-5. Radial Flow of Heat Through the Wall of a Cylinder. Just as the heat flow equation was written for a flow through a plane area, one writes the rate of flow through a cylindrical wall of 1 unit length ($L = 1$) as

$$q = Q/t = -KA\ (dT/dr) = -2\pi rK\ (dT/dr), \tag{3-17}$$

the minus sign meaning that with increase of r the temperature decreases (direction of heat flow in this problem is from warmer region to cooler one, if $T_1 > T_2$). Refer to Fig. 3-8.

Integration between T_1 and T_2, or r_1 and r_2, gives

$$-\int_{T_1}^{T_2} dT = \int_{T_2}^{T_1} dT = \frac{q}{2\pi K}\int_{r_1}^{r_2} \frac{dr}{r}, \tag{3-18}$$

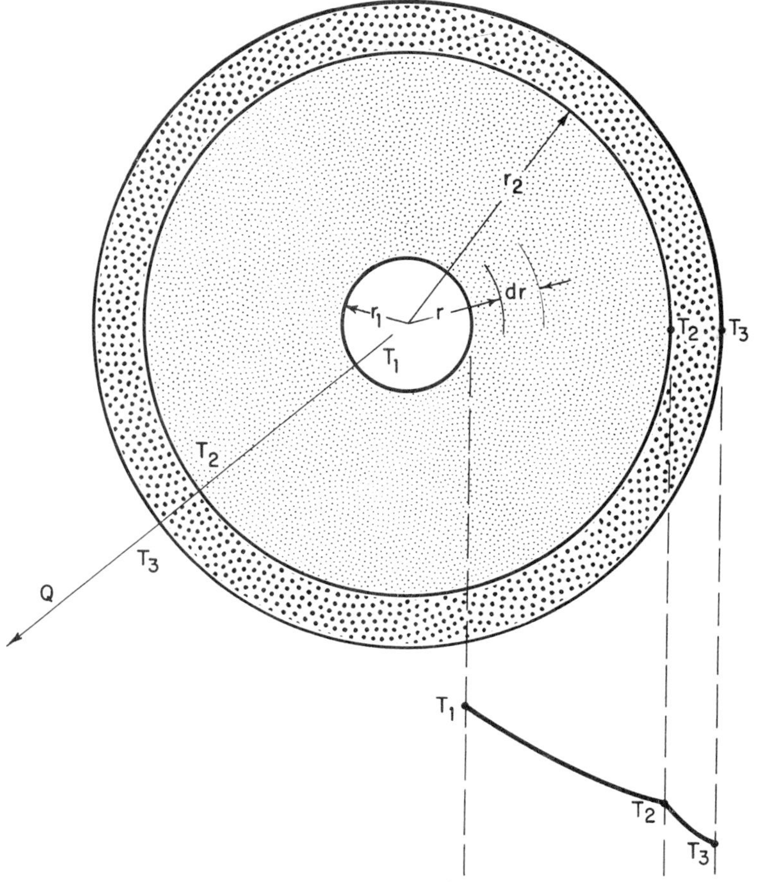

FIG. 3-8 Radial flow of heat.

or

$$T_1 - T_2 = \frac{q}{2\pi K}\left(\ln \frac{r_2}{r_1}\right), \tag{3-19}$$

and

$$q = 2\pi K \frac{T_1 - T_2}{\ln(r_2/r_1)} \qquad \left[\frac{\text{Cal}}{(\text{m})(\text{hr})}\right]. \tag{3-20}$$

For a cylinder of length L,

$$q_L = 2\pi KL \frac{T_1 - T_2}{\ln(r_2/r_1)}, \tag{3-21}$$

or it may be written in a manner similar to the equation for heat flow through a plane surface:

$$q_L = KA_{\text{av}} \frac{T_1 - T_2}{r_2 - r_1}. \tag{3-22}$$

In such a case

$$\frac{2\pi L}{\ln(r_2/r_1)} = \frac{A_{\text{av}}}{r_2 - r_1}, \tag{3-23}$$

and

$$A_{\text{av}} = \frac{2\pi L(r_2 - r_1)}{\ln(r_2/r_1)} = \frac{2\pi r_2 L - 2\pi r_1 L}{\ln(2\pi r_2 L/2\pi r_1 L)} = \frac{A_2 - A_1}{\ln(A_2/A_1)}, \tag{3-24}$$

where A_{av} is the logarithmic mean of areas A_1 and A_2.

3-6. Insulated Electric Cable. Assume a cross section of an electric cable as shown in Fig. 3-9. Designate drop in temperature by dT. Then the differential rate of heat flow for $L = 1$ (one unit of length of cable) through the cylindrical concentric surfaces may be written, analogous to heat flow through a plane surface, as

$$dq = -KA\,(dT/dr) = -Kr\,d\phi(1)\,(dT/dr), \tag{3-25}$$

the minus sign meaning that with increase of r the temperature decreases [direction of heat flow is from the warmer region in the core of the cable to cooler one (outside), if $T_1 > T_2$].

Integrating Eq. (3-25) first with respect to ϕ from $\phi = 0$ to $\phi = 2\pi$, obtain

$$\frac{1}{K}\frac{dr}{r}\int_0^q dq = -dT\int_0^{2\pi} d\phi,$$

or

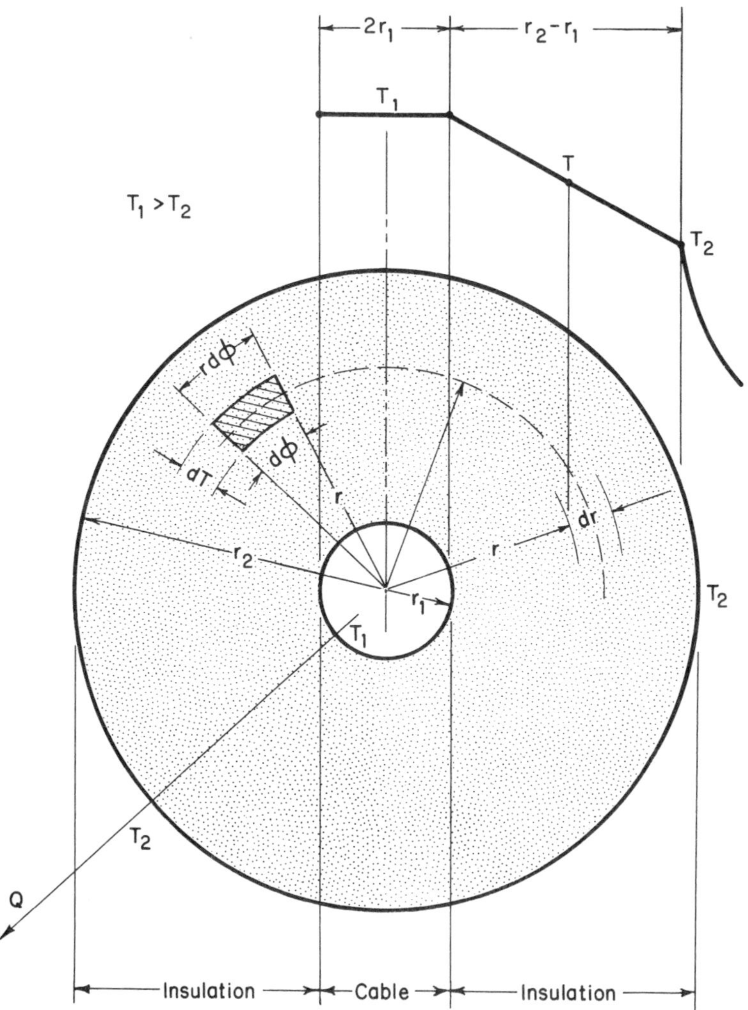

FIG. 3-9 Cross section of an insulated electric cable.

$$q \frac{dr}{r} = -2\pi K \, dT. \tag{3-26}$$

Then integrate Eq. (3-25) with respect to r from r_1 to r_2:

$$q \int_{r_1}^{r_2} \frac{dr}{r} = -2\pi K \int_{T_1}^{T_2} dT,$$

or

$$q \ln(r_2/r_1) = 2\pi K(T_1 - T_2). \tag{3-27}$$

The rate of heat flow is then calculated as

$$q = 2\pi K \frac{T_1 - T_2}{\ln(r_2/r_1)}, \tag{3-28}$$

where $T_1 - T_2$ is the temperature drop across the thickness of the insulation of the cable, and $\ln(r_2/r_1)$ is the geometric factor of the insulated cable.

3-7. Insulated Steam Pipe

Example. Given a steam pipe whose outer diameter is $d_1 = 100$ mm. The pipe is covered with two layers of insulation against heat loss. Each of the two insulating layers is 25 mm thick. The properties of these insulations are given as follows.

Insulation	*Thickness of Insulation* (in mm)	*Coefficient of Thermal Conductivity, K*
Insulating material directly on hot pipe: magnesium	25	$K_1 = 0.06 \dfrac{\text{Cal}}{(\text{m})(\text{hr})(°\text{C})}$
Insulating material exposed to air: asbestos	25	$K_2 = 0.075 \dfrac{\text{Cal}}{(\text{m})(\text{hr})(°\text{C})}$

Temperature on the outside surface of the hot pipe: $T_1 = 200°\text{C}$. Temperature on the outside surface of asbestos insulation: $T_3 = 40°\text{C}$.

Calculate the heat loss per unit length of the pipe and the temperature T_2 at the contact surface between the magnesium and asbestos insulating covering.

Solution. Heat loss (by Eq. 3-28):

$$q = \frac{2\pi K(T_1 - T_3)}{\ln(r_3/r_1)} = \frac{2\pi(T_1 - T_3)}{(1/K_1)\ln(r_2/r_1) + (1/K_2)\ln(r_3/r_2)} =$$

$$= \frac{(2)(3.14)(200 - 40)}{(1/0.06)\ln(75/50) + (1/0.075)\ln(100/75)} = \underline{95.6 \quad \left[\frac{\text{Cal}}{(\text{m})(\text{hr})}\right]}.$$

Temperature T_2:

$$T_2 = T_1 - \frac{q}{2\pi K} \ln(r_2/r_1) = 200.0 - \frac{95.6}{(6.28)(0.06)} (2.3)\lg_{10}(75/50) =$$

$$= \underline{97.3°\text{C}.}$$

3-8. Snow as an Insulating Material. The Igloo. Depending upon its age and density, snow is about six to ten times a better insulator than soil.

The Eskimo makes good use of the insulating properties of snow under severe freezing conditions with the igloo, or snow house (see Fig. 3-10). The igloo is built very skillfully in the form of vaults and domes, and the interior walls and floor are covered with reindeer skins. While the temperature outdoors may be as low as −50°F (−45.6°C), the temperature inside just above one's head and about 1 ft below the highest point of the dome may be as high as 60°F (15.6°C). If the snow on the inside wall of the igloo begins to melt, the Eskimo knows that the insulating snow wall is too thick. He will then take a knife, go outside, and shave the snow wall thinner in order to in-

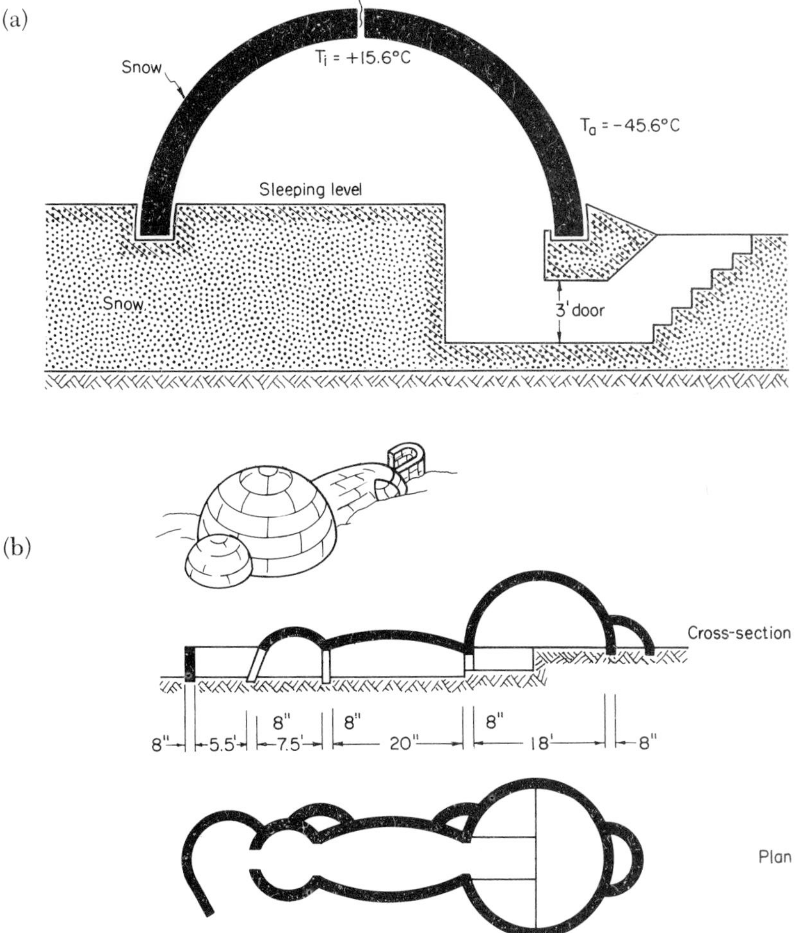

FIG. 3-10 (a) Cross section of an igloo. (b) Igloo in Baffinsland.

crease the rate of heat flow and keep the inside walls just below freezing.

3-9. Heat Transfer by Convection. The amount of heat Q transferred from a wall by convection is directly proportional to the area A, in square meters through which the heat flows, to time t in hours, and to the difference between the temperature T_1 of the liquid or gas and the temperature T_2 of the wall:

$$Q = \alpha At(T_1 - T_2) \qquad \text{(Cal)}, \tag{3-29}$$

where α is coefficient of heat convection (release) depending upon the properties of the fluid, nature of its motion, shape and nature of the surface characteristics of the solid surface and other possible factors. Its units are

$$\frac{\text{Cal}}{(\text{m}^2)(\text{hr})(°\text{C})}.$$

Some values of the heat convection coefficients α are given in the appendix of this book.

Dividing Eq. (3-29) by At, obtain the expression for the rate of heat flow by convection per unit of area:

$$q = \frac{Q}{At} = \alpha(T_1 - T_2) \qquad \left[\frac{\text{Cal}}{(\text{m}^2)(\text{hr})}\right], \tag{3-30}$$

or

$$q = \frac{T_1 - T_2}{1/\alpha}. \tag{3-31}$$

The quantity $1/\alpha$ is the thermal resistance to heat transfer by convection.

3-10. Heat Exchange by Radiation. Generally, radiant heat energy partly is absorbed by a body and transformed into heat and partly passes through the body. In a special case, all radiating heat energy may pass through a body. Such bodies are termed absolutely heat transparent (diathermal) (one- and two-atom gases). A body which reflects (not absorbing nor passing it through) all radiant heat energy is termed absolutely white. One which absorbs all radiant heat energy transferred to it is called absolutely black. All solid bodies partly absorb and partly reflect radiant energy.

The degree of absorption of radiant heat energy by a body is expressed by the coefficient of blackness a. This is a number showing what part of the energy transferred to the body is absorbed by it. If the coefficient of blackness of a certain body is $a = 0.85$ (lamp black, for instance), then 85% of all of the radiant heat energy transferred to the body is absorbed by it and 15% is reflected to the surrounding space. For an absolutely white body, $a = 0$. For an absolutely black body, $a = 1.00$.

The coefficient of blackness a depends upon the nature of the body, its surface condition, and temperature.

Radiation from an absolutely black body as a function of its temperature is expressed as

$$E_0 = C_0 \left(\frac{T}{100}\right)^4 \quad \left[\frac{\text{Cal}}{(\text{m}^2)(\text{hr})}\right], \tag{3-32}$$

where E_0 = amount of radiant energy, emanating from 1 m² during 1 hr;

C_0 = coefficient of radiation of an absolutely black body:

$$C_0 = 4.96 \quad \left[\frac{\text{Cal}}{(\text{m}^2)(\text{hr})(^\circ\text{C})^4}\right];$$

T = absolute temperature of the radiating body.

Or,

$$E_0 = (4.96)(T/100)^4 \quad \left[\frac{\text{Cal}}{(\text{m}^2)(\text{hr})}\right]. \tag{3-33}$$

When the absolute temperature of a body is doubled, its radiating capacity increases 16 times.

The amount of radiant energy actually emanating from a body is less than that from a theoretically absolutely black body, and is written as

$$E = C(T/100)^4 \quad \left[\frac{\text{Cal}}{(\text{m}^2)(\text{hr})}\right], \tag{3-34}$$

where C = coefficient of radiation of a body in Cal/(m²)(hr)(degrees)⁴, whereby $C < C_0$.

The radiating capacity of a body is proportional to its absorbing capacity:

$$C = aC_0, \tag{3-35}$$

where a = coefficient of blackness.

Consequently,

$$E = aC_0(T/100)^4 = (4.96)a(T/100)^4. \tag{3-36}$$

When the temperatures of two mutually acting bodies at a given instant are T_1 and T_2, and $T_1 > T_2$, then the amount of heat $q_{1,2}$ in

Calories transferred in 1 hr from a unit area of surface 1 m² of the first body to the second one is expressed as

$$q_{1,2} = C_n \left[\left(\frac{T_1}{100} \right)^4 - \left(\frac{T_2}{100} \right)^4 \right] \quad \left[\frac{\text{Cal}}{(\text{m}^2)(\text{hr})} \right], \tag{3-37}$$

where C_n = a reciprocal coefficient of radiation to be determined for two parallel plates from the following equation:

$$\frac{1}{C_n} = \frac{1}{C_1} + \frac{1}{C_2} - \frac{1}{C_0}, \tag{3-38}$$

where C_1, C_2 = radiation coefficients of first and second bodies, and $C_0 = (4.96)$ Cal/(m²)(hr)(degree)⁴.

By Eq. (3-30), the rate of heat flow in heat transfer by convection is expressed as

$$q = \alpha(T_1 - T_2), \tag{3-39}$$

from which is derived the coefficient α of heat release from gas (or liquid) at the wall boundary:

$$\alpha = \frac{q}{T_1 - T_{\text{wall}}}. \tag{3-40}$$

If, instead of q, one substitutes in the latter equation $q_{1,2}$ [from Eq. (3-37)], and replaces $(T_1 - T_{\text{wall}})$ by $(T_1 - T_2)$, then the *conventional coefficient of radiation* is obtained:

$$\alpha_c = \frac{q_{1,2}}{T_1 - T_2} \quad \left[\frac{\text{Cal}}{(\text{m}^2)(\text{hr})(\text{degree})} \right]. \tag{3-41}$$

This conventional coefficient of radiation α_c is numerically equal to the amount of radiant heat in kilo-calories transferred by 1 m² of surface during 1 hr at a temperature difference of 1°C.

Upon the simultaneous presence of heat exchange partly by convection and partly by radiant heat exchange, the equation of heat flow is

$$q_{\text{general}} = (\alpha + \alpha_c)(T_1 - T_2) \quad \left[\frac{\text{Cal}}{(\text{m}^2)(\text{hr})(\text{degree})} \right]. \tag{3-42}$$

Example. Calculate heat loss from 1 linear meter of an uncovered steam pipe 30 cm in diameter. The inside temperature is $T_i = 450$°C, and the temperature of the outside medium is $T_0 = 50$°C. The coefficient of blackness for the pipe is given as $a = 0.80$.

Solution.

$$q = \pi d a C_n \left[\left(\frac{T_i + 273°}{100}\right)^4 - \left(\frac{T_0 + 273°}{100}\right)^4\right] =$$

$$= (3.14)(0.30)(0.80)(4.96)\left[\left(\frac{450 + 273}{100}\right)^4 - \left(\frac{50 + 273}{100}\right)^4\right] =$$

$$= 9700 \quad \left[\frac{\text{Cal}}{(\text{m})(\text{hr})}\right].$$

3-11. Example of Combined Heat Exchange. Given a vertical, one-layered wall (Fig. 3-11). Assume heat flows from left to right. T_1 is the temperature of the heating fluid and T_2 is the temperature of the fluid to be heated. Hence, $T_1 > T_2$. The process of heat exchange in the given system consists of these three stages:

1) heat transfer from the first fluid to the wall,
2) heat conduction through the wall, and
3) heat transfer from the right-hand surface of the wall to the second fluid.

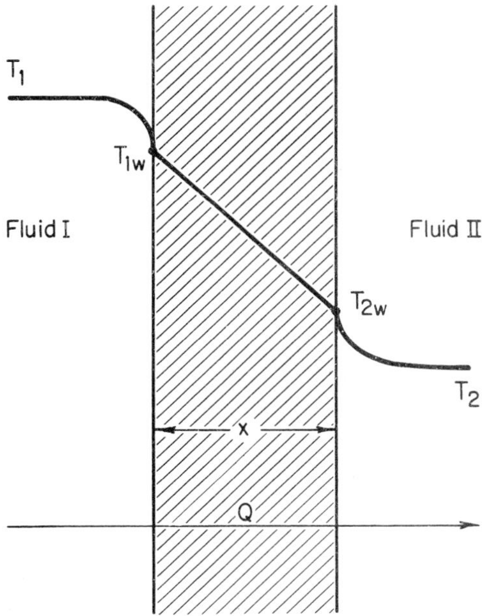

FIG. 3-11 Vertical wall.

The three heat flow equations for the above three kinds of heat transfer are:

1) $$q = \alpha_1(T_1 - T_{1w}) \quad \left[\frac{\text{Cal}}{(\text{m}^2)(\text{hr})}\right], \tag{3-43}$$

where T_{1w} = temperature at the left surface of wall. For pure convection

$$\alpha_1 = \alpha + \alpha_c \quad \left[\frac{\text{Cal}}{(\text{m}^2)(\text{hr})(^\circ\text{C})}\right].$$

2) For heat conduction through the wall

$$q = (K_{\text{wall}}/x)(T_{1w} - T_{2w}) \left[\frac{\text{Cal}}{(\text{m}^2)(\text{hr})}\right], \tag{3-44}$$

where K_{wall} = coefficient of heat conduction of wall material in Cal/(m)(hr)(°C);
x = thickness of wall in meters, and
T_{2w} = temperature at right-hand surface of wall.

3) Heat transfer from right-hand surface of wall to second fluid:

$$q = \alpha_2(T_{2w} - T_2) \quad \left[\frac{\text{Cal}}{(\text{m}^2)(\text{hr})}\right], \tag{3-43a}$$

where α_2 = coefficient of heat transfer in Cal/(m²)(hr)(degree).

Temperature differences:

$$T_1 - T_{1w} = q/\alpha_1 \tag{3-45}$$

$$T_{1w} - T_{2w} = (x/K_{\text{wall}})(q) \tag{3-46}$$

$$T_{2w} - T_2 = q/\alpha_2. \tag{3-47}$$

Addition of these three equations gives

$$T_1 - T_2 = \left(\frac{1}{\alpha_1} + \frac{x}{K_{\text{wall}}} + \frac{1}{\alpha_2}\right) q. \tag{3-48}$$

From here, the rate of heat flow is

$$q = \frac{T_1 - T_2}{\dfrac{1}{\alpha_1} + \dfrac{x}{K_{\text{wall}}} + \dfrac{1}{\alpha_2}} \quad \left[\frac{\text{Cal}}{(\text{m}^2)(\text{hr})}\right], \tag{3-49}$$

or

$$q = K(T_1 - T_2), \tag{3-50}$$

where K = combined coefficient of heat transfer and

$$K = \frac{1}{\dfrac{1}{\alpha_1} + \dfrac{x}{K_{\text{wall}}} + \dfrac{1}{\alpha_2}} \quad \left[\frac{\text{Cal}}{(\text{m}^2)(\text{hr})(\text{degree})}\right]. \tag{3-51}$$

For a wall n layers thick the coefficient of heat transfer is

$$K = \frac{1}{\dfrac{1}{\alpha_1} + \dfrac{x_1}{K_1} + \dfrac{x_2}{K_2} + \dfrac{x_3}{K_3} + \cdots + \dfrac{x_{n-1}}{K_{n-1}} + \dfrac{x_n}{K_n} + \dfrac{1}{\alpha_2}}. \tag{3-52}$$

For cylindrically shaped bodies such as rods or pipes,

$$K = \frac{1}{\dfrac{1}{\alpha_i d_i} + \dfrac{1}{2K_{oi}} \ln \dfrac{d_o}{d_i} + \cdots + \dfrac{1}{\alpha_o d_o}}, \tag{3-53}$$

where index "i" means inside diameter and "o" means outside diameter.

The heat transfer from a non-insulated pipe is

$$q = \frac{\pi(T_i - T_o)}{\dfrac{1}{\alpha_i d_i} + \dfrac{1}{2K} \ln \dfrac{d_2}{d_1} + \dfrac{1}{\alpha_o d_2}} \quad [\text{Cal}/(\text{m})(\text{hr})], \tag{3-54}$$

where T_i = temperature inside the pipe,
T_o = temperature of outside air,
α_i = coefficient of internal heat loss from water to metal wall of pipe, in Cal/(m²)(hr)(degree),
α_o = coefficient of external heat loss from external surface of pipe to air, in Cal/(m²)(hr)(degree),
K = coefficient of heat conduction of material of wall of pipe, in Cal/(m)(hr)(degree),
d_1 = inside diameter of pipe, in m, and
d_2 = outside diameter of pipe, in m.

The amount of heat transferred from the inside of the pipe to the outside air may also be written as

$$q = K_r \pi (T_i - T_o) = \frac{\pi(T_i - T_o)}{R}, \tag{3-55}$$

where K_r = equivalent linear coefficient of heat transfer of a round, uninsulated pipe.

$$K_r = \frac{1}{\dfrac{1}{\alpha_i d_1} + \dfrac{1}{2K} \ln \dfrac{d_2}{d_1} + \dfrac{1}{\alpha_o d_2}} \quad [\text{Cal}/(\text{m})(\text{hr})(\text{degree})]. \tag{3-56}$$

The reciprocal of the coefficient K_r is $1/K_r$, and the equivalent linear thermal resistance to heat transfer is

$$R_r = \frac{1}{K_r} = \frac{1}{\alpha_i d_1} + \frac{1}{2K} \ln \frac{d_2}{d_1} + \frac{1}{\alpha_o d_2} \quad [(\mathrm{m})(\mathrm{hr})(\mathrm{degree})/\mathrm{Cal}]. \quad (3\text{-}57)$$

For pipes with n concentric layers of insulation with diameters d_2, $d_3, \ldots, d_{n+1}$, the linear thermal resistance is

$$R_{\mathrm{ins}} = 1/K_{\mathrm{ins}} = \frac{1}{\alpha_i d_i} + \sum_1^n \left(\frac{1}{2K_i} \ln \frac{d_{i+1}}{d_i}\right) + \frac{1}{\alpha_o d_{n+1}} \quad [(\mathrm{m})(\mathrm{hr})(\mathrm{degree})], \quad (3\text{-}58)$$

and the heat transfer per one linear unit of length, say 1 meter, from the insulated pipe is

$$q_{\mathrm{ins}} = \frac{\pi(T_i - T_o)}{R_{\mathrm{ins}}}. \quad (3\text{-}59)$$

For water flowing through a metal pipe the coefficient of internal heat transfer may be taken as approximately $\alpha_i = 1000$ Cal/(m^2)(hr)(degree), and the coefficient of external heat transfer as $\alpha_o = 12$ Cal/(m^2)(hr)(degree).

***Example.* Heat Given Up by a Human Body.** How much heat q_1 is normally given up by 1 m^2 skin area of a human body in one hour at an ambient temperature of $T_a = -20°C$ if the body is covered with wool $x = 5.00$ mm thick? The coefficient of heat conductivity of wool is $K = 0.035$ Cal/(m)(hr)(°C).

Solution. Clothing, like the fur of animals, is heat insulating because the temperature drop between the body and the air is largely taken up by a calm layer of air between the fibers of the fabric of the clothing (or the hairs of the fur). This medium has a very low heat conductivity.

Assume a steady-state conduction of heat (when the temperature at a fixed point does not change with time). In such a case, the heat flow q_1 through the clothing must be completely transferred through its surface to air by convection, (q_2), i.e., by the principle of continuity of flow, $q_1 = q_2$.

Between the skin surface and the outside surface of the clothing there is a definite temperature gradient ΔT_1 (see Fig. 3-12).

The total temperature drop ΔT between the temperature of the surface of the skin T_s and the ambient temperature T_a is

$$\Delta T = T_s - T_a = 36.6°C - (-20°C) = 56.6°C,$$

where $T_s = 36.6°C$ = surface temperature of the skin, i.e., normal

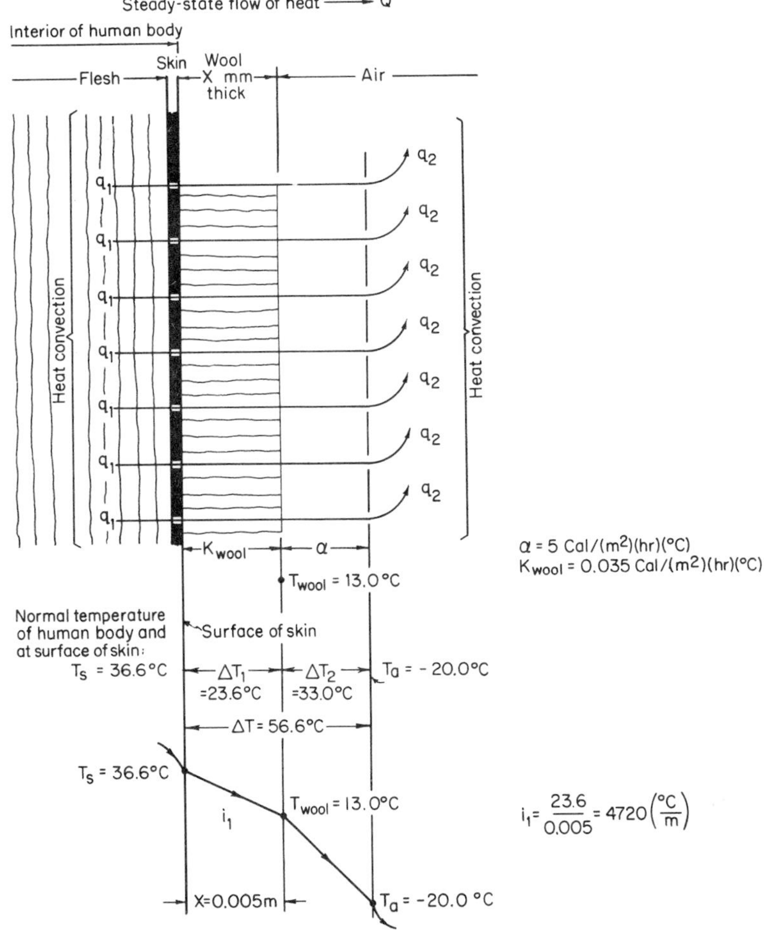

FIG. 3-12 Heat transfer of the clothed human body by conduction and convection.

temperature of the human body, and $T_a = -20°C$ = given ambient temperature.

The heat flows are:

1. Conduction: $q_1 = KA(\Delta T_1/x) = (K/0.005)(\Delta T_1)$ (Cal/hr), where $A = 1.00$ m^2, and 5 mm = 0.005 m.

2. By convection to air, the amount of heat transferred is

$$q_2 = \alpha A(\Delta T) = (5.0)(1.0)(\Delta T_2) \qquad \text{(Cal/hr)},$$

where $\alpha = 5$ = coefficient of thermal convection.

By the principle of continuity of heat flow, $q_1 = q_2$,

$$(K/0.005)(\Delta T_1) = (5.0)(\Delta T_2),$$

and

$$(\Delta T_2)/(\Delta T_1) = (1/0.025)K = 40K = 1.40,$$

$$\Delta T_2 = (1.40)(\Delta T_1).$$

Because

$$(\Delta T_1) + (\Delta T_2) = \Delta T = 56.6°\text{C},$$

$$(\Delta T_1) + (1.40)(\Delta T_1) = 56.6°\text{C},$$

and

$$\underline{\Delta T_1 = 56.6/2.4 = 23.6°\text{C}.}$$

This is to say that with this kind of clothing [$K = 0.035$ Cal/(m²)(hr)(°C), 5 mm thick], (23.6/56.6)100 = 41.7% of the total temperature difference is taken up by the clothing and 58.3% by the temperature drop from convection. At the outer surface of clothing the temperature T_{wool} in this example is

$$T_{\text{wool}} = T_s + \Delta T_1 = 36.6°\text{C} - 23.6°\text{C} = \underline{13.0°\text{C}}.$$

The amount of heat transferred through 1 cm² = 10^{-4} m² surface of skin:

$$q_1 = KA(\Delta T_1/x) = (0.035)(10^{-4})(23.6)/0.005 =$$

$$= \underline{0.01652}\ \underline{\text{cal/(cm}^2\text{)(hr)}}.$$

3-12. Example of Heat Exchange Between Soil and Building Floor. Given a thermal system as shown in Fig. 3-13. Calculate the rate of heat flow Q per hour through 1 m² of area. For the given system the thermal resistance $1/K$ is expressed as

$$\frac{1}{K} = \frac{1}{\alpha_1} + \frac{x_1}{K_1} + \frac{x_2}{K_2} + \cdots + \frac{x_n}{K_n}, \tag{3-60}$$

where the symbols are the same as before.

Given: $\alpha_1 = 5$; $K_1 = 1.1$ Cal/(m)(hr)(°C) for layer 1;
$K_2 = 0.5$ Cal/(m)(hr)(°C) for layer 2;
$K_{n=3} = 1.3$ Cal/(m)(hr)(°C) for layer 3.

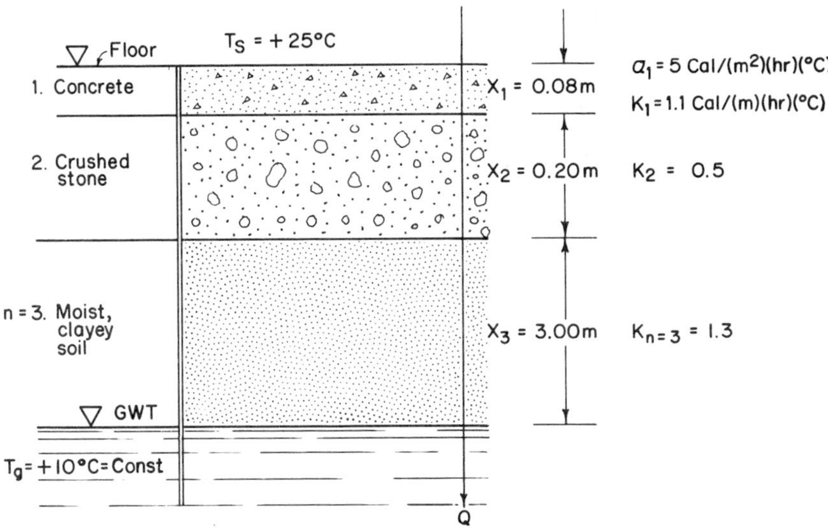

FIG. 3-13 Floor-soil system.

The surface temperature of the concrete slab is $T_s = 25°C$. The temperature of the groundwater is $T_g = 10°C$. The thicknesses of the layers are

layer 1 (concrete slab): $x_1 = 0.08$ m,
layer 2 (crushed stone): $x_2 = 0.20$ m,
layer 3 (moist, clayey soil): $x_{n=3} = 3.00$ m.

Solution.

$$\frac{1}{K} = \frac{1}{5.0} + \frac{0.08}{1.1} + \frac{0.2}{0.5} + \frac{3.0}{1.3} = 2.98 \qquad [(\text{m})(\text{hr})(°\text{C})/\text{Cal}],$$

and the system's coefficient of heat transfer is

$$K = 1/2.98 = 0.34 \text{ Cal/(m)(hr)(°C)}.$$

The rate of heat transfer is

$$q = K(T_s - T_g) = (0.34)(25 - 10) = \underline{5.1 \text{ Cal/(m}^2\text{)(hr)}}.$$

3-13. Electric Wire Cooled by Air

Example. An electric wire the diameter of which is $d_1 = 2$ mm is at a temperature of $T_1 = 90°C$ and is cooled by calm air, the temperature of which is $T_2 = 20°C$. The coefficient of heat transfer from wire to air is $\alpha_1 = 20$ Cal/(m²)(hr)(degree). Calculate temperature T_{11} of the wire if the wire is covered by rubber insulation 4 mm thick, and if the power of current in the wire is left unchanged. The coefficient of heat conduction of the rubber insulation is $K = 0.15$ Cal/(m)(hr)(degree). The coefficient of heat transfer from the surface of the rubber insulation to air is $\alpha_2 = 10$ Cal/(m^2)(hr)(degree).

Solution. By the principle of continuity, the amount of heat given up by the bare wire is equal to the amount of heat given up to the air by an insulated wire. Hence,

$$q = \pi d_1 \alpha_1 (T_1 - T_2) = \frac{\pi (T_{11} - T_2)}{\dfrac{1}{2K} \ln \dfrac{d_2}{d_1} + \dfrac{1}{\alpha_2 d_2}}. \tag{3-61}$$

The sought temperature T_{11} of the insulated wire is

$$T_{11} = T_2 + d_1 \alpha_1 (T_1 - T_2)\left[\frac{1}{2K} \ln(d_2/d_1) + \frac{1}{\alpha_2 d_2}\right] =$$

$$= 20 + (0.002)(20)(90 - 20)$$

$$\times \left[\frac{1}{0.30} (2.3)(\log 10.0/2.0) + 1/(0.01)(10)\right] =$$

$$= 20 + (2.8)(5.36 + 10) = \underline{63.00(°\text{C}) < 90°\text{C}}. \tag{3-62}$$

The temperature of the insulated wire is lower than that of the bare wire. This is so because the diameter of the wire, $d_1 = 2.00$ mm, is less than the critical diameter d_{cr} of the insulation:

$$d_{cr} = \frac{2K_{ins}}{\alpha_2} = \frac{(2)(0.15)}{10} = \frac{0.30}{10} = \underline{0.03 \text{ (m)} = 30 \text{ mm}}.$$

3-14. Heat Flow and Course of Temperature in a Thick-Walled Tube. Assume a constant heat flow through the wall of a tube x units thick (see Fig. 3-14). The tube is filled with a flowing fluid (F) of constant temperature T_i. A flowing medium U surrounding the tube has a constant temperature T_o, and x is the body of the tube carrying the heat flow. The discontinuity in temperature, B_2A_2 and A_1B_1, is the consequence of transitional resistance (= contact resistance). This resistance must be overcome by the heat flow upon entering and leaving the wall of the tube.

The following equations are valid for a wall of tube one unit long for the amount Q of flowing heat, expressed in Cal/(m)(hr):

$$Q = 2\pi r_2 \alpha_2 \tau_2 \tag{3-63}$$

$$Q = 2\pi K \frac{T_2 - T_1}{\ln(r_2/r_1)} \tag{3-64}$$

$$Q = 2\pi r_1 \alpha_1 \tau_1, \tag{3-65}$$

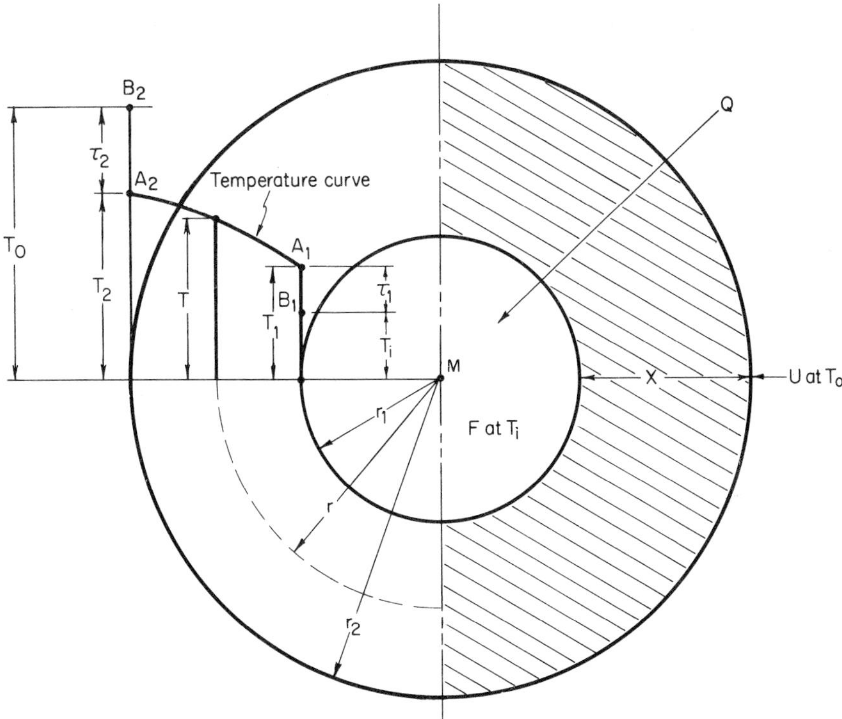

FIG. 3-14 Course of temperature in a thick-walled tube at steady flow of heat.

where α_2 and α_1 are the heat transfer coefficients in Cal/(m²)(hr)(degree) at the outside and inside surfaces of the tube, and K is the coefficient of thermal conductivity of the wall of the tube in Cal/(m)(hr)(degree). Also,

$$T_1 = T_i + \tau_1 \tag{3-66}$$

and

$$T_2 = T_o - \tau_2, \tag{3-67}$$

in which the positive sign designates the heat flow toward the inside of the tube.

At a distance r from the center of the tube the radial heat flow q per unit area, expressed in Cal/(m²)(hr), is

$$q = K\frac{\partial T}{\partial r} \qquad \text{Ref. (20).} \tag{3-68}$$

From the steadiness of the heat flow, which characterizes the steady condition, it follows that

$$q = Q/2\pi r. \tag{3-69}$$

Hence,

$$\partial T = \frac{Q}{2\pi K}\frac{\partial r}{r}. \tag{3-70}$$

Integration yields

$$T = \frac{Q}{2\pi K}\ln r + C. \tag{3-71}$$

From the boundary conditions, whereby temperatures T_1 and T_2 are coordinated with radii r_1 and r_2, respectively, obtain the constant of integration C by substituting Eq. (3-64) in Eq. (3-71):

$$C = T - \frac{T_2 - T_1}{\ln(r_2/r_1)}. \tag{3-72}$$

When $r = r_1$, then $T = T_1$, and

$$C = \frac{T_1 \ln r_2 - T_2 \ln r_1}{\ln(r_2/r_1)}. \tag{3-73}$$

The simultaneous solution of the five equations, Eqs. (3-63) to (3-67) gives

$$\tau_1 = \frac{T_o - T_i}{\dfrac{\alpha_1 r_1}{K}\ln\dfrac{r_2}{r_1} + \dfrac{\alpha_1 r_1}{\alpha_2 r_2} + 1} \tag{3-74}$$

$$\tau_2 = \frac{T_o - T_i}{\dfrac{\alpha_2 r_2}{K}\ln\dfrac{r_2}{r_1} + \dfrac{\alpha_2 r_2}{\alpha_1 r_1} + 1} \tag{3-75}$$

$$Q = 2\pi\frac{T_o - T_i}{\dfrac{1}{K}\ln\dfrac{r_2}{r_1} + \dfrac{1}{\alpha_1 r_1} + \dfrac{1}{\alpha_2 r_2}}. \tag{3-76}$$

T_1 and T_2 can then be calculated from Eqs. (3-66) and (3-67). The applications of these equations are seen in the following example.

Example. A concrete tube is surrounded by moving air at temperature $T_o = 15$°C. Inside the tube water flows at a temperature $T_i = 5$°C.

Given: $r_1 = 1.20$ m; $r_2 = 1.40$ m; $K = 2.0$ Cal/(m)(hr)(degree); $\alpha_1 = 1800$ Cal/(m²)(hr)(degree); $\alpha_2 = 10$ Cal/(m²)(hr)(degree).

Solution. With the quantities given above obtain, by Eq. (3-74),

$$\tau_1 = \frac{15° - 5°}{\dfrac{(1800)(1.20)}{2.0}\ln\dfrac{1.40}{1.20} + \dfrac{(1800)(1.20)}{(10)(1.40)} + 1} = \underline{0.0312°\text{C.}}$$

By Eq. (3-75),

$$\tau_2 = \frac{10°}{\dfrac{(10)(1.40)}{2.0}\ln\dfrac{1.40}{1.20} + \dfrac{(10)(1.40)}{(1800)(1.20)} + 1} = \underline{4.80°\text{C.}}$$

By Eq. (3-66),

$$T_1 = 5° + 0.03° = 5.03°\text{C.}$$

By Eq. (3-67),

$$T_2 = 15° - 4.80° = 10.20°\text{C.}$$

By Eqs. (3-63), (3-64), and (3-65),

$$Q = (2)(1.40)(\pi)(10)(4.80) = 422 \text{ Cal/(m)(hr)},$$

$$Q = (2)(\pi)(2.0)\frac{5.17}{\ln\dfrac{1.40}{1.20}} = 422 \text{ Cal/(m)(hr)},$$

$$Q = (2)(\pi)(1.20)(1800)(0.0312) = 422 \text{ Cal/(m)(hr)}.$$

The equality of the three values of Q confirms the correctness of the solution.

By Eq. (3-73),

$$C = \frac{(5.03)\ln(1.40) - (10.2)\ln(1.20)}{\ln(140/120)} = -1.08,$$

and finally, from Eq. (3-71) obtain

$$\underline{T = \frac{Q}{2\pi K}\ln r - 1.08.} \qquad (3\text{-}77)$$

By means of Eq. (3-77), the course of the temperature in the wall of the tube can readily be calculated.

The values α_1, α_2, and K vary considerably; hence the results depend very much upon these quantities. In a closed room in which air is circulating naturally, α may be from 5 to 7. Outside, at an air velocity of about 5 m/sec, $\alpha = 20$ Cal/(m^2)(hr)(degree).[21] For water, $\alpha = 500$ to 3000 Cal/(m^2)(hr)(degree), increasing with the temperature of the water.[22]

REFERENCES

1. A. R. Jumikis, *The Frost Penetration Problem in Highway Engineering,* Rutgers University Press, New Brunswick, N.J., 1955.
2. L. B. Wickoff, "Some Observations on Effect of Frost in Raising Weight," *Engineering News-Record,* **80,** 13, March 28, 1918, pp. 627–628.
3. R. D. Chellis, *Pile Foundations,* McGraw-Hill Book Company, Inc., New York, 1951, p. 104.
4. A. R. Jumikis, Frost Action Research Memorandum, 1948–1956: "Formulation of Upward Moisture Transfer Upon Freezing by Various Soil Moisture Transfer Mechanisms." Submitted to the Engineering Research Advisory Committee at Rutgers—The State University, College of Engineering, December 1956, New Brunswick, N.J.
5. A. R. Jumikis, "Some Concepts Pertaining to the Freezing Soil Systems," *Highway Research Board Special Report,* No. 40, on "Water and Its Conduction in Soils" (an international Symposium), National Academy of Sciences–National Research Council publication 629, Washington, D.C., 1958, pp. 178–190.
6. H. P. Hutchison, I. S. Nixon, and K. G. Denbigh, "The Thermo-Osmosis of Liquids Through Porous Materials," *Discussion of the Faraday Society,* **3,** 1948, Interaction of Water and Porous Materials. Gurney and Jackson, London, pp. 86–94.
7. Smithsonian Physical Tables, Publication 4169, Smithsonian Institution, 1954, Washington, D.C., p. 161.
8. G. Tammann, *The States of Aggregation,* translated by R. F. Mehl. D. Van Nostrand Company, Inc., New York, 1925, p. 3.
9. W. Bernatzik, *Baugrund und Physik,* Schweizer Druck- und Verlagshaus, Zürich, 1947, p. 87.
10. N. E. Dorsey, *Properties of Ordinary Water-Substance,* Reinhold Publishing Corp., New York, 1940, p. 399.
11. P. W. Bridgeman, *Proceedings, American Academy of Arts and Sciences,* **70,** 1935, p. 25.
12. *International Critical Tables,* **3,** published by McGraw-Hill Book Company, Inc., New York, 1928, for the National Research Council of the U.S.A., pp. 210–211.
13. Arthur and Elizabeth Rose, *The Condensed Chemical Dictionary,* 5th ed., Reinhold Publishing Corp., New York, 1956, p. 414.
14. J. B. J. Fourier, *The Analytical Theory of Heat,* translated by A. Freeman, Cambridge University Press, London, 1878.
15. M. Gaston Darboux, Oeuvres de Fourier, Vol. 1: *Théorie Analytique de la Chaleur,* Gauthier-Villars et Fils, Paris, 1888.
16. H. L. F. von Helmholtz, "Theorie der Wärme," *Vorlesungen über Theoretische Physik,* Vol. 6: Johann Ambrosius Barth, Leipzig, 1903.
17. R. V. Churchill, *Fourier Series and Boundary Value Problems,* McGraw-Hill Book Company, Inc., New York, 1941.
18. M. Jacob, *Elements of Heat Transfer,* John Wiley and Sons, Inc., New York, 1950.
19. H. S. Carslaw, *Introduction to the Mathematical Theory of the Conduction of Heat in Solids,* Macmillan, London, 1921, p. 21.
20. "Hütte," *Des Ingenieurs Taschenbuch,* Vol. 1, Wilhelm Ernst und Sohn, Berlin, 1935, p. 492.
21. "Hütte," *Des Ingenieurs Taschenbuch,* Vol. 3, Wilhelm Ernst und Sohn, Berlin, 1934, p. 352.
22. "Hütte," *Des Ingenieurs Taschenbuch,* Vol. 1, Wilhelm Ernst und Sohn, Berlin, 1931, p. 502.

Part II

Thermal Solidification of Soil

Chapter 4

Firing and Natural Freezing and Thawing of Soil

Soil may be solidified by means of thermal processes at temperatures above freezing and below freezing. The most common method of soil solidification above freezing is firing (baking). The firing method is applied to roads, tunnels, vertical shafts, and embankment slopes. Soil is solidified below freezing by (a) natural freezing and (b) artificial freezing. Natural freezing is utilized in climates where freezing seasons occur. This method is also known as *winter freezing*. Artificial freezing is used where no sheet piling in soil can be used, no caissons can be sunk, and where there is much flowing water in the soil.

4-1. Firing (or Baking) of Soil. Soil is stabilized by firing when moisture is driven out of it by heat. The method is applicable to cohesive soils.

Cohesive soil dried unintentionally can damage the structure that rests upon it. The heat source can be baker's ovens, brick kilns,[(1)] steel plant furnaces, deep-lying heating installations, boilers, steam pipes and hot water pipes, buried electric cables, and other heat-producing installations. Under such installations, the direction of heat flow is down into the soil.

Heat flowing from a hot source, say a furnace, through its foundations to the underlying cohesive soil may bring about uneven drying and shrinking of soil. Many brick kilns and baker's ovens have been damaged by the drying effect of their fires.[(1)]

4-2. Heat Treatment. The physical and mechanical properties of water-saturated cohesive soils may be improved by decreasing the soil moisture content. Bendel,[(2)] for example, writes that a slide-prone slope has been stabilized by driving into it horizontal shafts from which the soil was dried by means of large blowers and stoves. Every day during the first six months, 1400 liters of water were removed from the soil. The method is very expensive, and when the artificial water removal is discontinued, water may again seep into the soil.

The improvement of the physical properties of clay and silty soils by heat depends on the elevation of temperature applied to the soil. Practically, there are three methods of thermal soil treatment by heating or firing:

1) heating, or thermal dehydration, of soil at temperatures from about 300°C to 500°C,

2) firing of road surfaces *in place* at temperatures from about 600°C to 800°C, and

3) firing in a factory (manufacture of clinkers) at temperatures above 1000°C.

The heating of soil from about 105°C to 110°C first evaporates the moisture, then increases the temperature of the soil.

Heat is used to recrystallize certain minerals, such as evaporation of crystallization and chemically bound water from aluminosilicates. Higher temperatures cause certain minerals to melt or decompose, thereby strengthening the heat-treated material. The best results in thermal treatment give soils a moisture content about 15% to 25% of the clay fraction.

The fired road surfaces (clay) wear out quickly under traffic, become dusty, and require surfacing.

4-3. Firing of Road Soil Surface. The essential features of road soil firing are illustrated by a method used in the so-called "black soil" areas in Australia, where gravel or crushed rock is not available.[(3)] A slow-moving, downdraft furnace with a speed of about 10 ft/hr was developed at Sydney, New South Wales, for baking the soil in place and converting it into a bricklike material. The machine is wood-fired, of the air-gas producer type, and is propelled on a wheeled chassis under its own power.

Prior to heating, the road is graded to the desired cross section, and the strip to be treated is scarified to a depth of about 4 in. As the machine advances over a particular area, the soil is first subjected to the exudation of the gases and then to gradually increasing temperatures until the full intensity of the heat of the gases issuing from the generator is reached. Work proceeds continuously day and night, a 6-ft wide machine completing about 500 ft of roadway 18 ft wide per week. The effect of the heat treatment is noticed to a depth of about 6 in.

4-4. Deep Thermal Treatment. Deep thermal treatment, or firing, is a method of stabilizing cohesive earth masses in order to improve the bearing capacity of soil or to stabilize slopes. There are several methods, some of which are

1) the burning of wood, coal, or oil in tunnels and galleries,
2) the burning of liquid fuel in vertical and inclined borings,
3) the burning of gas in borings.

Burning fuel in tunnels and galleries is time-consuming: it takes several months to fire out each individual gallery, and it is very difficult to guide and control the firing process.

According to Beles and Stankulescu,[4] the firing of soil by burning liquid fuel in borings has been practiced in Rumania as an efficient and economical means of deep thermal treatment for stabilizing clayey and loess soils. In this method, two boreholes are made, about 20 cm in diameter and spaced about 80 cm apart. Through one of these borings, the firing boring, the soil is fired, and through the other boring, the free draft boring, connected at its bottom to the firing boring by a small passage through the soil, the burnt gases are evacuated. Many pairs of firing-draft borings (twin borings) can be operated simultaneously.

Instead of liquid fuel, gas may be burned in the firing boring, or hot air may be introduced into the borehole. There are several ways to do this. In one method, compressed air is heated in a central heating plant to about 600°C. The hot air is forced from the central heater into the borings, where the hot air solidifies the cohesive soil around the boring (see Fig. 4-1). The main disadvantage is the relatively great loss of thermal energy because of the long pipes through which the hot air is conveyed from the central heating plant to the firing holes. Attempts have been made to use mobile heating plants to reduce this heat loss.

Another method of soil firing is the one in which gas and air are mixed and then introduced into a firing pipe (or firing needle) at the top of the borehole. Several "points," or boreholes, can be fired simultaneously and independently. The heat loss is minimum. The main disadvantage in this method of soil solidification is the necessity for many sets of machinery, mainly compressors for each firing point, and the initial cost of the installation.

4-5. Necessary Amount of Heat. The amount of heat Q necessary for firing a soil has two component heats, the amount of heat Q_s necessary to fire 1 m^3 of soil skeleton, and the amount of heat Q_w neces-

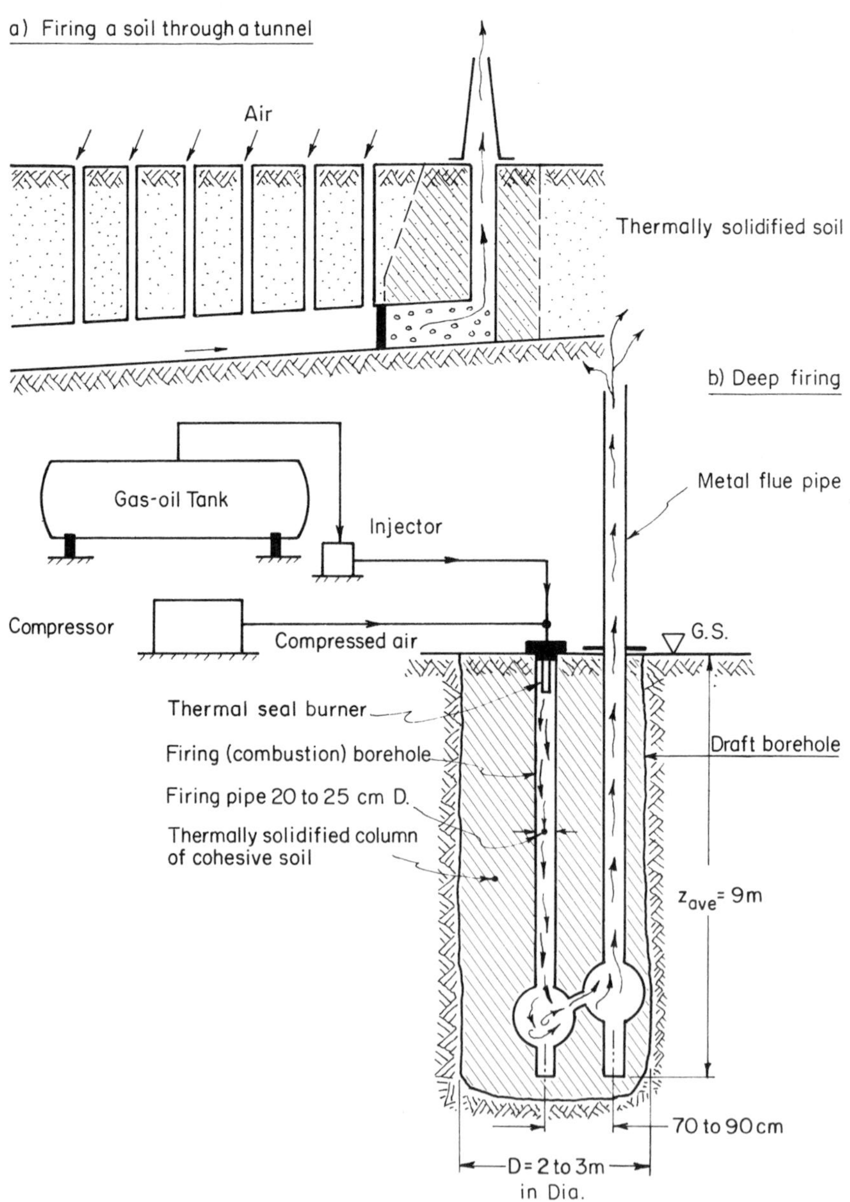

FIG. 4-1 Thermal solidification of soil.

sary to heat soil water in 1 m³ of soil till evaporation at $T_v = 100°C$ is completed. The total amount of heat Q may be calculated as follows:

$$Q = Q_s + Q_w = \gamma_s c_s (T_f - T_i) + W_w[c_w(T_v - T_i) + L_v] \quad \text{(Cal)}, \quad (4\text{-}1)$$

where γ_s = weight of soil skeleton or solids in 1 m³ of soil;
$\dot{c}_s = 0.19$ = heat capacity of soil solids, in cal/(m³)(°C);
T_f = average firing temperature, say 600°C;
T_i = initial temperature of soil before firing;
W_w = weight of water in 1 m³ soil at moisture content w% by dry weight;
$c_w = 1.0$ = heat capacity of water;
$T_v = 100°C$ = temperature of vaporization, and
$L_v = 540$ cal = latent heat of vaporization.

The calculation of the necessary amount of heat for firing a point in the soil is illustrated by the following example.

Example. Calculate the necessary amount of heat and fuel for firing a point (i.e., a cylindrical column) of soil 10 m deep and 2 m in diameter.

Given. Volume of soil to be fired:

$$V = \frac{\pi D^2}{4} h = \frac{(3.14)(2^2)(10)}{4} = 31.4 \text{ (m}^3\text{)}.$$

Unit weight of soil:

$$\gamma = 1.77 \text{ t/m}^3 \ (= 110 \text{ lb/ft}^3).$$

Moisture content of soil, by dry weight:

$$w = 12.0\%$$

Unit weight of solids in soil:

$$\gamma_s = \frac{\gamma}{1 + w} = \frac{1.77}{1 + 0.12} = 1.58 \text{ (t/m}^3\text{)}.$$

Weight of water in voids of soil:

$$W_w = \gamma - \gamma_s = 1.77 - 1.58 = 0.19 \text{ (t/m}^3\text{)}.$$

Initial temperature of soil: $T_i = 0°C$.
Average soil temperature during firing: $T_f = 600°C$.

Heat consumption for firing 1 m³ *of soil solids from* $T_i = 0°C$ *to* $T_f = 600°C$:

$$Q_s = \gamma_s c_s (T_f - T_i) = (1580)(0.19)(600 - 0) = \underline{180{,}120 \text{ (Cal)}}.$$

Heat required for heating water contained in 1 m³ *of soil till evaporation at* $T_v = 100°C$:

$$Q_w = W_w[c_w(T_v - T_i) + L_v] = (190)[(1.0)(100 - 0) + 540] =$$
$$= \underline{121{,}600 \text{ (Cal)}}.$$

Total heat required for firing 1 m³ *of soil:*

$$Q = Q_s + Q_w = 180{,}120 + 121{,}600 = 301{,}720 \text{ (Cal/m}^3) = \underline{310{,}000 \text{ Cal/m}^3}.$$

Amount of fuel oil necessary for firing 1 m³ *of soil:*

$$Q/Q_0 = 310{,}000/10{,}000 = 31.0 \text{ (kg)},$$

where $Q_0 = 10{,}000$ Cal/kg is the heating value (calorific value) of combustion of the fuel used in these calculations.

Amount of fuel oil for firing of $V = 31.4$ m³ *of soil:*

$$(Q/Q_0)V = (31.0)(31.4) = 973.4 \text{ (kg)}.$$

If the firing equipment is such that in 1 hour and for 1 linear meter of firing pipe 0.50 kg of fuel oil is consumed, then for one day and for one firing pipe, or borehole, there are needed

$$(0.5)(10)(24) = 120.0 \text{ kg}$$

of fuel oil.

Duration of firing of one firing point:

$$t = 973.4/120.0 = \underline{8.11 \text{ (hours)}}.$$

Of course, heat losses must be added to make the system work efficiently.

Chapter 5

Natural Freezing

5-1. Freezing of Bodies of Water. Water in ponds, lakes, rivers, reservoirs and other basins freezes from the surface downwards. This is a function of two principal factors: 1) density of water and 2) latent heat of fusion of water.

Water is densest at +4°C (Figs. 5-1 and 5-2). Also, latent heat, released upon freezing of water, dissipates upwards through the surface of the body of water (heat flows from points at higher temperature to points at lower temperature—in this case cold air is at the surface).

When the water at the surface cools, it becomes heavier and sinks to the bottom of the basin. This sinking continues until the water temperature drops to +4°C. The water at the bottom of the basin is now about +4°C. Upon further cooling of the water at the surface—from +4°C to just above freezing—water expands and becomes lighter per unit of volume and remains above the denser water at the bottom. Upon continued freezing, the surface water cools to 0°C. The colder water, lighter in density than that at +4°C, remains at the surface of the basin. Thus ice, being lighter than water, forms at the surface first. Solidification of water into ice begins in the form of a thin sheet of ice. The thickness of the ice sheet depends upon the rate of heat loss through the ice by conduction.

5-2. Thickness of Ice Sheet. The thickness of a freezing ice sheet, x cm after t sec from the start of freezing of a calm lake, can be approximately calculated as set forth here:

Assume that

1. the upper surface of the ice sheet is at temperature $T_2 = T_s = 0°C$ (Fig. 5-3);
2. the lower surface of the ice sheet is at temperature $T_1 = T_{fr} = T°C$; where T_{fr} = freezing temperature, say 0°C;

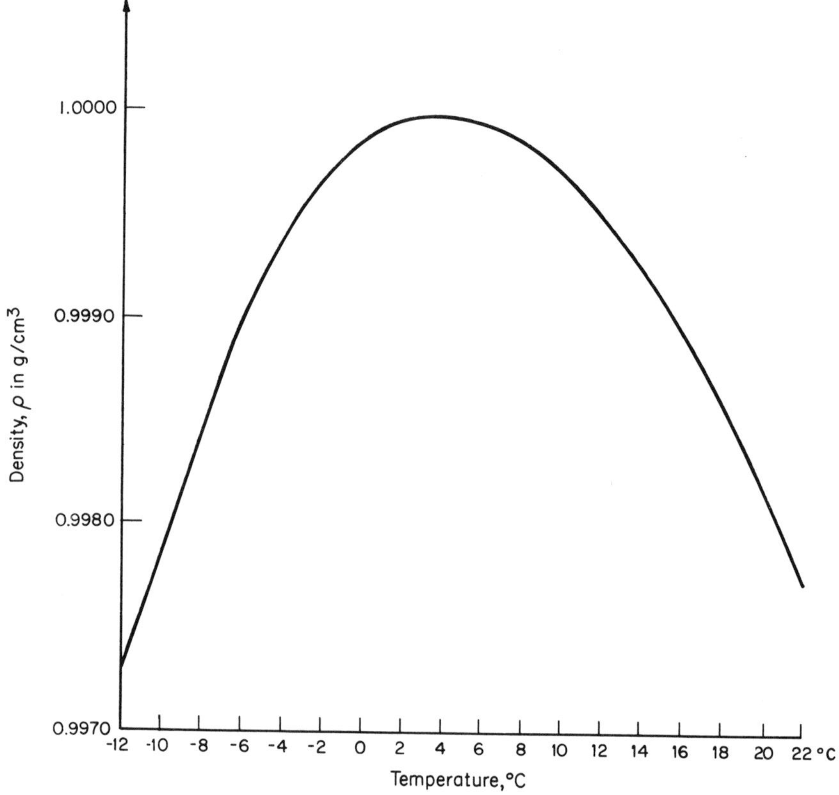

FIG. 5-1 Density of water as a function of temperature.

3. the density of ice at 0°C is ρ g/cm^3;
4. the coefficient of thermal conductivity of ice at 0°C is K (cal)/(cm)(sec)(degree);
5. the increase in thickness of the ice sheet during a differential time dt is dx;
6. the horizontal surface area A of ice through which the upward-flowing heat dissipates is one square unit large, say $A = 1$ cm^2.

When the conditions are such that the temperature gradient between the upper and lower surfaces of the ice sheet x cm thick is linear, then the temperature gradient across the ice sheet may be written as [5]

$$\frac{T_1 - T_2}{x} = \frac{\Delta T}{x} \qquad (°\text{C/cm}). \tag{5-1}$$

A gradient generally denotes the change in certain elements per unit distance or length.

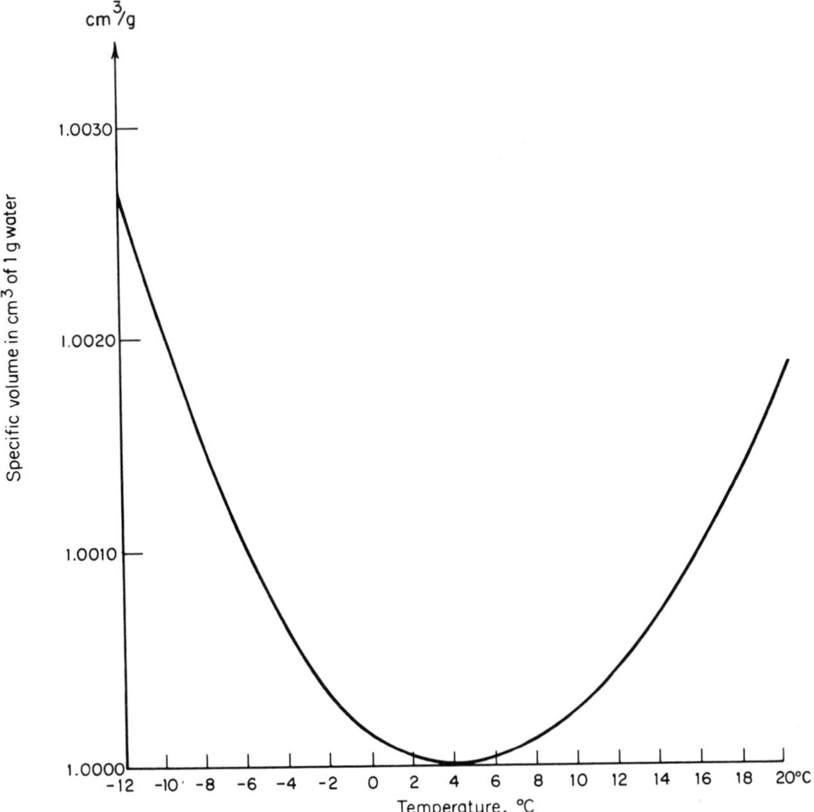

FIG. 5-2 Specific volume of water as a function of temperature.

During time dt, a volume of $[(1 \times 1)(dx)]$ cm³ of ice is formed, whose mass m is

$$m = \rho(1)(dx) \qquad \text{(g)}. \tag{5-2}$$

The amount of latent heat Q flowing upward through the area $A = 1$ cm², is

$$Q = L\rho\, dx \qquad (\text{cal/cm}^2), \tag{5-3}$$

where $L = 80$ cal/g = latent heat of fusion of ice.

The amount of heat that flows upward per unit area through the ice sheet in time dt is

$$K\frac{\Delta T}{x}\,dt \qquad (\text{cal/cm}^2). \tag{5-4}$$

This amount of heat is equal to that released and dissipated when the

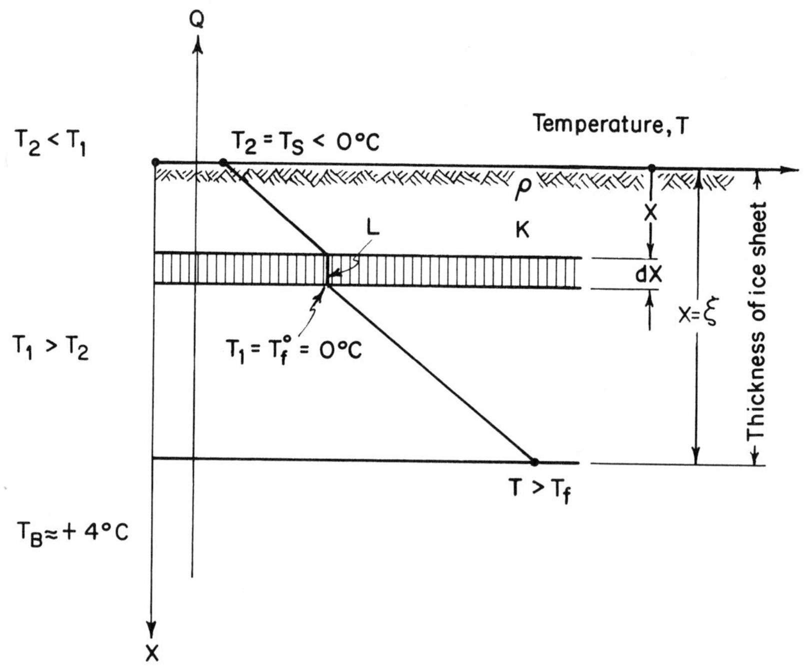

FIG. 5-3 Calculation of thickness of ice sheet.

thickness of the ice sheet increases by dx; thus,

$$K\frac{T}{x}\,dt = L\rho\,dx, \tag{5-5}$$

where $T = \Delta T$.

Separation of variables gives

$$x\,dx = \frac{KT}{L\rho}\,dt. \tag{5-6}$$

The limits of integration for the physical conditions are evaluated as follows: the thickness of ice is $x = 0$ when time $t = 0$:

$$\int_{x_1=0}^{x_2=\xi} x\,dx = \frac{KT}{L}\int_{t_1=0}^{t_2=t} dt. \tag{5-7}$$

Integration of Eq. (5-7) yields the thickness ξ of the ice sheet frozen during time t:

$$x = \xi = \sqrt{\frac{2KT}{L\rho}\,t} \qquad \text{(cm)}. \tag{5-8}$$

The thickness of the ice sheet is proportional to the square root of temperature difference T between both sides of the ice sheet and proportional to the square root of time.

Equation (5-8) is known as Stefan's formula,[5,6] and may be written as

$$\xi = \sqrt{\frac{2KT}{L\rho}} \cdot \sqrt{t}. \tag{5-9}$$

Example.

With $K = 0.0053$ cal/(cm)(sec)(degree) for ice at 0°C,
$T_2 = T_s = -6$°C = surface temperature,
$T = T_1 - T_2 = 0 - (-6) = 6$(°C),
$L = 80$ cal/g, and
$\rho = 0.99$ g/cm^3 at 0°C,

the thickness of the ice sheet frozen over a pond in two days (172,800 sec) since the beginning of freezing is, by Eq. (5-8),

$$\xi = \sqrt{\frac{(2)(0.0053)(6)(172800)}{(80)(0.99)}} = \underline{11.78 \text{ (cm)}}.$$

Water containing impurities or salt would require more than two days to freeze an ice sheet 11.78 cm thick. Atmospheric pressure also affects the rate of freezing.

5-3. Effects of Freezing Upon Soil. The freezing process in soil and the heat and moisture transfer from warm regions to colder ones are very complex phenomena. Indeed, some of the processes which take place during the freezing of a soil system are not yet well understood.

Studies show that a variation in any one of the factors in the soil freezing process influences to a greater or lesser extent the other factors, such as the properties of soil, water, and ice. The entire soil-water-temperature system is influenced by the application of a freezing thermal potential such as heat.

Depending upon the texture of the soil and the packing and shape of the soil particles, the voids in the soil system form channels of various sizes, shapes, and roughness for the passage of liquids and gases. Thus the soil moisture flows upward through poorly defined flow paths in a zigzag motion and also disperses through the constrictions of the void lattice.

Freezing of a soil system is brought about when cold temperature comes in contact with the surface of the soil system. Upon the application of a freezing thermal potential, the upper part of the soil system freezes, after releasing the latent heat of the soil water. Across the soil system, from the top down, a curvilinear temperature gradient sets in (Fig. 5-4). Then an upward heat transfer from a region of higher

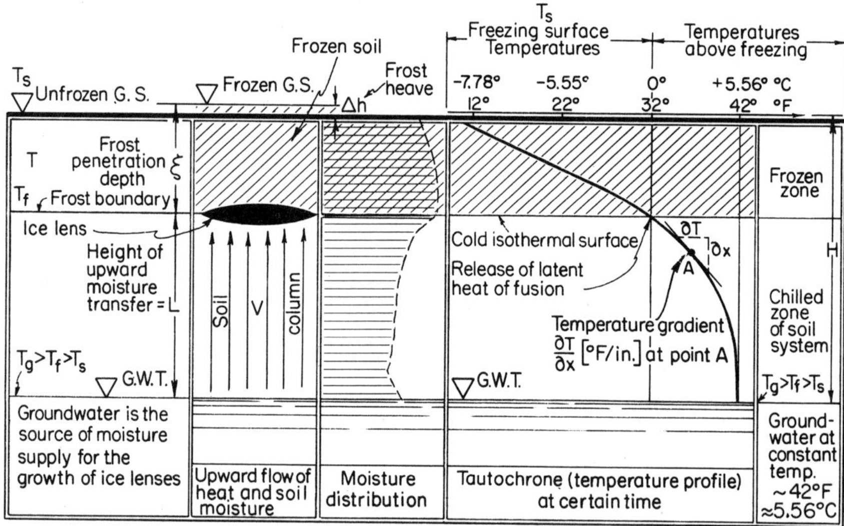

FIG. 5-4 Unidirectional upward flow of soil moisture upon freezing. Open system.

temperature (groundwater) towards a region of colder temperature (frozen layer of soil) takes place. This is one of the striking characteristics of heat—its tendency to translocate continuously from points of higher temperature to points of lower temperature. Thus application of a thermal potential difference to the soil system means that energy has been applied. The source of heat is in the groundwater. The soil receives its heat from the radiation of the sun and from conduction from the interior of the earth.

Thermal energy, measured by work done across the porous soil system, starts the upward migration of soil moisture. During the course of the upward migration, the flowing water loses some of its driving pressure. This means that the driving pressure performs some mechanical work which is lost. In doing external, overall work, the entire soil system loses some of its energy, so that the system does not work with 100% efficiency. Depending upon the state of packing, the soil moisture may first undercool and then freeze. Generally, the finer the voids in the soil in which the soil water is held, the lower is its freezing point.

During the freezing process in soil, many other changes take place—changes in thermal properties of the various substances present in soil, undercooling of water (in proper environment), change in density and viscosity of water, changes in the dielectric constant of water, electric breakdown of the liquid, and changes in the structure of the double layer around the soil particles. The resulting frost heaves, frost penetration depth and thawing of the frozen soil, and changes within the soil ultimately contribute to road damage, and especially to pavement damage.

5-4. Some Principal Modes of Moisture Transport in Soil Upon Freezing. Basically, soil moisture can be transported upward through the porous medium of soil upon freezing as

a) a vapor,
b) a liquid (water in bulk, or stressed water),
c) both liquid and vapor.

5-5. Vapor Transport. If the voids are relatively large, and there is no continuous soil moisture in liquid form in the voids connecting the groundwater with the downward-freezing ice lenses, the moisture from the groundwater is transported upward by way of vapor diffusion.[(7)] The driving pressure is the vapor pressure difference between the partial vapor pressure at the warmer end (the free water surface = groundwater table) and the partial vapor pressure in the upper region of the soil system just below the frozen ice, where it can be very small or negligible compared with that at the free surface.[(8)] This is to say that moisture migration in the vapor phase takes place in the direction along the drop of the thermal gradient. The vapor pressure decreases from the groundwater table up curvilinearly as the temperature decreases from the groundwater table up to the freezing isothermal surface (Fig. 5-5).

Vapor diffusion in soil upon freezing along soil particles coated with film moisture is difficult to comprehend analytically because of the difficulty in expressing by an equation the geometry of the voids of the system or the surface topography of the soil particles. This, however, may be done most readily by experiments.

If soil is fully saturated with water, the moisture migration cannot take place in the vapor phase. If the packing of the soil particles is very dense, moisture transfer in the vapor phase is ineffective.[(7)]

The various modes of soil moisture transfer[(9, 10, 11)] are illustrated in Fig. 5-6.

5-6. Film-Capillary Moisture Transport. The moisture migration process determines the moisture distribution in soil, and thereby the so-called drying out of the soil. If there is no groundwater present (approximately a closed system), the soil freezing is a drying process until all the soil moisture has been transferred into the freezing zone.

If the packing of the soil particles is such that the soil moisture can occupy absolutely all voids continuously connected to the ground-

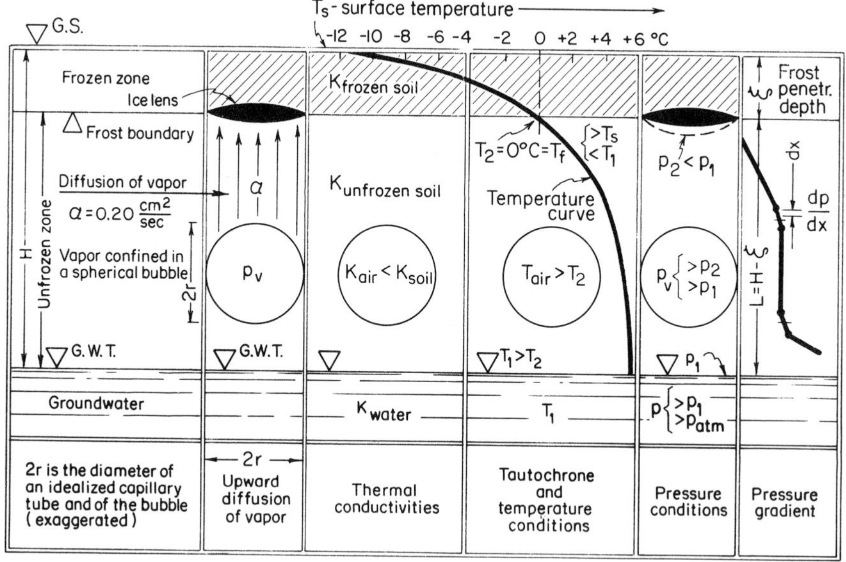

FIG. 5-5 Freezing soil system. Upward diffusion of vapor.

water table via the capillary and film waters, then, upon freezing, an upward motion of film-capillary soil moisture from the groundwater table takes place. Because of the temperature difference between the warmer groundwater and the downward freezing isothermal surface, the driving pressure for the upward-directed capillary moisture flow is again the difference in the vapor pressure at the free water surface and that at the curved surfaces, or menisci, at the freezing ice lenses, plus the flow pressure (molecular, viscous, or both) caused by molecular motion of the warmer particles of water from the groundwater upward to the cold front. Under certain conditions of temperature, surface topography, and configuration of soil particles and ice lenses, the magnitude of the vapor pressure at the freezing isotherm may be negligible, or nonexistent.[8, 12]

Both M. Faraday (1850) and J. Tyndall (1858) presented theories, plausible even today, in which it was assumed that ice is coated by a mobile, noncrystalline film of water that is stable even below the freezing point.[13] The surface film on ice represents a gradual transition layer from the rigid structure of the bulk of the ice crystal to the double layer of soil moisture on the surfaces of the soil particles.

Nakaya and Matsumoto[14] performed experiments on the adhesive force between ice particles and observed a phenomenon which seemed to show the existence of a liquid water film around two small ice spheres. This liquid-water film is not supercooled water but is in

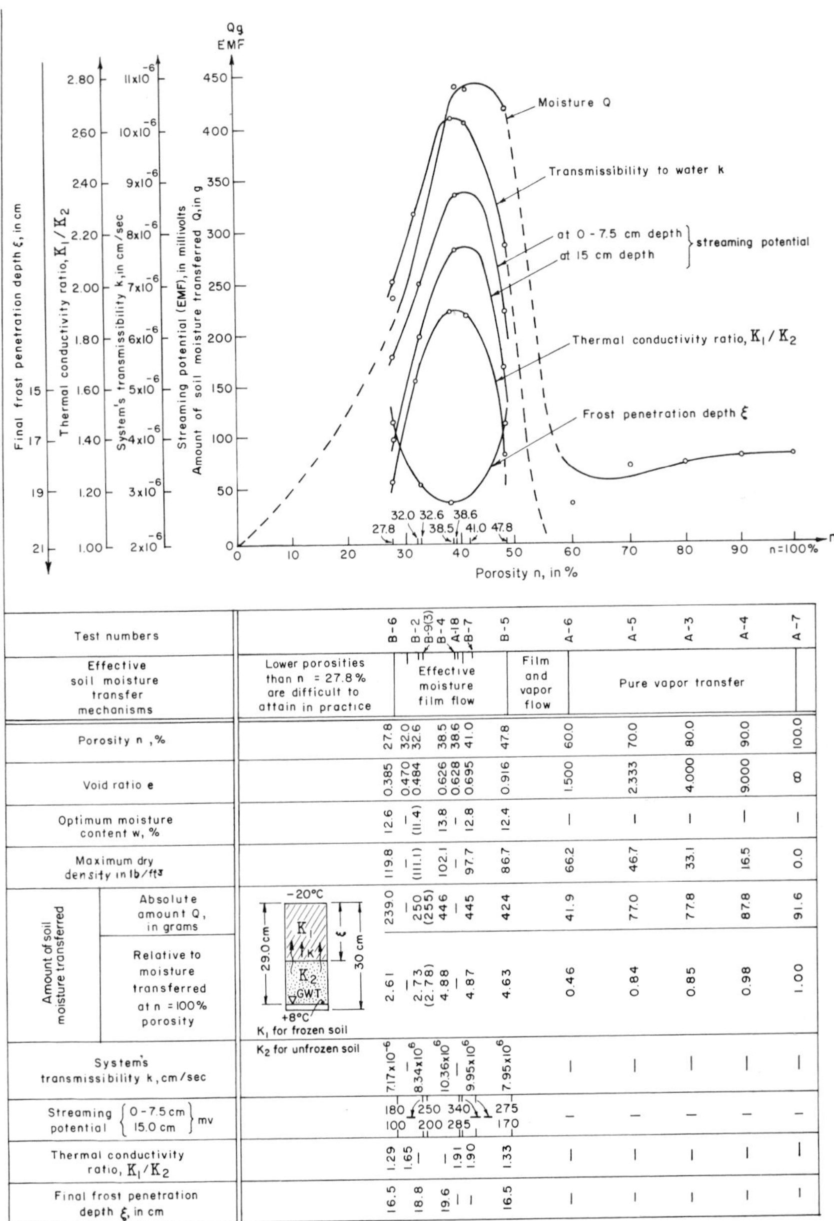

Test numbers		B-6	B-2	B-9(3)	B-4	A-18	B-7	B-5	A-6	A-5	A-3	A-4	A-7
Effective soil moisture transfer mechanisms	Lower porosities than n = 27.8% are difficult to attain in practice	Effective moisture film flow						Film and vapor flow	Pure vapor transfer				
Porosity n, %		27.8	32.0	32.6	38.5	38.6	41.0	47.8	60.0	70.0	80.0	90.0	100.0
Void ratio e		0.385	0.470	0.484	0.626	0.628	0.695	0.916	1.500	2.333	4.000	9.000	∞
Optimum moisture content w, %		12.6	—	(11.4)	13.8	—	12.8	12.4	—	—	—	—	—
Maximum dry density in lb/ft³		119.8	—	(111.1)	102.1	—	97.7	86.7	66.2	46.7	33.1	16.5	0.0
Amount of soil moisture transferred: Absolute amount Q, in grams		239.0	—	250 (255)	446	—	445	424	41.9	77.0	77.8	87.8	91.6
Amount of soil moisture transferred: Relative to moisture transferred at n = 100% porosity		2.61	—	2.73 (2.78)	4.88	—	4.87	4.63	0.46	0.84	0.85	0.98	1.00
System's transmissibility k, cm/sec		7.17×10^{-6}	—	8.34×10^{6}	10.36×10^{6}	—	9.95×10^{6}	7.95×10^{6}	—	—	—	—	—
Streaming potential 0-7.5 cm, mv		180		250		340		275	—	—	—	—	—
Streaming potential 15.0 cm, mv		100		200		285		170					
Thermal conductivity ratio, K_1/K_2		1.29	1.65	—	—	1.91	1.90	1.33	—	—	—	—	—
Final frost penetration depth ξ, in cm		16.5		18.8	19.6	—	—	16.5	—	—	—	—	—

FIG. 5-6 Amount of soil moisture transferred upon freezing as a function of porosity of soil. Author's study (Refs. 7, 8, 9, 10, 11).

equilibrium with its vapor phase on one side and with the ice crystal on the other.

To continue the discussion on film-capillary transport, it is assumed that the ice lenses are connected via the ice water films, and further via the soil moisture films and capillary moisture (where such exists), with the groundwater.[15] In such a case the film-capillary water supply to the freezing ice lenses is uninterrupted. Because the capillary water is less stressed by molecular (i.e., electrical) forces attractive to soil particles than the films surrounding the soil particle, the capillary moisture transport mechanism seems to be more effective in the combined film-capillary flow than the moisture transport via the capillary moisture and films surrounding (and separating) the soil particles. Stressed water-like film water, as we have seen, has properties different from those of free moisture in bulk.

5-7. Film Transport. In a very dense, close packing of soil particles (for which there is a theoretical and practical limit), where the soil particles are so close to each other (small porosity) that the moisture around and between them forms uninterrupted liquid films through the entire soil system down to the groundwater supply, then, depending upon the texture of the soil (whether silt, silty clay, clayey silt, or clay), the film transport mechanism becomes more effective than the capillary transport[11] (Fig. 5-7). The moisture transport in the vapor phase is then very ineffective compared with the movement of liquid. Of course, the process of the upward moisture migration via the films in the freezing soil is slow. A considerable amount of soil moisture, however, can flow from the groundwater upward over a period of several months, as during the winter. It is this slow process of flow which is often overlooked and which is one of the main factors in damage to highways and runways.

In the film transport mechanism, ice lenses are connected via moisture films at the ice surface and via the soil moisture films with the source of groundwater supply (Figs. 5-4 and 5-7). The driving pressure is the pressure difference between two points under consideration, and it is caused by the thermo-viscous flow of the film moisture and other potentials. These may be differences in density of moisture at different temperatures, differences in electrolyte concentration at different elevations in the soil system (temperature), induced secondary electrical potentials effecting additional flow of soil moisture in a direction that depends on the properties of the porous material, and other conditions. The film seems to be two-dimensional, i.e., it is immobile perpendicular to the surface of soil particle, but is mobile parallel to the surface. The movement of the film moisture is hence a slip, by overcoming the shearing resistance of the liquid.

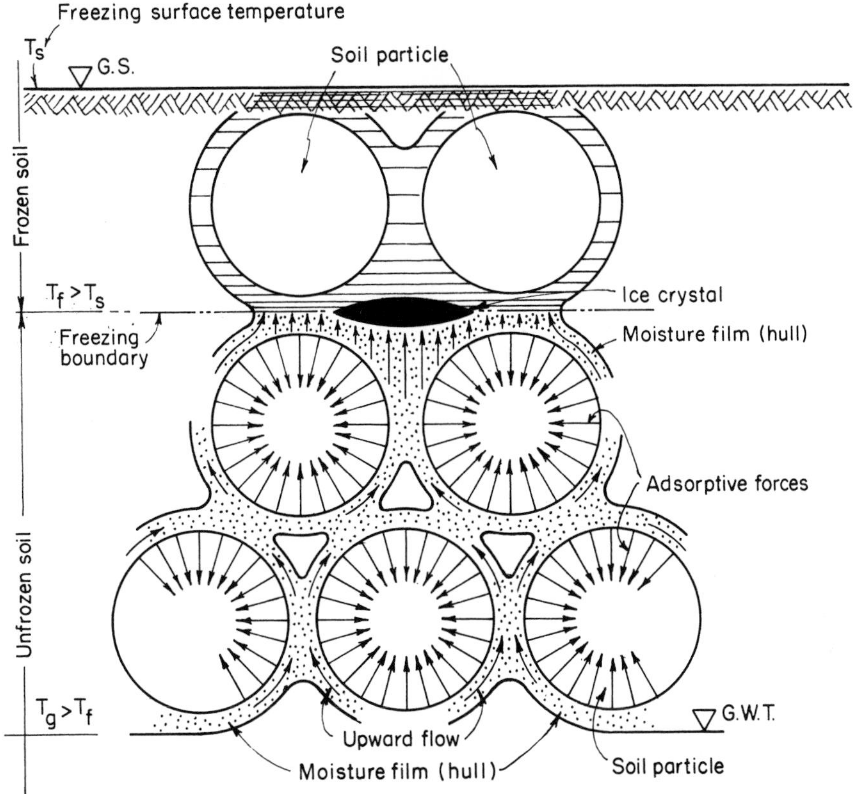

FIG. 5-7 Sketch illustrating the concept of the upward flow of soil moisture by way of film toward an ice crystal.

The amount of moisture transferred by means of film flow is proportional to the specific surface area of the soil particles in a unit of volume. The increase in density of the soil mass means more specific surface, more moisture films, and consequently more film moisture transferred.

5-8. Combination of Various Modes of Transport of Moisture. Depending upon the texture and gradation of the soil, the degree of the packing of the soil particles, and the presence of a multilayered soil system, a combination of the various soil moisture transport mechanisms may exist simultaneously upon freezing. With large porosities, for example, it is more likely that upward soil moisture transport in the vapor phase will be more effective than a film flow. In a densely packed clayey silt or silty clay the film transport mechanism will be more effective than vapor flow. Between the maximum possible densities, for different textures of soil, and in various combinations other than gravel and clay, several upward soil moisture transport mechanisms may set in, and in various proportions. There are no sharply defined boundaries between different transport mechanisms. It is quite reasonable to assume, rather, that a transition from one kind to another constitutes the combination of several kinds of transport acting simultaneously. One deduces that in reporting results on moisture transfer in soils upon freezing, it is essential to report also the porosity of the soil, because for each degree of packing there is a different moisture transport mechanism in action.

5-9. Ice Segregation in Soil. The amount of segregated ice in a frozen system of soil (i.e., the number, thickness, and distribution of visible ice layers or lenses) depends very much upon the intensity and rate of freezing. When the soil system is frozen quickly, say 8 in. (= 20 cm) frost penetration in three days at a temperature difference between surface and groundwater of 24.8°C (= 45°F), no ice layers are visible. When the soil sample is split longitudinally immediately after the test, examination of the frozen sample by eye or with the aid of a magnifying glass does not reveal any ice segregation in layers, although the moisture content in the soil after freezing is larger than before the test, and the moisture content is larger at the ends of the soil column than at its mid-height. Slow freezing, on the contrary, causes clearly visible ice layers of various thicknesses, for example, from $\frac{1}{2}$ mm to about 12 mm. If there are layers in the soil with voids or air gaps, and if a combination of moisture transport mechanisms is active, segregated ice layers about 10 cm (= 4 in.) thick may be observed at mid-height of a 30 cm (= 12 in.) high cylindrical soil sample (silt).

Ice segregation is also influenced by thermal properties of the soil and by the solvents and electrolytes in the soil water. Heat transfer through unfrozen and frozen soil particles is different from that through unfrozen water, chilled water, and ice. Ice lenses develop in the downward-freezing soil in jump-wise layers, leaving unfrozen water between two separately spaced ice lenses. (If the freezing continues long enough, the space between two ice layers may be dried out by the moisture migration towards the two ice layers.) There may therefore be both ice and unfrozen water in frozen soil at the same time. As the temperature goes down, some of the unfrozen water freezes.

5-10. Soil Freezing. Under natural conditions, the various kinds of soil water—such as free water in bulk, capillary water, film water, and hygroscopic water—are seldom present singly. They usually exist simultaneously and have different freezing points, which makes the freezing process in soil extremely complex (Fig. 5-8). The free water in bulk in the voids of the soil is the first type of soil water to

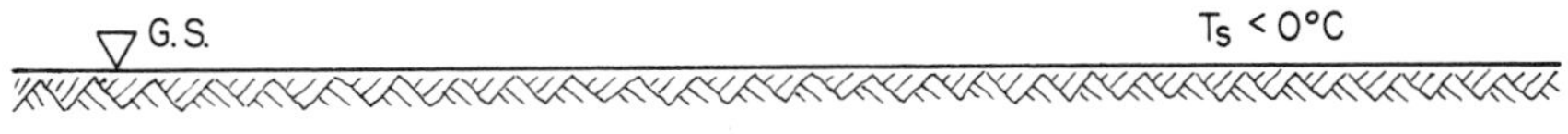

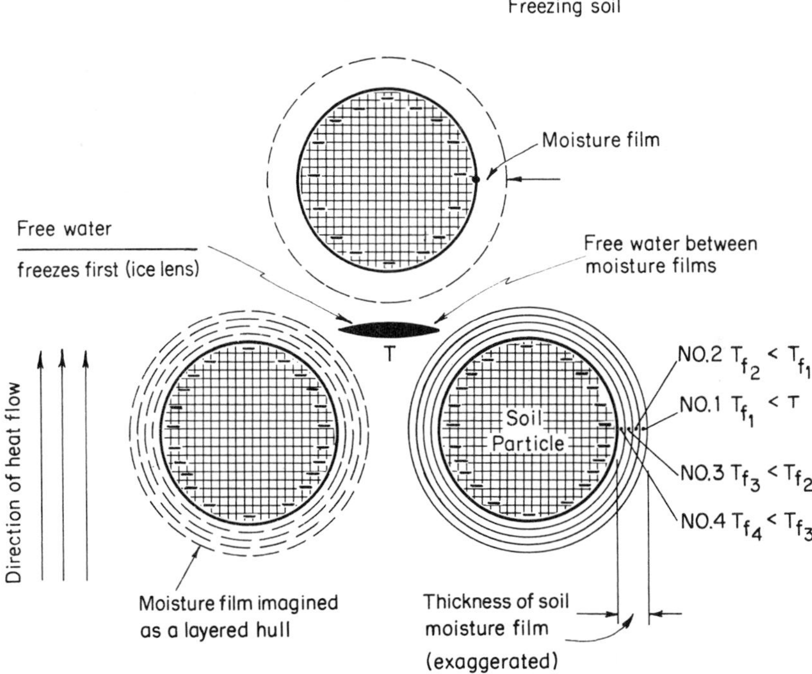

FIG. 5-8 Diagrammatic illustration of freezing of soil moisture.

freeze, then the less stressed films, and so on. Free water in bulk freezes at 0°C, and capillary water freezes at about −1.4°C. According to Bouyoucos,[16] combined water does not freeze at −78°C.

After the free water in bulk is frozen, that part of the soil moisture film freezes which is less stressed by the attractive electrostatic forces and is farther away from the surface of the soil particle. At the same time and temperature, the layered parts of the moisture film, which are nearer to the surface of the soil particle, are liquid, being subjected to a more intense attraction (less drop in zeta-potential)[17] and having, therefore, a lower freezing point. The viscosity of the different kinds of stressed and unstressed water also affects the freezing process in soil. The variation of dynamic viscosity of water as a function of pressure and temperature is shown in Fig. 5-9.

To visualize the freezing of the moisture film, assume that the thickness of the film can be arbitrarily divided into four layers, Nos. 1 to 4

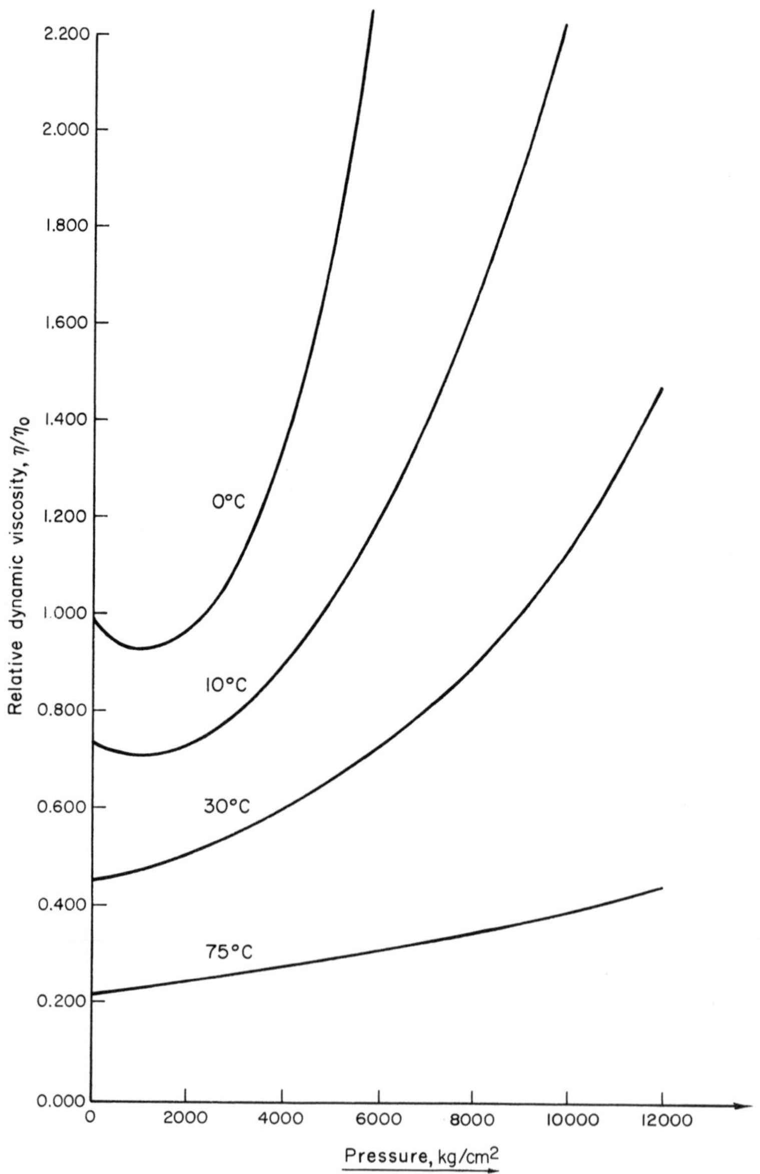

FIG. 5-9 Dependence of dynamic viscosity of water upon pressure and temperature.

(Fig. 5-8). Layer No. 1, whose freezing point is $T_{f1} < T$, freezes first. The freezing point of free water is designated by T. Then, as the temperature drops, layer No. 2 freezes at $T_{f2} < T_{f1}$, then layer No. 3, and so on. Of course, if free water in bulk in the voids is also present and is not subjected to attracting forces,[(17)] then it will freeze first, because its freezing point T is just somewhat below 0°C.

Depending upon the presence of ice crystals, soil can be

1) in the process of freezing,
2) in the frozen state, or
3) in the process of thawing.

In the freezing of stressed water, the bond between the particles of water is broken so that the particles leave the mass of water and join the growing ice crystals. This action causes some of the migration of water in the soil.

Because of this migration of soil moisture in freezing, moisture moves continuously toward the freezing zone, and the growing ice crystals gradually lift the frozen soil above, resulting in frost heave. The heave is conspicuously pronounced if the soil is a silt and if the freezing soil is near groundwater or perched groundwater.

It is possible with laboratory equipment (Fig. 5-10) to study freezing soil samples at a continuous supply of "groundwater" from below. Field conditions are simulated as closely as possible. Experimental work makes it possible to predict the order of magnitude of the expected performance of a given type of soil under the influence of water and temperature.

5-11. Rhythmic Banding of Ice in Soil Upon Freezing. Superficially, the rhythmic banding of ice (Fig. 2-4) appears to be analogous to the "Liesegang rings" [(18)] or Liesegang's rhythmically precipitated crystals of silver, as in a gel. However, for ice to form in water, it is necessary for a nucleation temperature to prevail. This nucleation temperature must be below the freezing temperature (0°C) of the free water in bulk. In soil the nucleation temperature of ice is lower than that of water in bulk because of the solid-liquid interfaces. Also, in the formation of ice lenses, there takes place an upward flow of water from groundwater toward the nucleating ice lenses, whereas in the Liesegang's rhythmic segregation of silver crystal layers no such upward groundwater supply takes place.

The formation of rhythmic ice bands in soil upon freezing appears to take place in a certain cycle. The cycle of banding, according to Martin,[(19)] may be described in three stages, as follows.

(a)

(b)

FIG. 5-10 Equipment used in studies of frost action in soils. (a) General view. (b) Freezing chamber with soil samples. (c) Auxiliary instruments.

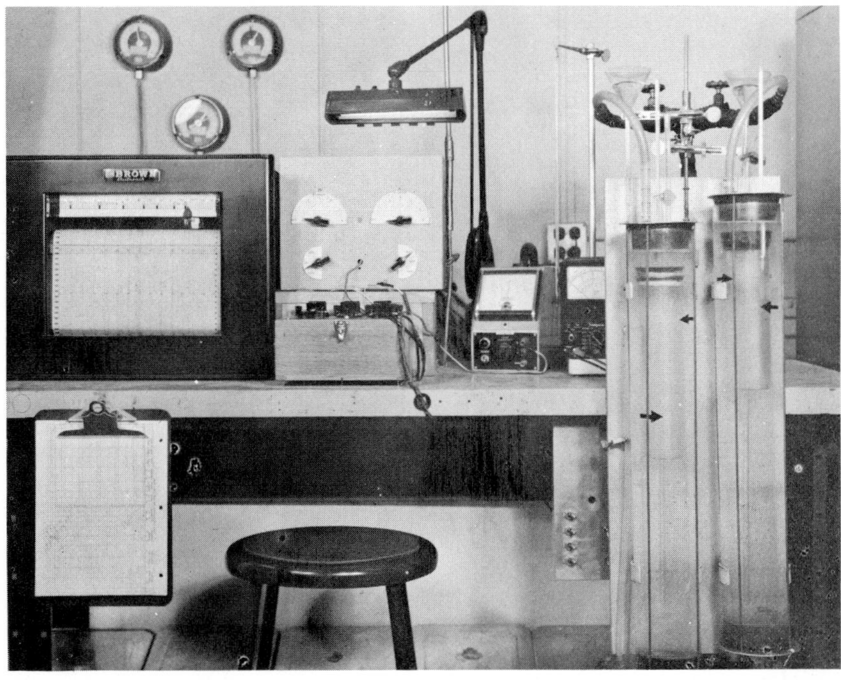

(c)

Stage 1, Nucleation of Ice Crystals. Spontaneous nucleation of ice in pure water takes place at some distance from an existing ice front or zero-isothermal surface at −39°C temperature.

Stage 2, Growth of Ice Crystals. The rapid growth of the nucleus into an ice crystal takes place at a temperature well above that of nucleation, i.e., when water changes from liquid to solid, latent heat of fusion is released. The driving force for the growth of ice crystals is the temperature difference between the growing ice crystal and the normal freezing point of water. In silts and clays there is usually an appreciable amount of water in the double layer.

When ice is nucleated, the instantaneous rate of growth of an ice crystal is very large. In silts and clays there is usually an appreciable amount of water in the double layer, and yet the amount of water in any pore of the soil is limited, thus restricting the growth of the ice crystal. This is to say that the rate of heat extracted upon the formation of ice crystals exceeds the rate of heat supply from the groundwater. The conversion of water to ice also decreases the water content of the soil, which in turn brings about a mechanical tension in the water films surrounding the soil particles. This "negative" pressure lowers the freezing temperature of the water. Water, for the growth of ice crystals, is supplied by its migration from a source (groundwater or perched groundwater) through the voids of the soil via the moisture films to the ice crystals because of the pressure deficiency (subpressure) at the ice front.

When a soil system is frozen from the top down, the driving force for the upward migration of water from groundwater to the cold front is contributed to by the greater kinetic energy of the warmer molecules of the groundwater,[20] i.e., the temperature gradient across the freezing soil system.[9,17] The electrokinetic effects in a freezing soil system also influence the process of the rhythmic banding of ice. Thus it is heat that provides the energy for the upward migration of water from groundwater to the cold front.

Stage 3, Termination of Growth. During the third stage of the freezing cycle the ice crystals stop growing and an ice band is completed. To establish water equilibrium in the water films (remember that upon adding water to the growing ice crystal water is under mechanical tension), water flows because of the pressure deficiency (subpressure) at the front of the ice crystals. *The flow along a temperature gradient* is thus triggered by the formation of ice, which instantaneously gives rise to the pressure deficiency at the ice front because of the undercooling. Once more, the main driving force for the flow of water to the ice front is the pressure deficiency induced by lower temperature at the ice front, i.e., by the temperature gradient applied to the freezing soil system. The lower the temperature at the ice front, the greater the magnitude of the driving force.

The necessary condition for rhythmic (or periodic) banding of ice in a freezing soil system is that the rate of heat extraction upon formation of ice crystals exceed the rate of heat supply by the flow of water from groundwater to the cold front. Under such a condition, the demand for water increases and the subpressure increases, but the ability of the soil to supply water decreases because of the decreased permeability of the soil. Thus the rate of ice formation decreases. The freezing thermal gradient then goes deeper into the soil towards a greater water supply, and the cycle of rhythmic banding of ice starts anew by nucleation of ice (stage 1).

Thermodynamically, the heat transfer is connected with the water transfer by the following free energy or maximum work equation:

$$W_{max} = pV = Q \frac{T_2 - T_1}{T_2} \quad \text{(g cm)}, \qquad (5\text{-}10)$$

where W_{max} = maximum work,
p = pressure difference,
V = volume of water,
Q = heat transferred from temperature T_2 to temperature T_1, including latent heat of fusion,
T_2 = groundwater temperature,
T_1 = temperature at the cold front.

From Eq. (5-10), the driving pressure p, i.e., the pressure difference of water, is calculated as

$$p = \frac{W_{\max}}{V} = \frac{Q}{V}\frac{T_2 - T_1}{T_2} = \frac{L}{1}\frac{T_2 - T_1}{T_2} = (3.4)(10^6)\frac{T_2 - T_1}{T_2} \quad \text{(g)}, \tag{5-11}$$

where $V = 1$ cm³ of water to be moved from groundwater to the cold front, and

$Q = L = 80$ (cal/g) $= (3.4)(10^6)$ (g cm). Only the latent heat of fusion has been considered.

5-12. Natural Freezing of a Foundation Pit. Miners in Siberia operate in the winter in order to penetrate saturated soil for gold and other minerals. In this method of mining, the soil of the foundation pit is frozen progressively. Before the freezing season sets in, the upper layer of soil is excavated down to the groundwater table (Fig. 5-11). This lowers the frost penetration depth below the groundwater. Then ice is removed, leaving an ice sheet about 5 to 10 cm thick to prevent the pit from flooding. Ice is a good heat conductor. When the ice has frozen thick enough, part of the ice sheet is removed and part is left for the protection of the pit against overflooding. If water fills the pit and freezes, the preparation of the pit is started by freezing all over again. By continued digging into the ice in this manner, the pit may be advanced to a considerable depth.

The rate of the downward freezing of soil under natural conditions is applied 5 to 10 cm per day at freezing temperatures of −10°C to −20°C. In about three weeks an advance of about one meter can be achieved.

Snow is a poor heat conductor, so it is removed from ice where pits are frozen in.

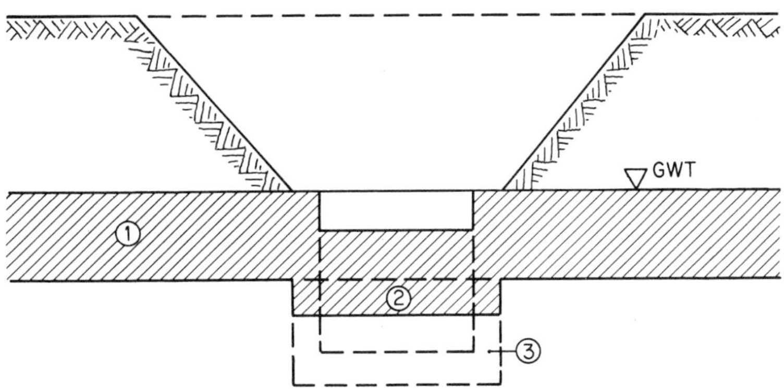

FIG. 5-11 Natural, progressive freezing of a foundation pit.

By means of natural winter freezing, relatively difficult foundation operations can be carried out.

Natural freezing is practiced also for preparing foundation pits for bridge piers.

5-13. Advantages of Natural Freezing of a Foundation Pit. Natural freezing, besides being inexpensive, effectively holds back water in waterlogged soil and can be applied to a wide range of saturated soils. In this method, no freezing point holes have to be drilled. This fact alone saves about 30% to 60% of the preparation time. With natural freezing there is no possibility of brine leaking into the soil, which would make the soil difficult or impossible to freeze.

Frozen soil has sufficient mechanical strength and imperviousness to water. No additional strutting and bracing of walls are needed. This method is very adaptable where pile-driving vibrations cannot be tolerated. Natural freezing of soil is also satisfactory when the permeation of groundwater is less than two meters a day.

5-14. Disadvantages of Natural Freezing of a Foundation Pit. Natural freezing is slow and dependent on the absence of warm spells. It may be applied only to about 10 m below the surface of the ground. In temperate climates the mining season by this method is short.

Chapter 6

Frost Penetration Depth in Soil

6-1. F. Neumann's Theory. Monolayer System. In soil and foundation engineering it is often necessary to know the maximum depth to which frost will penetrate a given type of soil and the rate of penetration. The depth depends upon the type of soil, its moisture content (latent heat of fusion), and the freezing temperature (its magnitude, intensity, and duration).

A satisfactory theory for calculating frost penetration depth in soil is given by Franz Neumann, the derivation of whose theory is given in the author's book *The Frost Penetration Problem in Highway Engineering* (5) and in Appendix 16 of this book. Neumann originally developed his theory to study the formation of ice on still water.(2, 3) However, when soil geotechnical constants are properly fitted into this theory, it can be applied also to frost penetration in soils. Neumann's theory considers the frozen part of the soil as well as the unfrozen (but chilled) part of the soil underneath the freezing isothermal surface 0°C.

The frost penetration depth ξ is proportional to the square root of the elapsed time of freezing:

$$\xi = m\sqrt{t} \qquad \text{(cm)}, \tag{6-1}$$

where m is the coefficient of proportionality to be determined from the following transcendental equation:

$$\underbrace{(0.5)L\rho_s\sqrt{\pi}\,wm =}_{Y_1 = f(m) = Cm}$$

$$= \underbrace{\frac{K_1}{\sqrt{\alpha_1}}(T_f - T_s)\frac{e^{-m^2/4\alpha_1}}{G\left(\dfrac{m}{2\sqrt{\alpha_1}}\right)} - \frac{K_2}{\sqrt{\alpha_2}}(T_0 - T_f)\frac{e^{-m^2/4\alpha_2}}{1 - G\left(\dfrac{m}{2\sqrt{\alpha_2}}\right)}}_{Y_2 = F(m)}, \tag{6-2}$$

where L = latent heat of fusion of water (ice),
ρ_s = density of ice, viz., frozen soil,
w = soil moisture content by dry weight of soil, in decimal fractions,
$K_{1,2}$ = thermal conductivity of frozen and unfrozen soil, respectively, in Cal/(m)(hr)(degree) [or in cal/(cm)(sec)(degree)],
$\alpha_{1,2}$ = coefficients of thermal diffusivity of frozen and unfrozen soil, respectively, in m²/hr,
$T_f = 0°C = 32°F$ = freezing temperature,
T_s = surface temperature $< T_f$, in °C,
$e = 2.7182 \ldots$ = base of natural logarithm system, and

$$G\left(\frac{m}{2\sqrt{\alpha_{1,2}}}\right) = G(\beta) = \frac{2}{\sqrt{\pi}}\int_0^\beta e^{-\beta^2}\, d\beta \qquad (6\text{-}3)$$

is Gauss's error function or the probability integral (see table of values of $G(\beta)$ in Appendix).

The transcendental function with one unknown, m, can be solved best graphically. Plot the straight line $Y_1 = Cm$ and the curve $Y_2 = F(m)$. The intersection of these two Y-functions (when $Y_1 = Y_2$) gives an abscissa m, which is the only root possible in order that $Y_1 = Y_2$. By means of m, the frost penetration depth ξ can be calculated for a given period of time t by Eq. (6-1).

Problem. Calculate frost penetration depth ξ into a soil, and plot the temperature profile for that soil after six days of freezing surface temperature T_s.

Physical constants:

unit weight of dry soil, $\gamma_d = 1.77$ (g/cm³),
amount of soil moisture, $W_w = 0.33$ (g/cm³),
moisture content, $w = (0.33/1.77)(100) = 18.7\%$ by dry weight,
heat capacity of soil solids, $c_s = 0.20$ (cal/g),
heat capacity of water, $c_w = 1.00$ (cal/g).

Thermal properties prior to freezing:

Coefficient of thermal conductivity:

$$K_2 = 16.00 \qquad [\text{cal/(cm)(hr)(°C)}].$$

Volumetric heat capacity:

$$C_2 = \gamma_d c_s + W_w c_w = (1.77)(0.20) + (0.33)(1.00) = $$
$$= 0.684 \text{ (cal/cm}^3\text{)}.$$

Thermal diffusivity:

$$\alpha_2 = \frac{K_2}{C_2} = \frac{16.00}{0.684} = 23.39 \qquad (\text{cm}^2/\text{hr}).$$

$$\frac{K_2}{\sqrt{\alpha_2}} = \frac{16.00}{23.39} = 3.31.$$

Thermal properties after freezing:
Coefficient of thermal conductivity:

$$K_1 = 20.00 \qquad [\text{cal}/(\text{cm})(\text{hr})(°\text{C})].$$

Heat capacity:

$$C_1 = (1.77)(0.20) + (0.33)(0.35) = 0.470 \qquad (\text{cal}/\text{cm}^3),$$

where 0.35 is the heat capacity of ice in cal/g.

Thermal diffusivity:

$$\alpha_1 = \frac{K_1}{C_1} = \frac{20.00}{0.470} = 42.55 \qquad (\text{cm}^2/\text{hr}).$$

$$\frac{K_1}{\sqrt{\alpha_1}} = \frac{20.00}{42.55} = 3.07.$$

Temperatures:
Initial temperature of soil before freezing: $T_0 = +2°\text{C}$.
Surface temperature (microclimate): $T_s = -10°\text{C}$.
Freezing temperature: $T_f = 0°\text{C}$.
Temperature differences: $T_f - T_s = 0 - (-10) = 10°\text{C}$.
$T_0 - T_f = 2 - 0 = 2°\text{C}$.

Auxiliary values:

$$\frac{K_1}{\sqrt{\alpha_1}}(T_f - T_s) = (3.07)\,[0 - (-10)] = 30.7$$

$$\frac{K_2}{\sqrt{\alpha_2}}(T_o - T_f) = (3.31)(2 - 0) = 6.62.$$

$$e^{-m^2/4\alpha_1} = e^{-m^2/(4)(42.55)} = e^{-(0.005875)m^2}.$$

$$G\left(\frac{m}{2\sqrt{\alpha_1}}\right) = G\left(\frac{m}{2\sqrt{42.55}}\right) = G[(0.07665)(m)].$$

$$e^{-m^2/4\alpha_2} = e^{-m^2/(4)(23.39)} = e^{-(0.010688)m^2}.$$

$$G\left(\frac{m}{2\sqrt{\alpha_2}}\right) = G\left[\frac{m}{(2)(4.84)}\right] = G[(0.10339)(m)].$$

$$1 - G\left(\frac{m}{2\sqrt{\alpha_2}}\right) = 1 - G[(0.10339)(m)].$$

Solution.

1. Frost Penetration Depth.

The coefficient of proportionality m. By linear equation (6-2),

$$Y_1 = Cm = (0.5)L\gamma_d w\sqrt{\pi}\, m = (0.5)(80)(1.77)(0.187)(1.77)(m) = = (23.43)(m).$$

Geometrically, this equation represents a straight line through the origin of the coordinates.

The transcendental equation (by Eq. 6-2) is

$$Y_2 = F(m) = (30.7)\frac{e^{-(0.005875)m^2}}{G(0.07665)m} - (6.62)\frac{e^{-(0.010688)m^2}}{1 - G(0.10339)m}.$$

Substituting in the Y_1 and Y_2 equations assumed values of $m = 0$, $m = 1$, $m = 2$; $m = 3$, $m = 4$ and $m = 5$, the Y_1 and Y_2 equations are plotted in Fig. 6-1. The intersection of line $Y_1 = f(m)$ and curve $Y_2 = F(m)$ gives the value sought, $m = 3.60$.

The frost penetration depth ξ is now calculated by Eq. (6-1) as

$$\xi = m\sqrt{t} = (3.60)\sqrt{t}. \tag{6-4}$$

In six days (144 hours), the frost would penetrate the soil

$$\xi = (3.60)\sqrt{144} = \underline{43.2\ (\mathrm{cm})} = 16.6\ \text{in.} = 1.38\ \text{ft.}$$

2. Temperature Profile. The temperature profile in soil for the given freezing conditions can be calculated by the following equations: (1)

(a) *For the frozen zone:*

$$T_1 = T_s + (T_f - T_s)\frac{G(x/2\sqrt{\alpha_1 t})}{G(m/2\sqrt{\alpha_1})}, \tag{6-5}$$

where T_1 = temperature at depth x below ground surface after t hours of freezing;

$m = 3.60$ (from Fig. 6-1). Other symbols are the same as before.

$$T_1 = -10 + [0 - (-10)]\frac{G[x/2\sqrt{42.55}\ \sqrt{t}]}{G(3.60/2\sqrt{42.55})} =$$

$$= 10\left\{\frac{G[(0.00640)(x)]}{G(0.27651)} - 1\right\}. \tag{6-6}$$

Assuming $x = 0$, 10, 20, 30, 40 and $x = \xi = 43.2$ cm, determine the

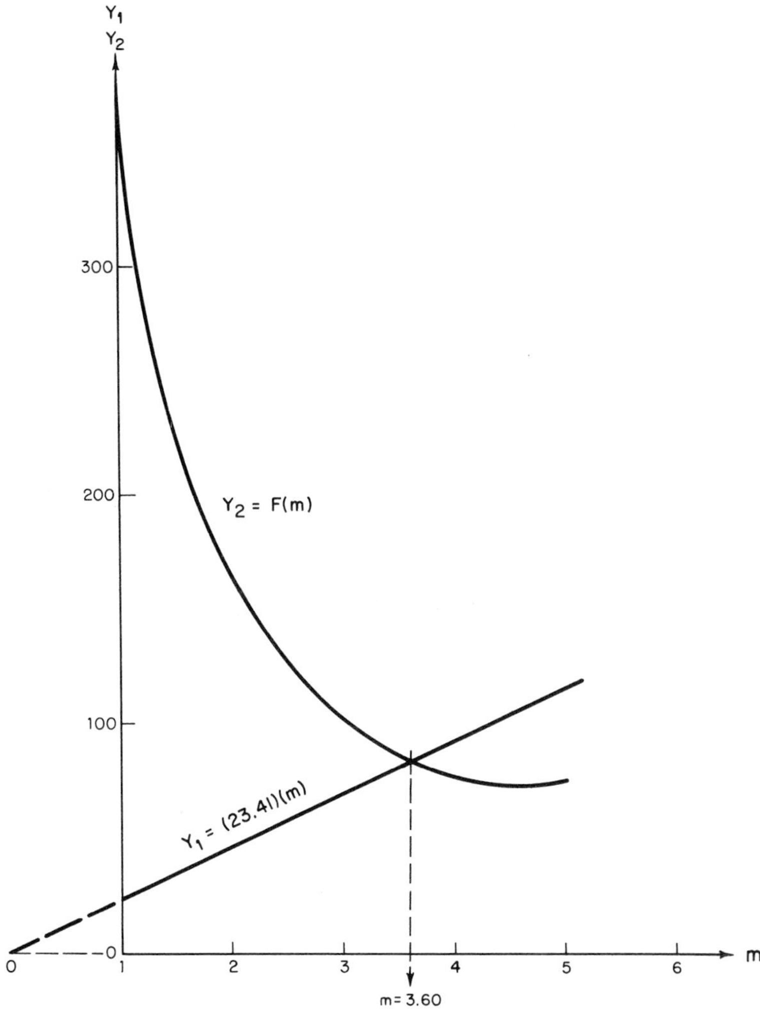

FIG. 6-1 Determining m graphically.

function $G[(0.00640)(x)]$, calculate temperatures T_1 at those depths by Eq. (6-6), and plot the temperature curve for the frozen zone (Fig. 6-2). These temperatures are

at depth $x = 0$ cm, $T_1 = -10.0°C$
$x = 10$ cm, $T_1 = -\ 7.8°C$
$x = 20$ cm, $T_1 = -\ 5.6°C$
$x = 30$ cm, $T_1 = -\ 3.4°C$
$x = 40$ cm, $T_1 = -\ 1.3°C$
$x = \xi = 43.2$ cm, $T_1 = \ 0.0°C = T_f$.

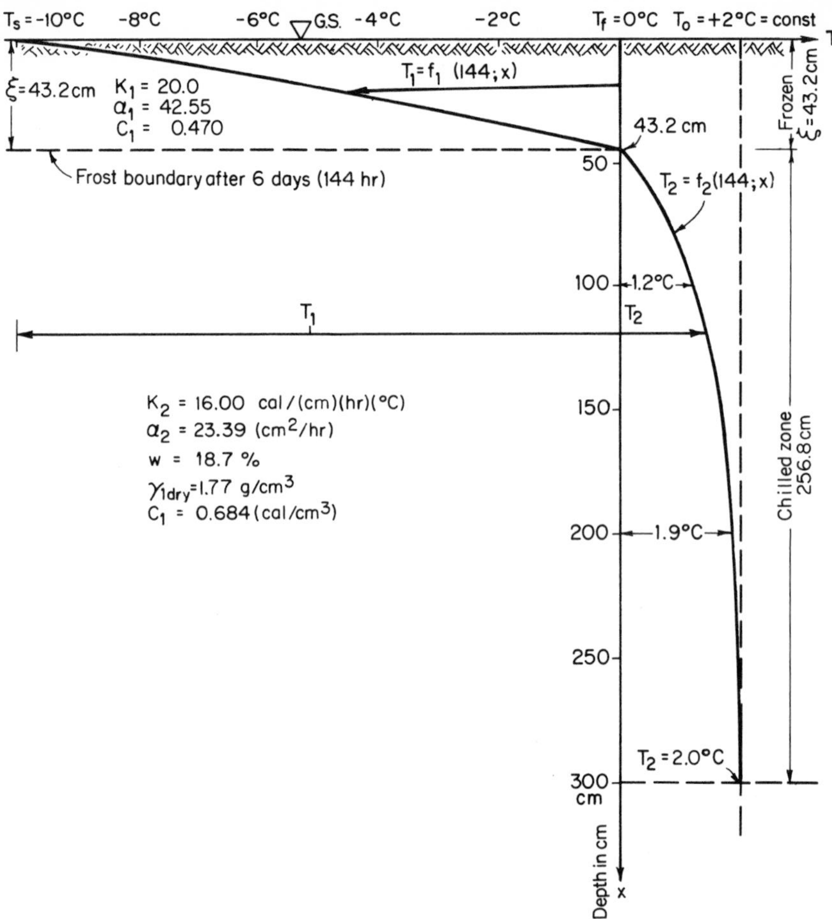

FIG. 6-2 Temperature profile after six days of freezing; $\xi = 43.2$ cm.

(b) *For the unfrozen (chilled) zone*[1]:

$$T_2 = T_o - (T_o - T_f)\,\frac{1 - G(x/2\sqrt{\alpha_2 t})}{1 - G(m/2\sqrt{\alpha_2})}, \tag{6-7}$$

where T_2 = temperature in the chilled (unfrozen) zone at depth x below the ground surface after 144 hours since the beginning of freezing;

T_o = initial temperature of the unfrozen zone before freezing started, i.e., temperature of the unchilled zone. Other symbols are the same as before.

Substitution of the auxiliary values into Eq. (6-7) renders the T_2

equation for calculating temperatures at various depths x in the chilled zone:

$$T_2 = 2\left\{1 - \frac{1 - G[(0.008608)(x)]}{0.600}\right\}. \tag{6-8}$$

The calculated T_2 temperatures are

at depth $\xi = x =$	43.2 cm,	$T_2 = 0.0°\text{C} = T_f$
$x =$	50 cm	$T_2 = 0.2°\text{C}$
$x =$	60 cm	$T_2 = 0.4°\text{C}$
$x =$	70 cm	$T_2 = 0.7°\text{C}$
$x =$	80 cm	$T_2 = 0.9°\text{C}$
$x =$	100 cm	$T_2 = 1.2°\text{C}$
$x =$	200 cm	$T_2 = 1.9°\text{C}$
$x =$	300 cm	$T_2 = 1.9966 \approx 2.0°\text{C} = T_0$.

The temperature profile sought is illustrated in Fig. 6-2 and Appendix 16.

Neumann's theory is an excellent mathematical treatment of the frost penetration problem in soil. In this theory, the moisture present is assumed to be motionless. The theory is of particular value if the thermal properties of the frozen and unfrozen parts of the soil are known.

6-2. J. Stefan's Formula. As mentioned in Chapter 5, Stefan developed a simple formula for the formation of ice, a formula which can also be applied for calculating the frost penetration depth in soil as a function of time.[5,6]

When conditions are such that the temperature gradient in the frozen zone (ice layer) of soil is linear, the thickness of the ice sheet (frost penetration depth) can be calculated as follows:

$$\xi = \sqrt{\frac{2K_1}{L\rho_i}(T_f - T_s)t}, \tag{6-9}$$

where all symbols are the same as before, and ρ_i = density of ice. This equation is based on the principle that the heat absorbed is equal to the heat conducted through 1 cm² area.

Taking into consideration the latent heat of fusion of ice relative to the amount of water in the soil ($W_w = w\gamma_s/100$), and volumetric heat capacities of ice and solids in the soil, Stefan's formula may be adjusted for calculating frost penetration depths in soil as follows:

$$\xi = \sqrt{\frac{2K_1(T_f - T_s)t}{Q_L + \dfrac{T_f - T_s}{2}c_{vf}}}, \tag{6-10}$$

where $Q_L = (80)(w/100)(\gamma_s)$ = total amount of latent heat of fusion for converting water into ice, in calories,

w = moisture content of water in soil, in percent of dry weight of soil (γ_s),

s = dry unit weight (density) of soil (= weight of solids in one unit volume of soil), in g/cm³,

c_{vf} = volumetric heat capacity of frozen soil, including soil moisture and solids, in cal/cm³. The volumetric heat capacity of frozen soil can be calculated by Eq. 2-13:

$$c_{vf} = \gamma_s \left[c_{ms} + \frac{(c_{mi})(w)}{100} \right] = \gamma_s \left[0.20 + \frac{(0.50)(w)}{100} \right],$$

where $0.20 = c_{ms}$ = heat capacity of dry soil in cal/(g)(°C), and
$0.50 = c_{mi}$ = heat capacity of ice in cal/(g)(°C).

The quantity

$$Q_L + \frac{T_f - T_s}{2} c_{vf} = L(w/100)(\gamma_s) + \frac{T_f - T_s}{2} \gamma_s \left[c_{ms} + \frac{(c_{mi})(w)}{100} \right]$$

in the denominator of Eq. (6-10) is termed by Beskow[21] the "frost storing capacity" of the soil material.

Problem. Using the same quantities as in the problem of Section 6-1, calculate the frost penetration depth by means of Stefan's formula.

Solution.

$$Q_L = (80)(18.7/100)(1.77) = \underline{26.48 \text{ (cal)}}.$$

$$\frac{T_f - T_s}{2} c_{vf} = (10/2)(1.77) \left[0.20 + \frac{(0.50)(18.7)}{100} \right] = \underline{2.60 \text{ (cal)}}.$$

The frost penetration depth ξ is calculated as

$$\xi = \sqrt{\frac{(2)(20)(10)(144)}{26.48 + 2.60}} = \underline{42.5 \text{ (cm)}}.$$

This depth is 0.7 cm less than the 43.2 cm calculated by the more rigorous Neumann's formula.

Stefan's theory can be considered as a special, simpler case of Neumann's theory. The soil moisture present in Stefan's calculation is motionless. Stefan's theory serves well as an approximation for the calculation of frost penetration depth if it is justified to assume that the temperature gradient in the soil is linear. Stefan's equation can also be used for calculating the thawing depth in soil. This theory takes into account the density of the soil, the moisture content present in the soil, the latent heat of fusion of ice (water), properties of the frozen zone of soil only, some climatic conditions and the duration of cold.

6-3. Frost Penetration Depth in a Multilayered Soil System. The calculation of frost penetration depth in a multilayered soil system can be performed based on Stefan's frost penetration depth equation (6-9) but without the term of volumetric heat capacity of ice and solids:

$$\xi = \sqrt{\frac{2K(T_f - T_s)t24}{Q_L}}, \tag{6-11}$$

where $Q_L = Lw\gamma_s = (80)(w)(\gamma_s)$, and the rest of the symbols the same as before.

Equation (6-11) thus contains the latent heat of fusion of ice in soil only. The elapsed time t of the duration of frost is given in days, hence the coefficient 24 in the numerator of the formula. The product in this equation, $(T_f - T_s)(t) = N$, is, therefore, in terms of degree-days. In order to convert the number of degree-days into degree-hours, multiply degree-days by 24 (hours). Now Eq. (6-11) can be rewritten as

$$\xi = \sqrt{\frac{(48)(K)(N)}{Q_L}}. \tag{6-12}$$

The number of degree-days required for frost to penetrate a layer of soil ξ units thick can be expressed from Eq. (6-12) as

$$N = \frac{Q_L\xi^2}{48K} \quad \text{(degree-days)}. \tag{6-13}$$

Designating the thicknesses of the various layers in the multi-layered system by $h_1, h_2, h_3, \ldots, h_{n-1}, h_n, h_{n+1}$ (Fig. 6-3), the number of degree-days N required for each layer to be penetrated by frost is calculated as follows:

$$N_1 = \frac{Q_1 h_1}{24}\frac{h_1}{2K_1} = \frac{Q_1 h_1}{24}\frac{R_1}{2}. \tag{6-14}$$

When frost penetrates from ground surface to a depth $h_1 + h_2$, or better, when heat flows up through layers h_2 and h_1, the total average thermal resistance is

$$\frac{R_1 + (R_1 + R_2)}{2} = R_1 + \frac{R_2}{2}. \tag{6-15}$$

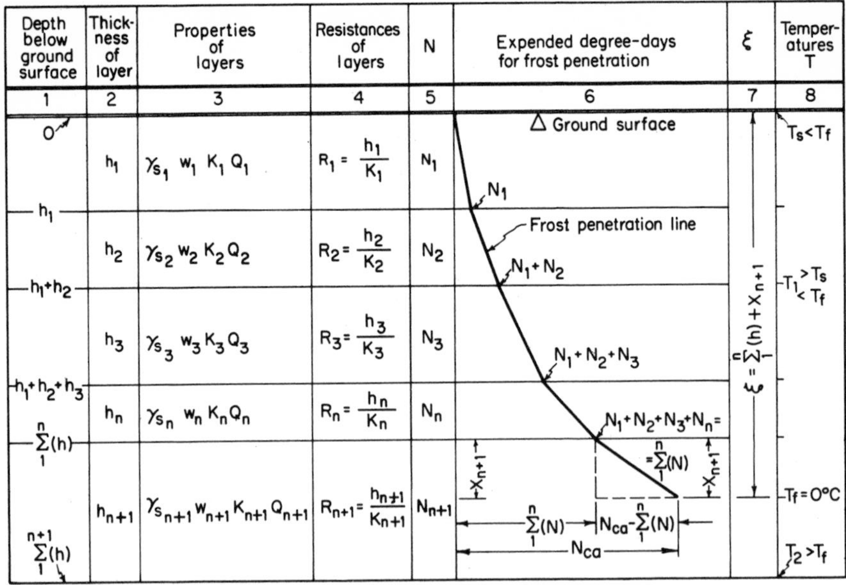

FIG. 6-3 Frost penetration in a multilayered soil system. (N_{ca} = climatologically available number of degree-days.)

Therefore the number of degree-days N_2 required for frost to penetrate a thickness of h_2 is calculated as

$$N_2 = \frac{Q_2 h_2}{24} \frac{R_1 + (R_1 + R_2)}{2} = \frac{Q_2 h_2}{24}\left(R_1 + \frac{R_2}{2}\right). \tag{6-16}$$

Similarly, to penetrate frost from depth h_2 to the bottom of layer h_3, the necessary number of degree-days is

$$N_3 = \frac{Q_3 h_3}{24}\left(R_1 + R_2 + \frac{R_3}{2}\right). \tag{6-17}$$

....

$$N_n = \frac{Q_n h_n}{24}\left[\sum_1^{n-1} (R) + \frac{R_n}{2}\right]. \tag{6-18}$$

$$N_{n+1} = \frac{Q_{n+1} h_{n+1}}{24}\left[\sum_1^{n} (R) + \frac{R_{n+1}}{2}\right]. \tag{6-19}$$

Here $Q_1, Q_2, Q_3, \ldots, Q_n, Q_{n+1}$ are the latent heats of fusion of ice of the individual layers in the multilayered system.

The sum $N_1 + N_2 + N_3 + \cdots + N_n + N_{n+1} = \sum_1^{n+1} (N)$ gives the total number of degree-days necessary for frost to penetrate layers $h_1 + h_2 + h_3 + \cdots + h_{n-1} + h_n = \sum_1^n (h)$.

In order to find the total frost penetration depth ξ, the climatologically available number of degree-days N_{ca} must be known. Compare the climatologically available number of degree-days N_{ca} during a certain duration of frost t with the number of degree-days $\sum_1^n (N)$ necessary to penetrate n layers of a total thickness of $\sum_1^n (h)$. If $N_{ca} > \sum_1^n (N)$, then the frost penetrates deeper than n layers. The frost penetration depth x_{n+1} in the $(n+1)$ layer depends upon the excess number of available degree-days, $\left[N_{ca} - \sum_1^n (N)\right]$. With the number of degree-hours of $\left[(24)(N_{ca} - \sum_1^n (N)\right]$, calculate the frost penetration depth x_{n+1} into the $(n+1)$-layer as follows:

$$x_{n+1} = \frac{(24)N_{n+1}}{(Q_{n+1})\left(\sum_1^n R + R_{n+1}/2\right)}. \tag{6-20}$$

$$x_{n+1} = \sum_1^n (R) + \frac{x_{n+1}}{2K_{n+1}} = \frac{(24)\left[(N_{ca} - \sum_1^n (N)\right]}{Q_{n+1}}. \tag{6-21}$$

$$(x_{n+1})^2 + (2)(K_{n+1}) \sum_1^n (R)(x_{n+1}) - \frac{(24)\left[N_{ca} - \sum_1^n (N)\right]}{Q_{n+1}} = 0. \tag{6-22}$$

The solution of this quadratic equation renders the depth x_{n+1} to which the unexpended amount of climatological degree-days $\left[N_{ca} - \sum_1^n (N)\right]$ would penetrate into layer $(n+1)$.

The total frost penetration depth ξ in this multilayered system is

$$\xi = \sum_1^n (h) + x_{n+1}. \tag{6-23}$$

Problem. Given a multilayered system of pavement and soil as tabulated below, establish the course and depth of frost penetration in the given layered system.

Concrete slab 15.0 cm thick; $\gamma_s = 2300$ kg/m^3; $w = 2.0\%$; $K_1 = 0.60$ Cal/(m)(hr)(°C)
Gravelly sand 20.0 cm thick; $\gamma_s = 2000$ kg/m^3; $w = 4.0\%$; $K_2 = 0.67$ Cal/(m)(hr)(°C)
Clayey silt 30.0 cm thick; $\gamma_s = 1800$ kg/m^3; $w = 24.4\%$; $K_3 = 1.10$ Cal/(m)(hr)(°C)
Silty clay 25.0 cm thick; $\gamma_s = 1700$ kg/m^3; $w = 29.4\%$; $K_4 = 1.20$ Cal/(m)(hr)(°C)
Clay, a very thick layer; $\gamma_s = 2000$ kg/m^3; $w = 16.0\%$; $K_5 = 1.22$ Cal/(m)(hr)(°C)

The number of climatologically available degree-days in 16 days of freezing is $N_{ca} = 175$. The surface temperature (microclimate) is $T_s = -10$°C, and the freezing temperature at the zero-isothermal surface is $T_f = 0$°C.

Solution.

Latent Heats Q_L. The quantity of latent heat for each layer in the given system is calculated by

$$Q_L = (80)(w/100)(\gamma_s) \qquad (\text{Cal/m}^3). \tag{6-24}$$

$$\begin{aligned} Q_1 &= (80)(0.020)(2300) = 3680 \text{ Cal/m}^3 \\ Q_2 &= (80)(0.040)(2000) = 6400 \text{ Cal/m}^3 \\ Q_3 &= (80)(0.244)(1800) = 35200 \text{ Cal/m}^3 \\ Q_4 &= (80)(0.294)(1700) = 40000 \text{ Cal/m}^3 \\ Q_5 &= (80)(0.160)(2000) = 25600 \text{ Cal/m}^3 \end{aligned}$$

Thermal Resistances R

$$R_1 = h_1/K_1 = 0.15/0.60 = 0.25 \quad [(\text{m}^2)(\text{hr})(°\text{C})/\text{Cal}]$$

$$R_2 = h_2/K_2 = 0.20/0.67 = 0.30 \quad [(\text{m}^2)(\text{hr})(°\text{C})/\text{Cal}]$$

$$R_3 = h_3/K_3 = 0.30/1.10 = 0.27 \quad [(\text{m}^2)(\text{hr})(°\text{C})/\text{Cal}]$$

$$R_4 = h_4/K_4 = 0.25/1.20 = 0.21 \quad [(\text{m}^2)(\text{hr})(°\text{C})/\text{Cal}]$$

$$R_5 = h_5/K_5 = h_x/1.22 = (0.82)(h_x) \quad [(\text{m}^2)(\text{hr})(°\text{C})/\text{Cal}]$$

Necessary Number of Degree-Days N for Each Layer

$$N_1 = \frac{Q_1 h_1}{24}\frac{R_1}{2} = \frac{(3680)(0.15)}{24}\frac{(0.25)}{2} = 2.875 \approx 3 \text{ (degree-days)}$$

$$N_2 = \frac{Q_2 h_2}{24}\left(R_1 + \frac{R_2}{2}\right) = \frac{(6400)(0.20)}{24}\left(0.25 + \frac{0.30}{2}\right) =$$

$$= 21.333 \approx 22 \text{ (degree-days)}$$

$$N_3 = \frac{Q_3 h_3}{24}\left(R_1 + R_2 + \frac{R_3}{2}\right) = \frac{(35{,}200)(0.30)}{24}\left(0.25 + 0.30 + \frac{0.27}{2}\right) =$$

$$= 302 \text{ (degree-days)}$$

$$N_4 = \frac{Q_4 h_4}{24}\left(R_1 + R_2 + R_3 + \frac{R_4}{2}\right) =$$

$$= \frac{(40{,}000)(0.25)}{24}\left(0.25 + 0.30 + 0.27 + \frac{0.21}{2}\right) = 385 \text{ (degree-days)}$$

$$N_5 = \frac{Q_5 h_5}{24}\left[\sum_1^n (R) + \frac{R_5}{2}\right] =$$

$$= \frac{(25{,}600)(1.00)}{24}\left(0.25 + 0.30 + 0.27 + 0.21 + \frac{0.82}{2}\right)$$

$$= 1536 \text{ (degree-days)}$$

(for $h_x = 1.00$ m).

Cold Degree-Days Expended for Penetration of Frost into the Given Layered System

Climatologically available degree-days: $N_{ca} = 175$.
Expended in first layer: $N_1 = 3$ degree-days
Expended in second layer: $N_2 = 22$ degree-days

Total: $\sum_1^n (N) = 25$ degree-days.

Degree-days left for frost penetration into the third layer:

$$N_{ca} - \sum_1^n (N) = 175 - 25 = 150 \text{ (degree-days).}$$

Because the third layer requires 302 degree-days for frost penetration through the entire thickness of that layer but only 150 degree-days are still left unexpended, the penetration of frost will stop at some depth within the third layer of the clayey silt. In order to find how deep ($x_{n+1} = x_3$) frost will penetrate in 150 cold degree-days into the third layer, the depth x_3 is calculated by Eq. (6-20) as shown:

$$x_3 = \frac{(24)\left[N_{ca} - \sum_1^n (N)\right]}{Q_3\left(R_1 + R_2 + \frac{R_3}{2}\right)} = \frac{(24)(150)}{(35{,}200)[0.25 + 0.30 + x_3/(1.10)(2)]};$$

$$(x_3)^2 + (0.55)(2.20)(x_3) - \frac{(24)(150)(2.20)}{35{,}200} = 0;$$

$$(x_3)^2 + (1.21)(x_3) - 0.225 = 0;$$

$$x_3 = \frac{-1.21 + \sqrt{1.464 + 0.900}}{2} = 0.165(\text{m}) = \underline{16.5 \text{ cm.}}$$

The Total Depth ξ of Frost Penetration. By Eq. (6-23), the frost penetration depth ξ in the given layered system is

$$\xi = \sum_1^n (h) + x_3 = h_1 + h_2 + x_3 = 0.15 + 0.20 + 0.165 =$$

$$= 0.515 \text{ (m)} = \underline{51.5 \text{ cm}} \text{ below the ground surface.}$$

The frost penetration graph can now be drawn as shown in Fig. (6-3). The thawing depth of a frozen soil can be calculated in a manner similar to that used in calculating the frost penetration depth in a layered system. In such a case the thawing degree-days must be used instead of the cold degree-days.

REFERENCES

1. W. H. Ward and E. C. Sewell, "Protection of the Ground from Thermal Effects of Industrial Plant," *Géotechnique* (London), **2**, 1, June 1950, pp. 64–81.
2. L. Bendel, *Ingenieurgeologie*, Vol. 2, Springer Verlag, Wien, 1948, p. 656.
3. C. A. Hogentogler, *Engineering Properties of Soil*, McGraw-Hill Book Company, Inc., New York, 1937, p. 283.
4. A. A. Beles and I. I. Stankulescu, "Thermal Treatment as a Means of Improving the Stability of Earth Masses," *Géotechnique* (London), **8**, 4, Dec. 1958, pp. 158–165.
5. A. R. Jumikis, *The Frost Penetration Problem in Highway Engineering*, Rutgers University Press, New Brunswick, N.J., 1955, pp. 91–92.
6. J. Stefan, "Probleme der Theorie der Wärmeleitung," *Sitzungsberichte der mathematisch-naturwissenschaftlichen Classe der Kaiserlichen Akademie der Wissenschaften* (Vienna), **XCVIII**, 2a, 1890, p. 474.
7. A. R. Jumikis, "Vapor Diffusion in Freezing Soil Systems of Very Large Porosities," *Highway Research Board Bulletin*, No. 331, on Soil Behavior Associated with Freezing, National Academy of Sciences–National Research Council Publication 1013, Washington, D.C., 1962, pp. 28–45.
8. A. R. Jumikis, "Soil Moisture Transfer in the Vapor Phase Upon Freezing," *Highway Research Board Bulletin*, No. 168, on Fundamental and Practical Concepts of Soil Freezing, National Academy of Sciences–National Research Council Publication 528, Washington, D.C., 1957, pp. 96–115.
9. A. R. Jumikis, "Some Concepts Pertaining to the Freezing Soil Systems," *Highway Research Board Bulletin*, Special Report No. 40, on Water and Its Conduction in Soils (an international symposium), National Academy of Sciences–National Research Council Publication 629, Washington, D.C., 1958, pp. 178–190.

10. A. R. Jumikis, "Streaming Potential and Moisture Transfer in Soil Upon Freezing as a Function of Porosity of Soil," *Highway Research Board Bulletin,* No. 287, on Discussions on Water and Its Conduction in Soils, National Academy of Sciences–National Research Council Publication 859, Washington, D.C., 1961, pp. 30–31.
11. A. R. Jumikis, "Effective Soil Moisture Transfer Mechanisms Upon Freezing," *Highway Research Board Bulletin,* No. 317, on Soil Behavior on Freezing With and Without Additives, National Academy of Sciences–National Research Council Publication 963, Washington, D.C., 1962, pp. 1–8.
12. A. R. Jumikis, "The Effect of Freezing on a Capillary Meniscus," *Highway Research Board Bulletin,* No. 168, on Fundamental and Practical Concepts of Soil Freezing, National Academy of Sciences–National Research Council Publication 528, Washington, D.C., 1957, pp. 116–120.
13. W. A. Weyl, "Surface Structure of Water and Some of Its Physical and Chemical Manifestations," *Journal of Colloid Science,* **6,** Academic Press, Inc., New York, 1951, pp. 395–396.
14. U. Nakaya and A. Matsumoto, "Evidence of the Existence of a Liquidlike Film on Ice Surfaces," Research Paper No. 4, 1953, Snow, Ice, and Permafrost Research Establishment, Corps of Engineers, U.S. Army, Wilmette, Ill., p. 1, p. 6.
15. A. R. Jumikis, "The Soil Freezing Experiment," *Highway Research Board Bulletin,* No. 135, on Factors Influencing Ground Freezing, National Academy of Sciences–National Research Council Publication 425, Washington, D.C., 1956, pp. 150–165.
16. G. J. Bouyoucos, "A New Classification of Soil Moisture," *Soil Science,* **11,** 1, January, 1921, pp. 33–47.
17. A. R. Jumikis, "Concerning a Mechanism for Soil Moisture Translocation in the Film Phase upon Freezing," *Proceedings, Highway Research Board,* **39,** 1960, Washington, D.C., pp. 619–639.
18. R. E. Liesegang, *Geologische Diffusionen,* Theodor Steinkopf, Dresden and Leipzig, 1913.
19. R. T. Martin, "Rhythmic Ice Banding in Soil," *Highway Research Board Bulletin,* No. 218, on Frost Effects in Soils and on Pavement Surfaces, National Academy of Sciences–National Research Council Publication 671, Washington, D.C., 1959, pp. 11–22.
20. A. R. Jumikis, "Experimental Studies on Moisture Transfer in a Silty Soil Upon Freezing as a Function of Its Porosity" (mimeographed, 89 pages, 24 illustrations). Rutgers—The State University, New Brunswick, N.J., 1963.
21. G. Beskow, *Tjälbildningen och Tjällyftningen.* Meddelande (Report) 48. Statens Väginstitut, Stockholm, 1935, p. 189 (with an English summary).

Part III

Soil Stabilization by Freezing

Chapter 7

The Soil Freezing System

7-1. Artificial Freezing of Soil. The presence of engineers' "opponent" water is the principal cause of difficulty in excavating a foundation pit. The excavation work becomes particularly difficult when groundwater is present in fine-particled sand. In such a situation the walls and the bottom of the pit can be stabilized by artificial freezing.

It should be kept in mind that soil freezing is not in itself a foundation: it serves only to provide a dry foundation pit and thus facilitate the excavation operation.

Artificial freezing of soil in excavation operations is an expedient, efficient, and successful means of stabilizing the walls and bottom of foundation pits in fine-particled, permeable, saturated soils, in water-bearing layers of soil, and in sandy soils subject to quick conditions.

In this method of thermal soil solidification, the soil layers are temporarily converted into solid ice. This is done by refrigerating the soil.

Soil water can freeze partly or fully. Depending upon the rate of freezing, there form either discrete ice crystals or segregated ice lenses. The method of artificial soil freezing presupposes that the soil contains a large quantity of water or that it is saturated. The permeability and thermal characteristics of frozen soil are different from those of unfrozen soil. Also upon freezing,

1) water expands 9% in volume;
2) ice cements the aggregate particles;
3) a saturated soil becomes sufficiently impermeable to water for excavation, and
4) soil acquires sufficient mechanical strength for its intended purpose.

By freezing the soil around a foundation pit, the influx of groundwater into the pit can be checked. Also, artificial soil freezing for foundation engineering is no longer seasonal but can be carried out in any season and in any climate.

The frozen condition of the soil lasts only as long as the refrigeration plant is in operation. After the foundation work in a "frozen-out" pit is completed, the frozen soil is allowed to thaw.

7-2. Some Applications of Artificial Freezing of Soil. Artificial soil freezing can be used to great advantage in foundation systems that exceed the depth limit for sheet piling, or where sheet piling cannot be applied because of unfavorable soil conditions (sheet piling is difficult to drive into gravelly soil, for example), or where open and/or pneumatic caissons cannot successfully be sunk because of quick conditions of fine sand occurring at great depth, or where the designed depth of the foundation exceeds the maximum economical draw-down of the groundwater table, or where pumping is difficult and impracticable. Artificial freezing of soil is difficult to perform if the velocity of groundwater flow is greater than two meters per day.

Soil freezing is also applicable for tunnel works, for sealing leaky cofferdams and locks, for underpinning structures,[1] in soils where pile driving vibrations cannot be tolerated, for placing of water-impermeable curtains in soil underneath power plants, dams, and other structures, and in combating slides in soil.

The soil physical limits for laying of foundations after Ref. (2) are shown in Figs. 7-1 and 7-2.

During the construction of the Grand Coulee dam, earth and mud was frozen into a retaining structure to prevent the mud from flowing into the foundation pit.[3] The frozen soil acted as a temporary earth- and water-retaining structure.

7-3. Historical Notes. The development of the freezing method for stabilizing soil has been closely linked to the sinking of mine shafts. The idea of protecting a shaft against inflowing water by means of an ice wall showed up first in 1852 with the construction of a mine shaft in Auzin in northern France, when, because of the setting in of winter, a natural course of ice formed around the shaft. Artificial soil freezing was first used by Siebe Gorman and Co. in 1862 in Wales, England, for stabilizing walls of mining shafts in loose, water-logged soils.[4] The freezing method was introduced in the Ruhr region of Germany in 1880 by Pötsch, a mining engineer from Aschersleben. His method has been used since, especially in Germany,[5,6,7] in the construction of the Archibald mine near Schneidlingen.

In the Pötsch method of artificial soil freezing, bore holes are made at 0.9 to 1.0 m intervals around the outer perimeter of the designed

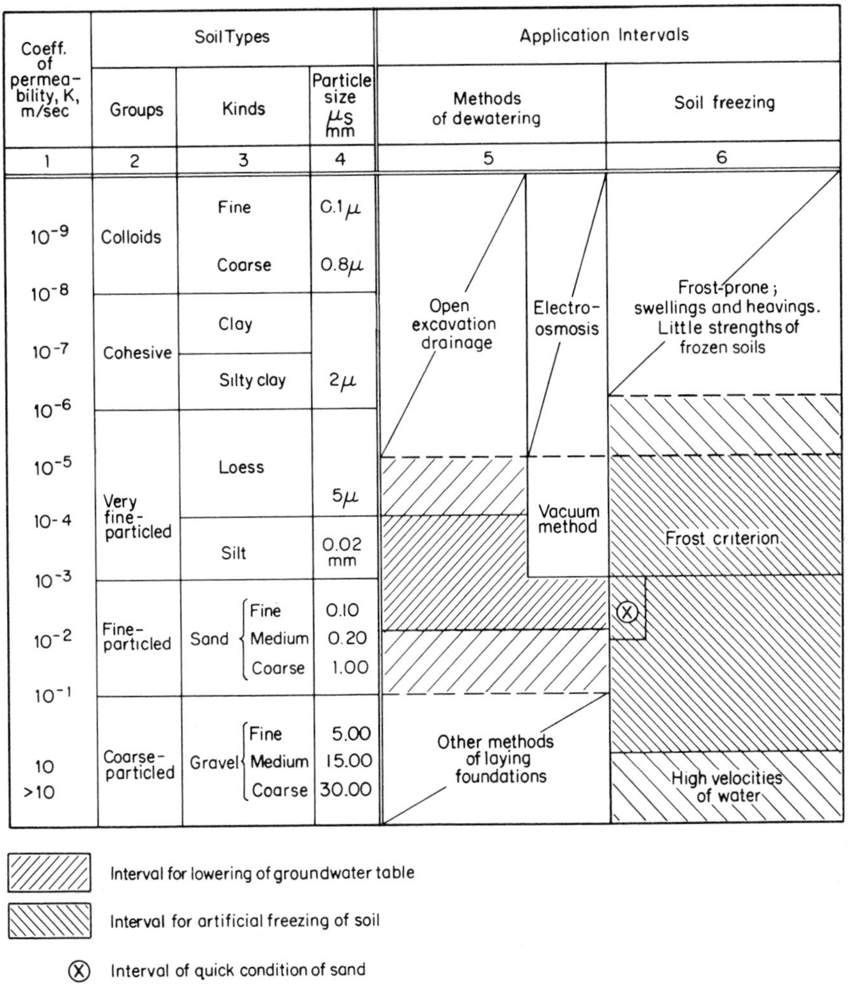

Coeff. of permea-bility, K, m/sec	Soil Types: Groups	Soil Types: Kinds	Particle size μs mm
1	2	3	4
	Colloids	Fine	0.1μ
10^{-9}		Coarse	0.8μ
10^{-8}	Cohesive	Clay	
10^{-7}		Silty clay	2μ
10^{-6}	Very fine-particled	Loess	
10^{-5}			5μ
10^{-4}		Silt	0.02 mm
10^{-3}	Fine-particled	Sand: Fine	0.10
10^{-2}		Sand: Medium	0.20
10^{-1}		Sand: Coarse	1.00
	Coarse-particled	Gravel: Fine	5.00
10		Gravel: Medium	15.00
>10		Gravel: Coarse	30.00

Application Intervals

5 Methods of dewatering: Open excavation drainage; Electro-osmosis; Vacuum method; Other methods of laying foundations

6 Soil freezing: Frost-prone; swellings and heavings. Little strengths of frozen soils; Frost criterion; High velocities of water

Interval for lowering of groundwater table

Interval for artificial freezing of soil

Ⓧ Interval of quick condition of sand

FIG. 7-1 Physical limits of soil for laying foundations.[2]

shaft, through water-logged soil down to impermeable strata. Freezer pipes, closed at the bottoms, are inserted into the holes, and smaller pipes, called pressure pipes, are introduced almost to the bottom of the freezer pipes. Through the pressure pipes, cold brine is pumped into the freezer pipes. The brine circulates up through the freezer pipes, carrying with it the heat absorbed from the freezing soil by the mantle surface in contact with the soil. The warmed brine is returned to the refrigeration plant, cooled, and returned again in continuous circulation to the freezer pipes.[7]

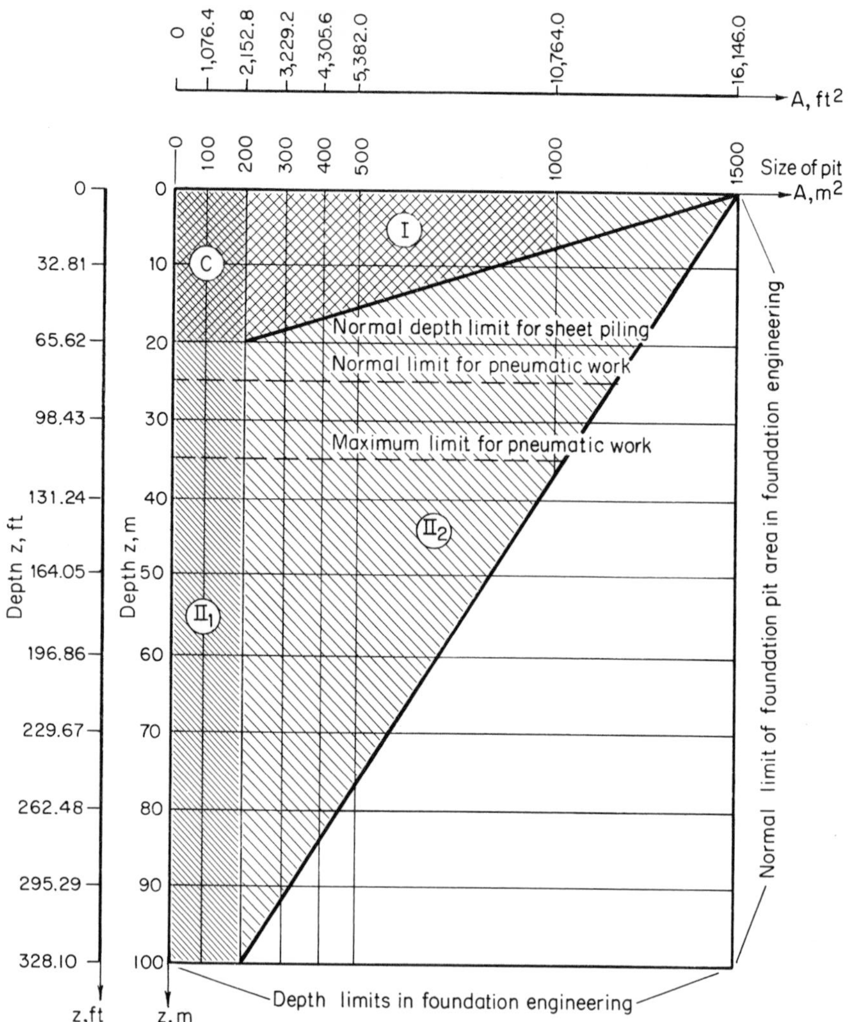

FIG. 7-2 Engineering and geometric limits of soil freezing as compared with other methods of laying foundations.[2] (I) Interval for lowering of groundwater table. Interval for artificial freezing of soil (II_1) for simple and (II_2) complex outline forms of foundation. (C) Competitive interval to other methods of laying foundations.

From 1884 to 1886, the soil freezing method was used in the construction of a pedestrian tunnel at Stockholm, Sweden. A tunnel 80 ft long was dug by freezing coarse gravel, sand, and clay.

In 1906, during the construction of a section of the Metropolitan, the subway system of Paris, a tunnel under the Seine was driven partly through artificially frozen soil. The section is 1092 m long, running from Place du Châtelet to Place St. Michel, under the Ile de la Cité and both arms of the Seine.[8]

Artificial freezing of soil was applied from 1931 to 1933 to the River Scheldt tunnel in Antwerp, Belgium. The tunnel shafts are 70 ft in diameter, and 87 ft deep. Six-inch freezer pipes and two-inch pressure pipes were used.[9]

In Moscow the method of artificial soil freezing was applied to subway construction from 1933 to 1946.

The method was first attempted in the United States in 1888 with the construction of a mining shaft in Louisiana for the National Sulphur Company. It was unsuccessful.[10] Another mining shaft was dug by freezing with better results in 1891 at the Chapin mine at Iron Mountain, Michigan.[11] Artificial freezing was successfully used to repair a leak in the cofferdam of the West River pier of the Detroit-Superior arch bridge over the Cuyahoga River at Cleveland.[12] Recently, many artificial soil freezing jobs in the United States have been completed successfully, among them the shaft for the Richmond water supply tunnel in Brooklyn.[13]

7-4. Protecting Excavations by Soil Freezing. The method of stabilizing of foundation excavation walls by freezing consists of the following. Around the area of the pit to be excavated a wall of frozen soil, called an *ice wall,* is formed (Fig. 7-3). After the ice wall is established, the foundation pit can be excavated.

Small foundation areas may be enclosed by straight walls (Fig. 7-3a), square or rectangular in outline. For larger areas, straight ice walls are not dependable. Therefore, in order to strengthen the wall of frozen soil, it is formed in a curve. Receiving water and earth pressure from outside of the excavation, the arch of frozen soil works in compression, and is able to withstand the pressure.

Long, straight walls of frozen soil may be strengthened by providing the walls with counterforts of frozen soil (Fig. 7-3). Depending upon the plan of the foundation the ice wall may have other outlines than merely straight or circular. Large foundation pits to be enclosed by freezing are most expediently subdivided into a number of smaller units. Whichever ice wall plan is used, the proposed site of soil freezing must be carefully explored and the soil properties thoroughly investigated.

7-5. Nature of Soil Exploration. The decision to freeze soil artificially in foundation engineering is based on careful geological, hydrogeological, and climatological investigations, and the soil is tested for its physical strength and thermal properties. Specifically, soil exploration should provide the following information.

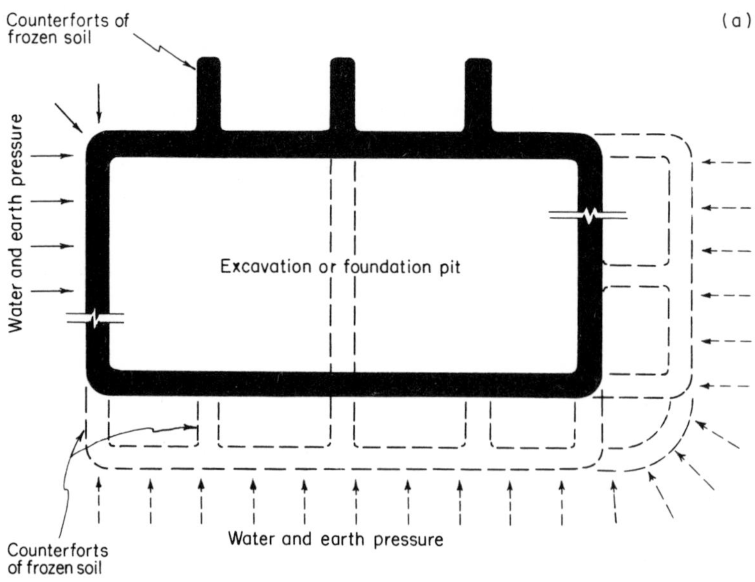

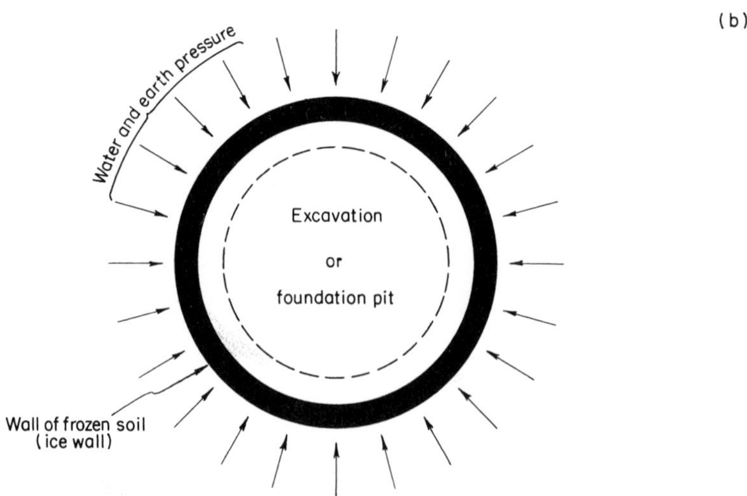

FIG. 7-3 Walls of frozen soil. Plan views. (a) Straight wall of frozen soil. (b) Curved wall of frozen soil.

1. The regimen of the groundwater: its depth below ground surface, its direction and velocity of flow and hydraulic gradient; seasonal fluctuations; its temperature, chemical content (salt, for example); and whether there is free or artesian groundwater present. Groundwater flowing faster than 2.0 m per day is very difficult to freeze. Groundwater can be used for cooling operations in the refrigeration plant.
2. The number, position, thickness, and nature of the soil to be frozen (soil structure, texture, mineralogical content, porosity, moisture content, and consistency limits).
3. The thermal properties of water, ice, frozen soil, and unfrozen soil.

The success of the operation depends to a great degree upon the porosity of the soil strata to be frozen.

7-6. Design of a Soil Freezing Installation. After soil exploration, the freezing installation is designed. The design consists basically of three parts: (1) the freezing project, which is the determination of the outline, position, spacing and number of freezer points, the thickness of the depth of the ice wall, and the volume of the soil to be frozen; (2) calculation of the amount of heat to be abstracted from the soil and determination of the time necessary for freezing the ice wall; (3) the design and selection of the refrigerating system and the calculation of its requirements.

7-7. Procedure in Artificial Soil Freezing. The procedure in artificial soil freezing consists of these five operations:

1. Installation of a freezer point network.
2. Installation of a refrigerating plant and the pipes for circulating brine.
3. Formation and freezing of the ice walls (for foundations).
4. Maintenance of the freezing during digging and laying of foundations or supporting shafts and tunnels.
5. Thawing after completion of the operation.

Chapter 8

The Soil Refrigeration System

8-1. General Description. The freezing installation used in foundation engineering consists of two essential parts, a system of soil freezer points and a refrigeration plant. The freezer points are installed in contact with the soil to be frozen. The refrigeration plant provides the freezer points with the necessary cold for abstracting heat from the soil.

There are four commonly used refrigeration methods. They use, respectively, natural or artificial ice, freezing mixtures, expanding gases, and evaporating liquids.

The cold is carried from the refrigeration plant to the freezer points with a brine solution. In this book, the refrigeration of brine by means of evaporating liquid ammonia will be discussed.

Ammonia (NH_3), a compound of nitrogen and hydrogen, is a colorless, pungent, suffocating gas that is very soluble in water.

8-2. Freezer Point. A wall of frozen soil (ice wall) is created by installing freezer points vertically or obliquely along the perimeter of the excavation site at predetermined spacing. The freezer point is a metal pipe 4–8 in. (100–200 mm) in diameter and 6–8 mm thick, through which circulates a liquid or gas cooling agent (Fig. 8-1). The lower end of the freezer pipe is closed. The freezer pipes of a freezer point are usually installed in holes predrilled vertically or obliquely in the soil. Bore-holes can be drilled with or without a casing. To advance a bore-hole without a casing, "drilling mud" (thixotropic drilling fluid) is used[14] to prevent the walls of the borings from caving in. A thixotropic drilling fluid was used in making borings for freezer pipes for the shaft of the Richmond water tunnel on the Brooklyn side.[13]

In the underpinning operations of the 26-floor "Companhia Paulista de Seguros" building in São Paulo, Brazil,[1] galvanized freezer pipes

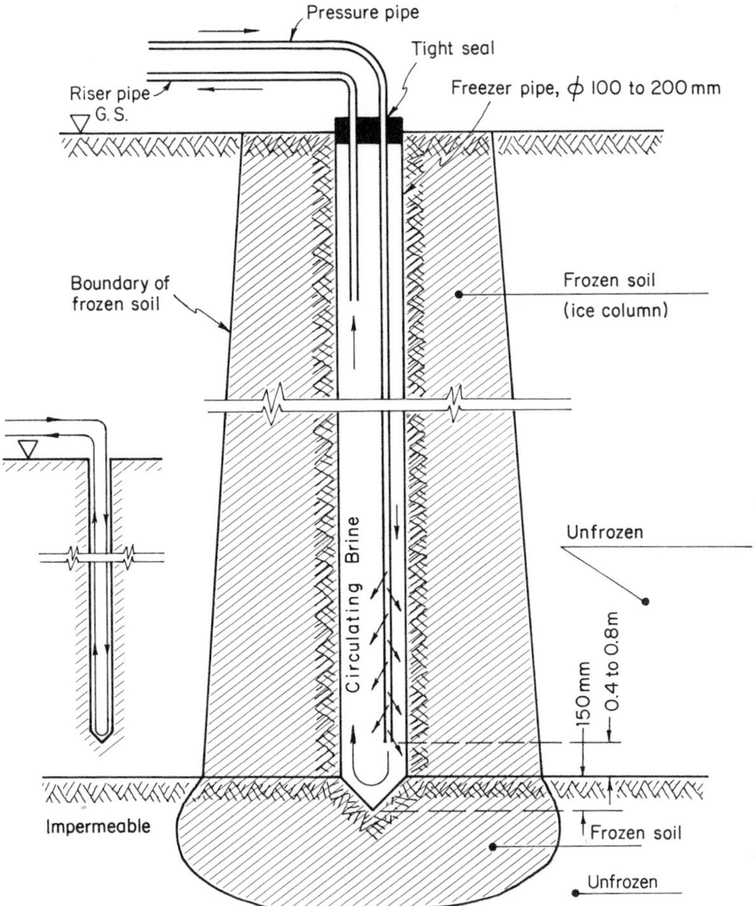

FIG. 8-1 Freezer point.

4 in. in diameter and 14 ft long were used. Brine of −20°C was used here.

If possible, the freezer pipe penetrates the entire thickness of the water-bearing layer of soil down to an impermeable stratum. This safeguards against hydrostatic uplift of the bottom of the excavation and influx of water into the pit. If water enters the pit from the bottom, the bottom must also be frozen. In light soils, the freezer pipes can be installed by the method of jetting.

8-3. Pressure and Riser Pipes. Inside the freezer pipe are installed two smaller pipes: the pressure (feeder) pipe and the riser (return) pipe. The diameter of these pipes is 1–2 in. (~25 mm to ~50 mm). Their lower ends are open. The pressure pipe may have side perforations at its lower end. Alternatively, the freezer pipe is connected directly to the collector pipe, in which case there is no riser pipe.

8-4. Circulation of Brine. The brine enters the freezer pipe through the pressure pipe with a velocity of about $v = 0.5$ to $v = 0.7$ m/sec at a temperature of about −20°C. Here the cold brine loses some of its velocity and takes heat from soil around the freezer pipe. The brine rises in the freezer pipe with a velocity of $v = 3$ to $v = 5$ cm/sec, enters the riser pipe, and returns by the collector pipe to the refrigerator, where cold is regenerated by evaporating liquids, such as ammonia. Thus the refrigerating brine circulates uninterruptedly within a closed system.

8-5. Formation of Wall of Frozen Soil. Because of the uninterrupted heat exchange in soil surrounding the freezer pipe, and as a result of heat removal from the soil by the freezer pipe, the soil and water in the voids of the soil cool and freeze gradually, thus forming around the freezer pipe a thick, pear-shaped cylinder or frozen soil column (Fig. 8-2).

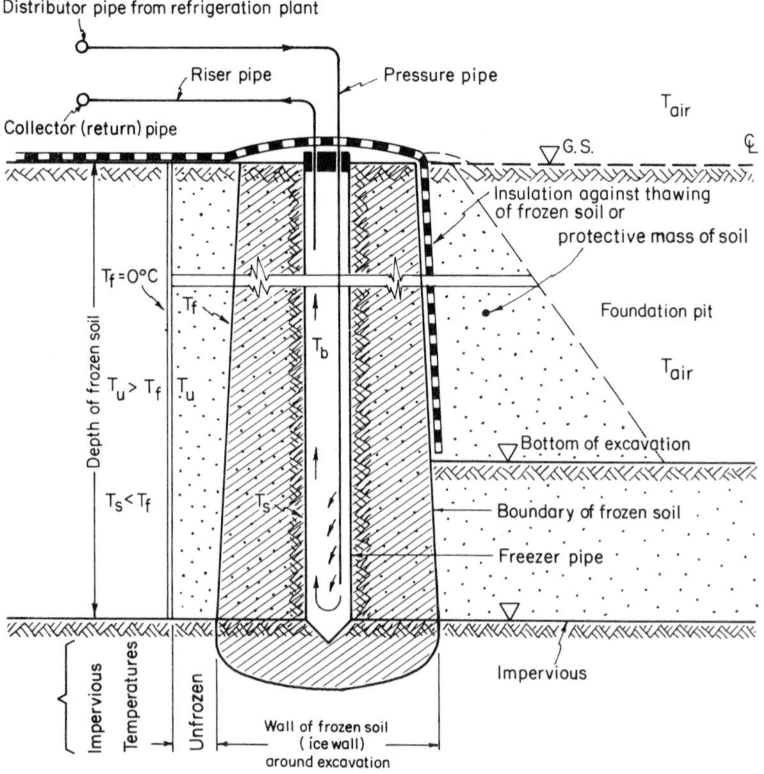

FIG. 8-2 Principle of freezing of a foundation pit.

As the diameter of the frozen soil columns increases, the columns merge with the adjacent ones to form a solid, rigid wall of frozen soil several feet thick (Fig. 8-3). After the ice wall has been formed, the pit is ready for excavation.

The ice wall prevents the groundwater and quicksand from flowing into the pit and is strong enough to make any bracing of the pit unnecessary.

In pits and shafts enclosed by ice walls that do not rest upon impermeable soil or rock, water may enter from underneath the base of the ice wall. Hence, the whole soil should be frozen in a solid block. When this is not possible, special freezer points are used (Fig. 8-3),[15] that have short freezer pipes, which permit freezing the soil of the

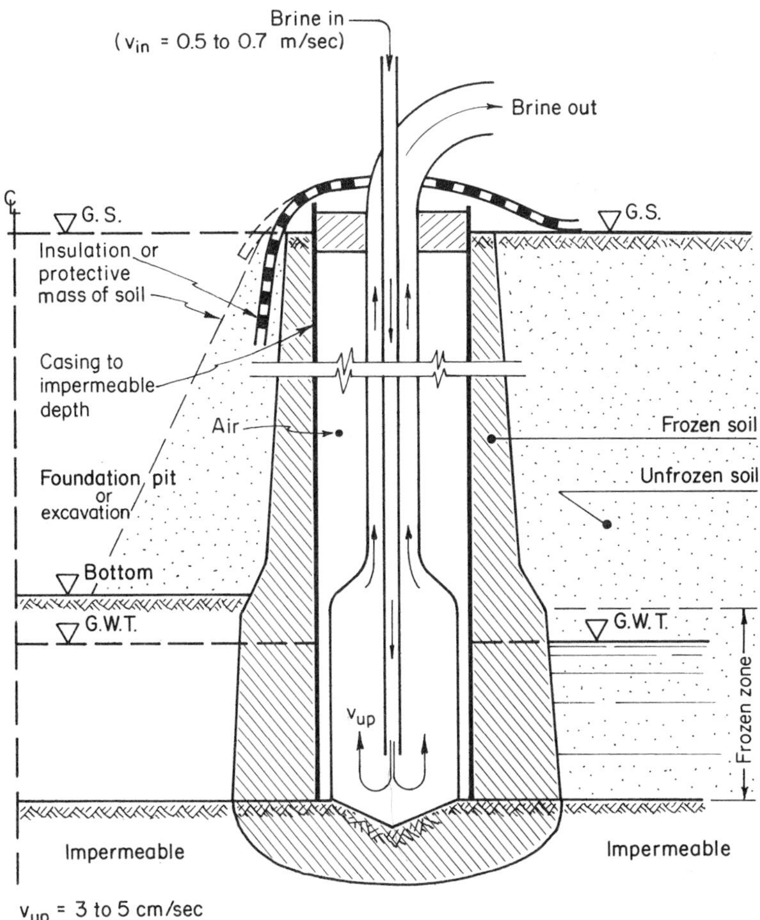

FIG. 8-3 A short freezer point.

bottom of the pit. In this way, the foundation pit may also be waterproofed by means of a course of frozen soil.

8-6. Freezer System's Requirements. The freezer system should be leakproof with respect to heat and brine.

To minimize heat loss, pipes should be well insulated.

Great care must be exercised in preparing, installing, and testing the freezer pipes, as well as the brine distributor and return pipes. The lower part of the freezer pipe must be subjected to a hydrostatic pressure test with water. The test pressure is 10–20 atmospheres higher than the working pressure in the freezer column. For the upper part of the freezer pipe the test pressure is gradually reduced. The very upper part of the freezer pipe may be subjected to the working pressure of the brine, 10–20 atmospheres.

Freezer pipes must not leak. Brine escaping into the soil forms "brine nests," or "brine pockets," which are difficult to freeze. Brine pockets may cause the groundwater to flow into the foundation pit or excavation.

The end of the freezer pipe above the ground must be sealed tightly to prevent the brine from spilling into the soil. The spilled brine will not freeze, leaving unfrozen pockets in the frozen wall.

The groundwater itself supplies heat to the freezing body of soil, thus retarding the formation of the size, shape, and density of the ice wall.

The presence in soil of brine with a lower freezing point than soil water slows the freezing process. A salt solution does not freeze instantly and uniformly, but only when the *cryohydratic point* is reached. For brine with a salt content of 22.4%, this point is at −21.2°C. At this temperature, the solution breaks down into ice and salt and solidifies into a mixture of both constituents.

8-7. Spacing of Freezer Points. The spacing of the freezer points is chosen with the idea that the frozen soil should form a continuous, solid, frigid wall. For thin walls, the freezer pipes are spaced in one row. For thick walls, the freezer pipes are staggered in two rows. An ice wall may also be formed in the shape of a cellular cofferdam.

For open pits the freezer points are spaced from about $s = 3$ ft to $s = 7.5$ ft (~1.0 m to ~2.5 m) center to center, depending upon the properties of the soil, soil and air temperatures, diameters of freezer pipes, and hence the rate of freezing (Fig. 8-4). Such spacing forms an ice wall 2.5–3.0 m thick in about 45–60 days.

The spacing of freezer points for shafts or small, round excavations is 3 ft to 4 ft (~0.9 m to ~1.2 m) center to center.

Hydrological and thermal check holes spaced at intervals of 20 ft

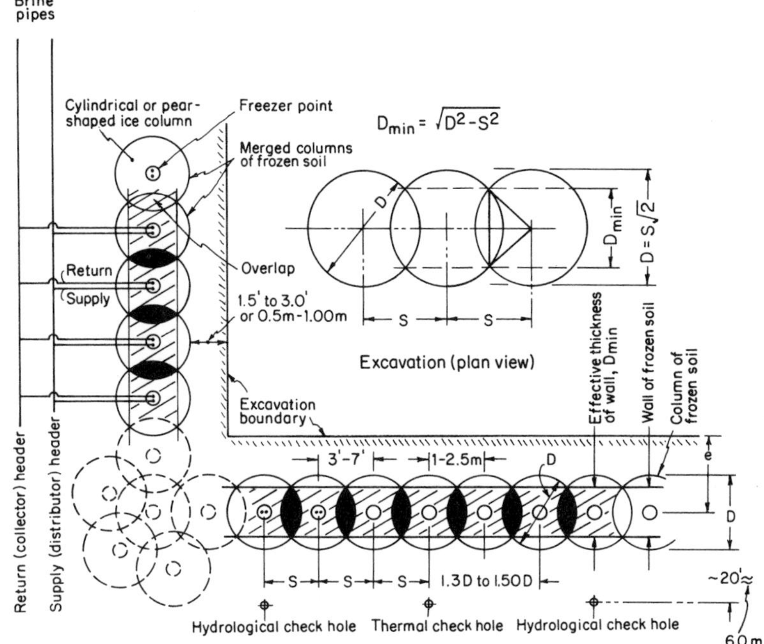

FIG. 8-4 Spacing of freezer pipes.

parallel to the ice wall are advisable. These holes are not drilled inside the excavation unless there is no possibility of thereby flooding it.

The spacing and depth of freezer pipes in the Richmond water supply shaft project in Brooklyn are illustrated in Fig. 8-5. The photographs in Fig. 8-6 were taken during the soil freezing operation at the Richmond water supply tunnel in Brooklyn. Notice the lined-out shaft, the air duct into the shaft, and the positions of the iced freezer pipes. The heads of the freezer and return pipes are covered with tarpaulin.

8-8. Depth of Ice Wall. The freezer point must be installed so as to intercept the entire thickness of the water-bearing stratum. Figure 8-7 shows how an ice wall on the uphill side of an excavation on a slope effectively seals off the groundwater.

The freezing operation must be designed so that the bottom of the excavated pit is not broken up by hydrostatic pressure of water. This is prevented by sinking the freezer points down about 2–2.5 m into the water-impervious layer of rock or clay. The alternative is to freeze the soil at the bottom of the excavation pit. Clays, generally, are more difficult to freeze than sand or gravel.

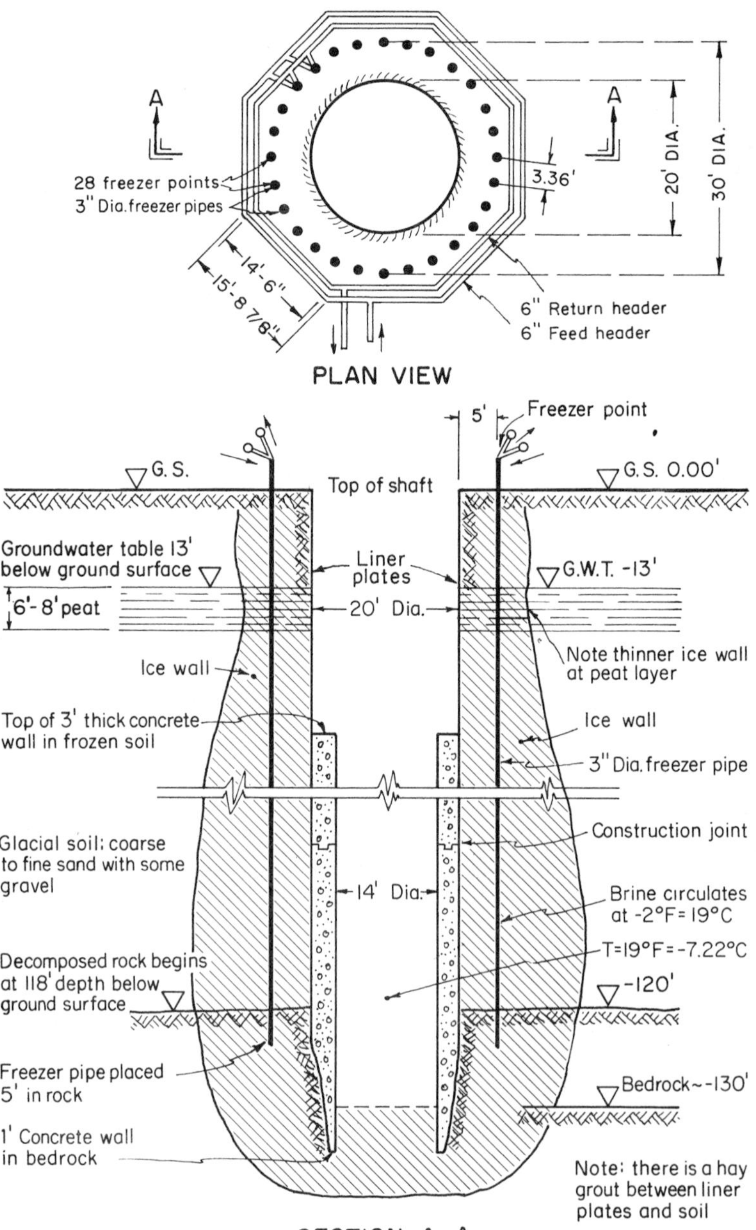

FIG. 8-5 Spacing and depth of freezer pipes in the Richmond water supply tunnel shaft project in Brooklyn, N.Y.

(a)

(b)

FIG. 8-6 Soil freezing operations for the Richmond water supply tunnel shaft in Brooklyn, N.Y. (a) Lined-out shaft and tarpaulin-covered freezer pipes. (b) Iced freezer pipe. (c) Lowering workmen into shaft. (d) Manifold for pneumatic tools for loosening frozen soil and rock in the shaft.

(c)

(d)

FIG. 8-6 (Continued)

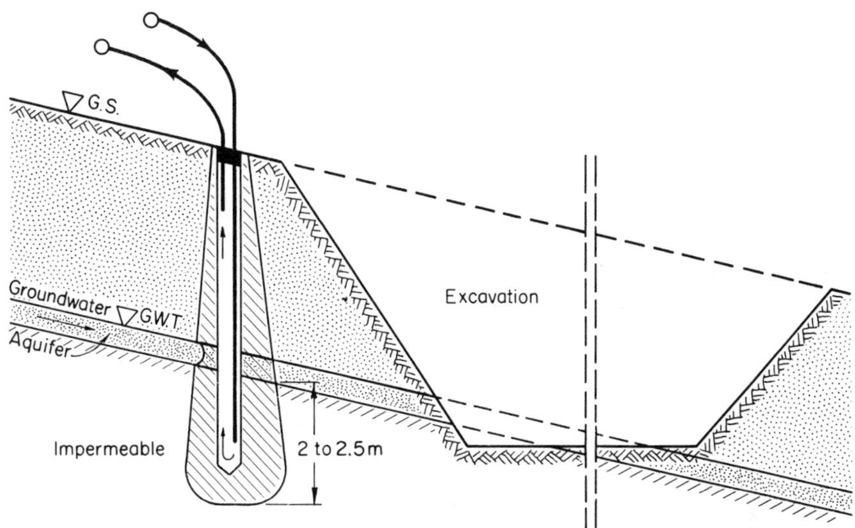

FIG. 8-7 Ice wall on the uphill side in a sloped soil.

The thickness of the frozen bottom of the pit depends chiefly on the hydrostatic pressure from below.

The floor of the excavation must be safeguarded against underground water pressure by a concrete bottom seal ("grouting"), by chemical injections, or by freezing. Otherwise, after the pit has been pumped out, uplift sets in with its full effect.

The required depth of the ice wall depends also upon the location and size of the head of the groundwater table. If the groundwater is inaccessibly deep, an artificial water-bearing layer is established by recharging the soil with water for the purpose of freezing an ice wall.

A fluctuating groundwater table is not suitable for freezing. If the freezing method must be employed, the groundwater table must be lowered before freezing is begun.

In uniformly textured soils, the shape of the frozen soil around the freezer point is fairly cylindrical. If there is flowing groundwater present, the warmth of the water may form an irregular, bulging column (Fig. 8-8).

Various layers of soil may have different heat capacities and other different thermal properties, causing bulges along the frozen soil column. In such instances great skill and care must be exercised in soil freezing operations.

The thickness and the height of the ice wall depend to a great extent on the strength properties of the frozen soil layers as well as on the sequence in which the various layers of various soil types are de-

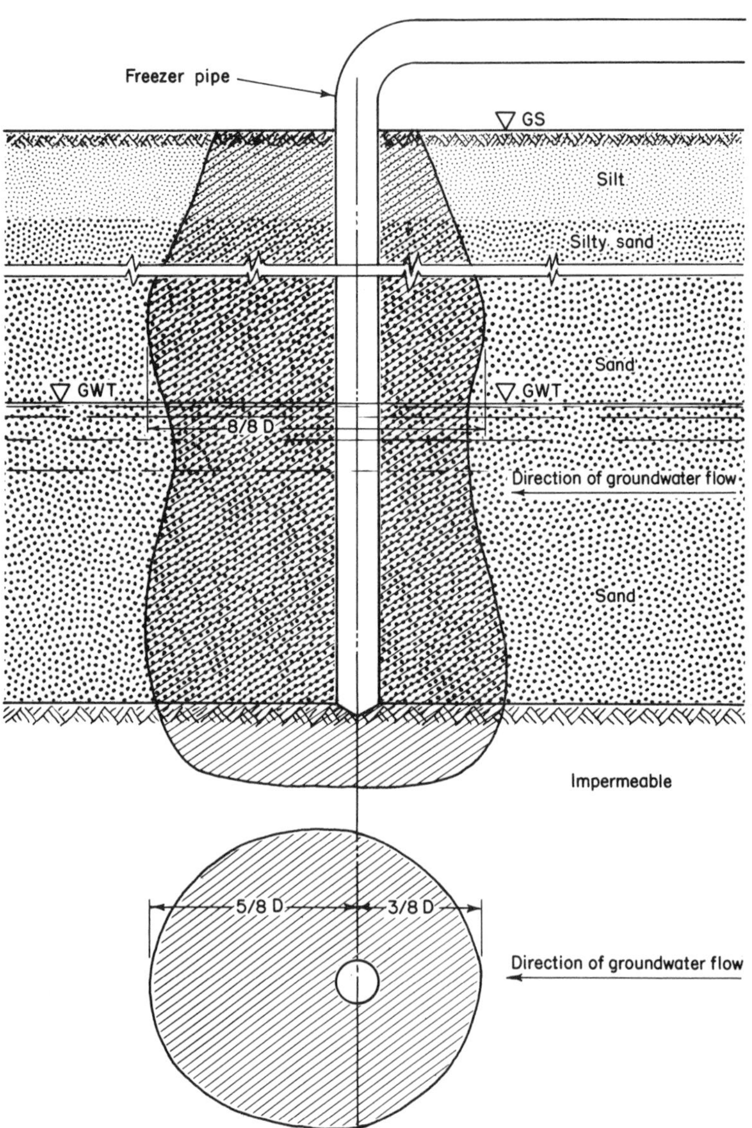

FIG. 8-8 Bulged column of frozen soil.

posited. Clay covering a sandy soil is less dangerous than sandy soil lying upon a clayey soil. This is so because the compressive strength of a frozen, water-logged soil at $T = -15°C$ is about 140 kg/cm^2, whereas that of frozen saturated clay is about 70 kg/cm^2 at the same temperature. This fact, as well as the depth and thicknesses of such layers of soils and the possible combinations of the sequence of the various types of soil, governs to a great extent the design of the ice wall.

Chapter 9

Refrigeration Plant

9-1. Description. A refrigeration plant consists of two basic parts, the refrigeration equipment for cooling the brine and a pumping station for circulating the brine through the freezer system (Fig. 9-1).

The refrigeration equipment consists usually of the following principal devices: (1) a compressor, (2) a condenser, (3) a throttling (expansion) valve, and (4) an evaporator or refrigerator.

Auxiliary equipment, such as precoolers and oil and grease traps between compressor and condenser, are also used.

Depending on the desired degree of freezing to be attained and on the purpose of refrigeration, the cooling of the circulating brine is produced by evaporating carbonic acid, ammonia, or other chemicals. Hence, the refrigeration plants are termed carbonic acid refrigeration plants or ammonia refrigeration plants, for example.

9-2. Ammonia Refrigeration Plant. Ammonia, NH_3, is a colorless gas with a sharp, specific odor. Technical ammonia is obtained as a by-product from dry distillation of coal in a coke oven or from the manufacture of illuminating gas. Ammonia is also obtained synthetically. In foundation engineering, the ammonia refrigeration plant is widely used because it is more economical than other types (Fig. 9-1).

Ammonia refrigeration plants cannot produce refrigerating temperatures below −25°C, whereas carbonic acid plants can produce temperatures to about −40°C.

Refrigeration plants may also be classified as central or local (decentralized) and stationary or mobile. For foundation engineering in thickly settled areas the refrigeration plant should be mobile and compact.

A central refrigeration plant is one from which the cold brine is distributed to the system of freezer points installed in the soil. Such

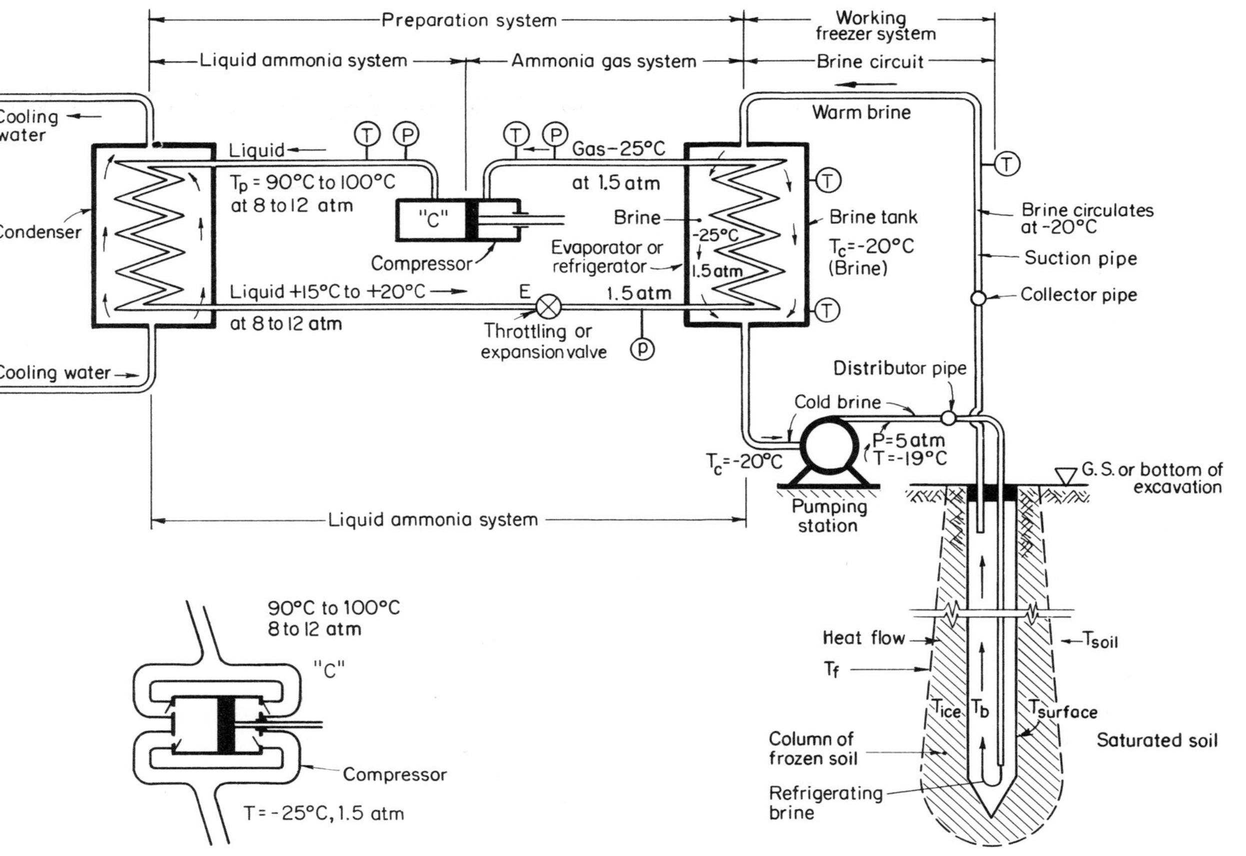

FIG. 9-1 Schematics of an ammonia refrigeration system.

a plant is usually stationary (Fig. 9-2), although mobile plants are occasionally used.

A local refrigeration system (rather than plant) is one installed at each freezer point, where the refrigerant is prepared, mixed and introduced into the freezer pipe.

9-3. Compressor. The compressor liquefies the ammonia gas at about 8–12 atmospheres. The temperature of the liquid ammonia rises to 90°C or +100°C. The ammonia is then pumped from the compressor to a condenser.

(a)

FIG. 9-2 A stationary, central refrigerating plant. (a) Refrigerating equipment. (b) Refrigerator plant and freezer pipes. (c) Throttling valve.

(b)

(c)

9-4. Condenser. In the condenser, the liquid ammonia passes through a system of coils and is cooled by circulating water to a temperature of 15°C to 20°C. The compressor maintains high pressure in the condenser and low pressure in the evaporator (refrigerator). The circulation of ammonia is constantly checked with thermometers and manometers (pressure gauges).

9-5. Throttling Valve. The liquid ammonia leaves the condenser at the same pressure and temperature and passes through a throttling valve, also called an expansion, or regulating, valve. In the throttling process, the liquid ammonia is sprayed at a constant, high pressure (8 to 12 atm) through a fine nozzle into another coil at a constant but lower pressure.

Passing through the throttling valve as a mixture of liquid and vapor, the pressure of ammonia drops rapidly to about 1.5 atm, changing into a state such that it is just about to evaporate. The drop in pressure is accompanied by a lowering of temperature of the ammonia to about –25°C.

9-6. Refrigerator. The refrigerator, or vaporizer (Fig. 9-1), a vessel through which brine circulates, cools the brine used to freeze the soil. Also in the refrigerator are coils of pipe for circulating the ammonia gas. The coils are rinsed by the surrounding brine.

In the refrigeration coils, as a consequence of the throttling process, a partial vaporization of the ammonia takes place. The throttling process plays the chief role in cooling the brine.

The refrigerator coils take some heat from the brine returning from the freezer points. This heat helps convert the remaining liquid ammonia into vapor, NH_3, whereby the latent heat of vaporization of the ammonia is released. The temperature of the ammonia in the coils drops to about –25°C, thus rechilling the brine.

The ammonia gas, in order to be converted back to a liquid, is drawn in by the compressor and pumped upward through a coil, thus returning to the low-pressure side of the compressor. This closes the ammonia (preparation) circuit. Compressed to about 8 to 12 atm, the ammonia rises in temperature to about 90°C or 100°C (194°F to 212°F). When it condenses, the compressed ammonia is changed into a liquid.

9-7. The Working Circuit. The working circuit of the freezer system (brine circuit) consists of a brine tank, a brine pumping station, a distribution system, pressure pipes, freezer pipes, riser pipes, and collector pipes. The freezer points are connected to distribution and collector lines in parallel, so that the brine reaches each freezer pipe at practically the same temperature.

The brine in the refrigerator is cooled by the vaporizer to about $T_{cr} = -20°C$. The brine is drawn from the refrigerator tank and pumped to the freezer points at a pressure of about 2 kg/cm^2. The cold brine in the freezer abstracts heat from the soil, warms up, rises by pressure into the riser pipe, and is returned to the brine tank, where it is cooled by the circulating gaseous ammonia in the refrigeration coil. In operation, the entire process is continuous and uninterrupted.

9-8. Brine. Brine (salt water) does not generate cold, but carries it to the freezer points and carries away heat absorbed from the soil around the freezer points. Brine should meet the following requirements:

1. It should be mobile.
2. It should have a high heat capacity.
3. It should have a low freezing point.
4. It should not affect the material of pipes through which it is circulated.
5. It should not settle out chemical salt at a given freezing temperature (this would clog up the pipes and retard the freezing process).

In removing heat from the soil the brine warms up. In the refrigerator, the brine gives off heat to the vaporizer (where the ammonia evaporates).

Refrigerating brine may be prepared from ordinary rock salt, sodium chloride (NaCl), from magnesium chloride ($MgCl_2$), or from calcium chloride ($CaCl_2$). These brines are difficult to freeze.

Sodium chloride brine freezes at –26°C. However, it corrodes the pipes and is not ideally suitable for foundation engineering. A 26% magnesium chloride solution freezes at –33°C (–27.4°F). Calcium chloride brine is more expensive than sodium chloride brine but is well suited for deep freezing.

The most common concentration of $CaCl_2$ brine is a 30% solution. Calcium chloride brine freezes at about –30°C to –40°C, depending upon its concentration.

The freezing point of a solution can be lowered by adding methyl alcohol, because alcohol freezes at –112°C (–81.5°F). There are two disadvantages to the use of alcohol alone as the coolant—its high cost and its flammability.

Brine may be prepared as a mixture of

85% brine of $CaCl_2$, $\gamma = 1204$ kg/m^3 = 75.13 lb/ft^3 (= 28°Bé),
heat capacity of 8 Cal/(kg)(°C),
10% brine of $MgCl_2$, and
5% methyl alcohol.[16]

Such brine freezes at –50°C (–58°F).

In the freezing operations of the shaft for the Richmond water supply tunnel at Brooklyn, N.Y. (in a tunnel under the Hudson River from Brooklyn to Staten Island), calcium chloride brine was used with a specific gravity of $G = 1.25$ and a freezing point of −31.68°C (−25°F).

9-9. Properties of Ammonia and Carbon Dioxide. Some important properties of ammonia and carbon dioxide relative to their use as refrigerants are compiled in Table 9-1.

Table 9-1

Some Properties of Ammonia and Carbon Dioxide [17]

Cold-Producing Substance	Temperature and Pressure of Liquefaction	Boiling Point
1	2	3
Ammonia, NH_3;	+15°C and 7.1 atm	−34.0°C at 1.0 atm
critical temperature	+20°C and 8.4 atm	−23.0°C at 1.5 atm
$T_{cr} = 131°C$	+25°C and 9.8 atm	−18.0°C at 2.0 atm
Carbon dioxide, CO_2;	+15°C and 52.2 atm	−49.0°C at 7 atm
critical temperature	+20°C and 58.8 atm	−45.0°C at 8 atm
$T_{cr} = 31°C$	+25°C and 66.6 atm	−42.0°C at 9 atm

A comparison of these properties reveals that ammonia is liquefied at less pressure than carbon dioxide. With a one-stage compressor, the temperature of ammonia can be reduced to −29°C. With two-stage or multistage compression, brine temperatures of −40°C can be attained.

9-10. Disadvantages of Carbon Dioxide as a Refrigerant. By means of carbon dioxide plants and a one-stage compressor, brine temperatures of −30°C to −35 C at pressures 60 to 80 atm may be achieved. With multistage compressors brine temperatures between −50°C and −55°C may be attained in carbon dioxide plants. Hence, in carbon dioxide plants the equipment and pipes must have thicker and stronger walls and other resisting parts. Also, because CO_2 is odorless, leaks in equipment may remain unnoticed for a long time. Another disadvantage of carbon dioxide as a refrigerant is its very low critical temperature, 31°C. Above this temperature, carbon dioxide gas cannot be liquefied. Therefore, large amounts of water must be provided for cooling it.

"Threads" of water in carbon dioxide-type equipment must be avoided so that, in passing through the throttling valve, they do not freeze, clogging the nozzle.

Therefore, carbon dioxide-type refrigeration plants are very seldom used in soil freezing operations in foundation engineering.

Carbon dioxide refrigeration equipment, however, is used in digging deep mining shafts. Such equipment works at high pressures (and is therefore expensive) and attains temperatures down to −55°C. Carbon dioxide equipment is particularly required when the groundwater contains soluble salts, for example, rock salt or potassium salt.[18] If the ground water does not contain salt, ammonia equipment is usually adequate.

9-11. Advantages of Ammonia as a Refrigerant. Some of the advantages of the ammonia refrigeration plant are as follows.

1. Leaks in equipment are small because low pressure is used.
2. Leaks are easily detected because of the specific odor of ammonia.
3. The presence of water "threads" in the system is of no significance.
4. Smaller motors and compressors are needed than in other types of refrigeration plants. Hence, both the initial and operating costs of an ammonia plant are less than for other types.

Ammonia refrigeration plants are preferred when the brine coolant need not be colder than −20°C. For lower temperatures, carbon dioxide refrigeration systems are used.

9-12. Disadvantage of Ammonia as a Refrigerant. Ammonia is more expensive than carbon dioxide. Ammonia is contaminated more easily than carbon dioxide by oil and grease from the compressors; this requires great care with respect to lubrication.

9-13. Other Kinds of Refrigeration Systems. Refrigeration systems are coming into use in which the direct vaporization of the refrigerant takes place at the head of the freezer pipes, thus making the brine system obsolescent. Heat may also be removed from soil by introducing vaporized carbonic dioxide directly into the freezer pipes. By this method it is possible to reach a temperature of about −60°C in the freezer pipes.

In these two methods the possibility of leakage in the refrigeration installation is reduced considerably compared with conventional plants. Costs are also reduced. Both methods are still undergoing improvements.

Freon. Some of the refrigerants supplied to the industry are those known under the trade name Freon, a group of polyhalogenated derivatives of methane and ethane containing fluorine, and in most cases, chlorine or bromine.

Freon refrigerants possess such noteworthy characteristics as nonflammability, excellent chemical and thermal stability, low toxicity, high density, low boiling point, low viscosity, and low surface tension. They are odorless, noncombustible, harmless cooling agents. Only at 30% by volume in the air, for an exposure of about two hours, can freon become dangerous to health.

The most commonly known freons are as follows.

F_{12} = difluordichlormethane, CF_2Cl_2. Next to ammonia, it is the most used coolant in piston compressors. It is the most commonly used of the freons for household and commercial refrigeration and air conditioning.

F_{22} = difluormonochlormethane, CHF_2Cl. This is used for low vaporizing temperatures (down to −60°C) in plunger type compressors.

F_{13} = trifluormonochlormethane, CF_3Cl. Can be used where CO_2 is used. It solidifies at −181°C, whereas CO_2 solidifies at −56°C.[19]

F_{11} = trichlormonofluormethane, CCl_3F. Suitable for turbocompressors. It is used in commercial and industrial air conditioning systems and water cooling.

F_{21} = dichlormonofluormethane, $CHCl_2F$. Used in absorption machines.

F_{113} = trichlortrifluorethane, $C_2Cl_3F_3$. Used for turbocompressors.

F_{114} = dichlortetrafluorethane, $C_2Cl_2F_4$. Frigidaire uses this for certain rotation compressors.

Freon was introduced into the refrigeration technology by the American scientists Midgley, Henne, and McNary.

Disadvantages of Freon. The main disadvantage of freon is its high cost. It also requires a relatively large compressor. In freezing soils, however, this is of no great significance. A tight system is required to prevent leaks.

9-14. Other Means of Freezing. Tunnel walls may be stabilized, in cold climates, by naturally available cold air, or by artificially cooled air.

According to Stini,[20] depending upon the size of the cross section of a tunnel, frost action may advance into a tunnel to a distance of about 1000 m and thus during the course of years lower the degree of the heat, i.e., temperature regimen in the tunnel. The 1431-m-long two-track Semmering tunnel near Vienna, Austria, is affected throughout by adverse icing conditions, thus greatly endangering train traffic. Coping with the ice conditions by providing and maintaining safety measures is costly.

Occasionally dry ice (solid carbon dioxide) has been used in foundation engineering. For example, dry ice was used to make frozen cofferdams for bridge pier repair.[21]

9-15. Commercial Ton. As a carryover from the early days of the art, the quantity of refrigeration is measured in the unit of a *ton of refrigeration,* known also as the *commercial ton.* A one-ton refrigeration plant is capable of extracting the amount of heat energy which could be realized through melting one ton of ice in 24 hours. This does not mean that such a plant could make one ton of ice. The actual effect usually exceeds the maximum, because commercial ice is necessarily distributed at a subcooled state, and the process of ice making requires that some of the energy be utilized to cool the water to 0°C before any actual freezing of water can take place.

In the freezing operation of the Richmond water supply tunnel at the Brooklyn end, the two compressors together produced 125 tons of refrigeration for the active stage of freezing and 40 tons of refrigeration during the passive (maintenance) stage of freezing. The soil temperature was kept at about −10°F (−23.3°C).

Chapter 10

Soil Freezing and Design of Ice Wall

10-1. Stages of Freezing. The process of artificial freezing of soil is carried out in two stages: active freezing and passive freezing.

10-2. Active Freezing. During active freezing, a dense wall of frozen soil is formed to the necessary thickness. After the ice wall has been established, active freezing ceases and passive freezing begins.

When it freezes, soil transforms from a two-phase soil (solids and water held in saturation), or from a three-phase soil (solids, water, and air or other gas), into a complex four-phase system of solids, ice, water, and air or other gas.

Upon freezing, the soil heaves. Soil does not heave as much if it is frozen quickly, because the freezing is relatively uniform throughout. Slow freezing results in ice segregation in layers, causing relatively large frost heaves.

10-3. Passive Freezing. The second stage of freezing, passive freezing, is the maintenance of the wall of frozen soil in the thickness required to resist pressure from unfrozen soil and water.

During passive freezing, when the refrigerating plant operates without interruption, the foundation is laid.

10-4. Temperature of Frozen Soil. The temperature of the frozen soil in contact with the outside wall of the freezer pipe is −10°C to −15°C. About 1.5 ft (~0.5 m) from the freezer pipe the temperature of the frozen soil is about −4°C or −5°C. At a distance of about 6 ft (~2.0 m), the soil temperature is about 2°C to 5°C.

For shallow pits, the temperature of the ice wall is −10°C; for deep pits, about −20°C, although temperatures as low as −40°C and −60°C have been reported, depending upon the type of the refrigerant. Thermal calculations determine the degree of coldness required.

Changes in soil temperatures lag considerably behind and are much less variable than changes in atmospheric temperatures. Daily fluctuations in soil temperature are much greater in summer than in winter. The cyclic temperature changes in soil from year to year are relatively small, particularly at depths between 3 m and 4 m (~9 ft and ~12 ft, respectively).

The higher the rate of freezing, the finer the crystalline structure. For a qualitative treatment, it is necessary that the freezing rate be mathematically and exactly defined.

Groundwater temperature measurements by the author through seven years (winters and summers) at 5 m (~15 ft) depth showed a variation of from 6°C to 10°C, the average of which, 8°C, for an entire freezing season can be considered as constant[(22)] for the area studied.

10-5. Time Required to Form an Ice Wall. The length of time necessary for freezing the ice wall depends on the required thickness and strength. By nature, soil freezing is a slow process; hence, the time necessary for the formation of an ice wall is a relatively long one. The rate of freezing the soil depends upon several factors, all of which must be determined before the freezing operation is started:

1. the type of soil;
2. stratification of soil;
3. its thermal properties;
4. its moisture content;
5. electrolyte content (salinity) of water in the soil;
6. proximity of water supply from groundwater or perched groundwater;
7. nature of the surface cover as an insulator against heat;
8. the overall amount of heat to be removed from soil plus heat losses;
9. climatic and weather conditions;
10. the capacity of the refrigerating plant.

The formation of the ice wall is very much retarded by flowing groundwater and by the presence of water-saturated peat. This is so because groundwater carries heat that warms up the ice wall continuously. Saline groundwater, too, retards freezing of soil.

Usually the active freezing of a soil column about 7.5 to 10.0 ft (~2.5 to 3.0 m) in diameter requires about three to four weeks. To close the ice wall takes about two to four months of refrigeration plant operation in the active stage of freezing.[(9,23)]

With a freezer pipe spacing of from 4.5 ft to 6 ft (1.5 m to 2.0 m), the active freezing of soil requires, on the average, 40 to 70 days. The time necessary for the formation of an ice wall is shorter when the freezer points are more closely spaced.

Likewise, the required depth of the ice wall of the frozen soil determines the freezing time. To create a water-impermeable wall takes, on the average, 2 to 4 months of active freezing. In this freezing period, the ice wall may attain a thickness of 4 to 5 m.[15]

In fine-particled soils, such as water-saturated sand and silt, with a brine temperature of about −20°C and a freezer point spacing of 1.5 m, active freezing may last for about 2.5 to 3 months, but in coarser and drier soils, active freezing may take only 1.5 to 2 months.

10-6. Strength of Ice Wall. The basis for the design of the wall of frozen soil is the strength of the frozen soil masses. Depending upon the freezing temperature and the time allowed for freezing, it is possible to attain a certain strength of the wall of frozen soil capable of resisting soil and water pressures behind it. The strongest ice wall is obtained when the soil is fully saturated. Uniform soil materials form stronger ice walls than nonuniform soil materials.

The plane, uncurved wall of frozen soil is usually proportioned as a simple gravity retaining wall. For this purpose, the author's books *Soil Mechanics, Mechanics of Soils—Fundamentals for Advanced Study,* and *Active and Passive Earth Pressure Coefficient Tables*[14,24,25] may be used to advantage.

The ice wall should be checked for its stability with respect to sliding, as well as overturning. It should be checked also against crushing (compression), tension, and shearing.

If soil freezing can occur behind the wall independently from the freezer point after the ice wall has been established, the freezing water in the voids behind the ice wall may exert a pressure on the ice wall. This may break or severely crack the ice wall. The possibility of hydrostatic pressure on the ice wall should also be considered.

Although ice usually has sufficient strength to withstand design loads, in building deep shafts the inside wall of the shaft is often provided with a steel lining for extra safety (Fig. 10-1). Liner plates of ribbed, curved steel were used in the Brooklyn shaft.[23] The liner plates were 12 in. by 24 in., and they lined a shaft of 20 ft inside diameter.

Upon freezing fine- to coarse-particled soils, the particle sizes of which are $d > 0.05$ mm, a homogeneously frozen texture of soil results. With fine-particled soils, $d < 0.05$ mm, a heterogeneously frozen soil texture results. If fine-particled soils, such as silts, are frozen slowly, there is the probability that visible, segregated ice

FIG. 10-1 Steel liner plates in the Brooklyn water supply tunnel shaft. View from below. (Author.)

lenses will be formed (subject to the proximity of a groundwater supply to the cold front). Also, heterogeneously frozen soil textures (resulting from slow freezing) possess less strength than homogeneously frozen soil textures. (With quick freezing, there is no visible ice segregation or lensing.) Figure 2-12 shows some of the results of quick and slow freezing of a silty soil sample, all other conditions being the same. Note the ice lensing near the cold front upon slow freezing at −20°C from the top of the sample down.

If nonuniform soil materials are frozen at a low temperature, say −40°C, they, too, would attain greater compressive strength and density than if frozen at a higher temperature, say −15°C, because at −40°C the process of crystallization of ice takes place faster and more effectively than at temperatures above −40°C (water in the voids of the soil which was not frozen at temperatures higher than −40°C and less than −15°C may become frozen at −40°C). Thus, at low temperatures a more complete solidification of ice is attained, resulting in a denser and stronger mass of frozen soil.

The available information on strength properties of frozen soil is very meager, lacking systematic data as to the moisture content of the soil, soil textural composition, fractional proportions, and the method of obtaining these strength figures. In general, however, the compressive strength of frozen soil increases with decreasing freezing temperatures and is dependent on the type of soil.

10-7. Mechanical Properties of Ice. A knowledge of the mechanical properties of ice is useful in properly organizing and adapting suitable drilling, blasting, and excavation methods. It is useful also in determining the suitability of lake ice as a landing and take-off field for aircraft and for temporary roads, for calculating the strength of a frozen wall of soil in artificial soil freezing operations for foundation engineering, for the use of ice, snow, and frozen soil for housing and storage, for preserving permafrost beneath foundations, for use as fill and construction material, and for other applications. The published values for ultimate strengths of ice, however, vary considerably. The variation in ice strength is governed by the crystal size of the ice, its orientation, structure, impurities, age, texture, temperature, rate of load application, method of testing, and other factors.

Ordinary ice, called *ice I*, can be considered as a solid, elastic substance. When subjected to stress, ice seems to behave up to a certain limit perfectly elastically, exhibiting no permanent deformation. However, if the stress exceeds a small elastic limit, deformation of the ice takes place. Other things being the same, the nearer the temperature of the ice to zero, the more rapidly deformation increases.

Modulus of Elasticity. From theory of elasticity, the modulus of elasticity E of a material is defined by

$$E = \frac{\sigma}{\epsilon} = \frac{\text{stress}}{\text{strain}} \qquad (\text{kg/cm}^2). \qquad (10\text{-}1)$$

According to various published values, the modulus of elasticity (Young's modulus) of normal ice at an average freezing temperature from 0°C to −15°C is about $E = 95{,}000$ kg/cm² parallel to the direction of freezing, and about $E = 112{,}000$ kg/cm² perpendicularly to it. At $T = -2$°C, $E = 0.28$ dynes/cm² $= (3.0716)(10^{-4})$ g/cm², since one dyne equals $(1.0197)(10^{-3})$ force grams.

The E-values vary greatly, depending upon the method of their determination, from $(0.3)(10^{10})$ to $(11.5)(10^{10})$ dynes/cm² between temperatures of 0°C to −60°C.[26]

The dependence of modulus of elasticity of pure ice and that of frozen soil upon freezing temperatures T (comparison between glacial ice and sandstone) is shown after Seydel[2] in Fig. 10-2. According to Seydel, the coefficient of thermal conductivity K of ice depends upon the modulus of elasticity of the ice-soil system. This dependence is illustrated in Fig. 10-3.

Poisson's Ratio. Poisson's ratio μ is defined as the ratio of the unit

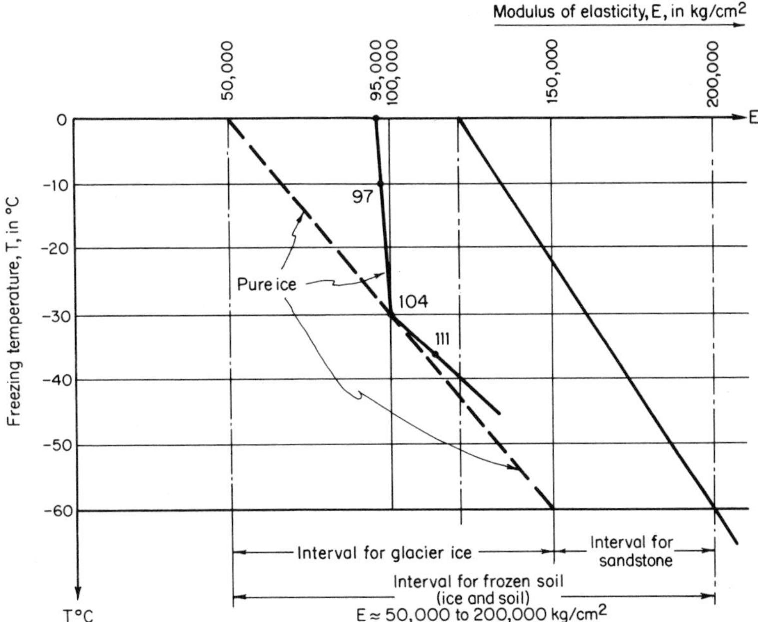

FIG. 10-2 Dependence of modulus of elasticity of pure ice and frozen soil upon freezing temperatures T; comparison between glacial ice and sandstone. (After Seydel.[(2)])

deformation (strain) perpendicularly and parallel to applied stress:

$$\mu = \frac{\epsilon_x}{\epsilon_z} = \frac{\epsilon_y}{\epsilon_z}, \tag{10-2}$$

where ϵ_z = strain in the z direction (parallel to stress), and
$\epsilon_z = \epsilon_y$ = strain in the x and y directions, respectively.

According to Reference (26) (SIPRE's Report No. 4, July, 1951),

at 0°C Poisson's ratio of ice is $\mu = 0.360$;
at −5°C Poisson's ratio of ice is $\mu = 0.380$;
at −15°C Poisson's ratio of ice is $\mu = 0.330$.

Between −5°C and −15°C, Poisson's ratio of ice for calculation purposes may be assumed as $\mu = 0.365$.

Ultimate Compressive Strength of Ice. An average value of the ultimate compressive strength of ice is 25 kg/cm² (= 355 psi). This value, however, is not constant, but varies because of the variation in ice structure and size of the ice specimen, as well as in the method of testing.

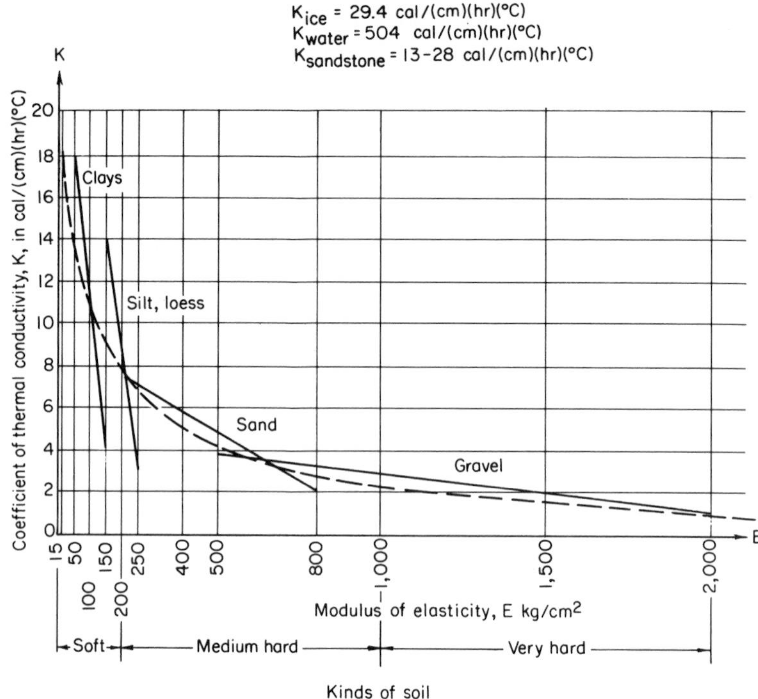

FIG. 10-3 Dependence of coefficient of thermal conductivity K upon modulus of elasticity E of the ice-soil system.[2]

Table 10-1 shows some values of the compressive strength of uniform ice parallel and perpendicular to the optical axis at various temperatures.

The average ultimate unconfined compressive strength of 12 ice specimens 7.2 cm high and 3.3 cm in diameter as tested in the Soil Mechanics and Frost Action in Soils Research Laboratory at Rutgers University at a temperature of $-8.5°C$ was $\sigma_u = 16.0$ kg/cm^2.

According to Barnes,[28] the allowable compressive strength of pure ice may be taken as 6 kg/cm^2 and the allowable tensile strength as 3 kg/cm^2.

Tensile Strength of Ice. The tensile strength of ice according to SIPRE[26] is from 90 to 150 psi, and the ultimate *bending stresses* are from 195 to 244 psi, although for warm melting of ice these values vary from 38 to 113 psi, with an approximate average of 60 psi = 4 kg/cm^2.

Shear Strength of Ice. The shear strength τ of ice is reported by Finlayson[29] as follows:

Table 10-1
Compressive Strength of Ice

Compressive Temperature (°C)	Compressive Strength σ_u (kg/cm²) $\parallel$	$\perp$	Source
1	2		3
0	26	25	Dorsey, Ref. (27), p. 449
− 2.2	†	21	
− 7.0	70	25	Dorsey
− 8.5	16	–	Author's study
−10.0		49	Ref. (27)
−11.7	124	72	Ref. (27)
−16.6	†	62	Ref. (27)

† Values not reported.

$\tau_{\perp} = 8.0$ kg/cm² = 114 psi perpendicular to optical axis, and
$\tau_{\parallel} = 6.9$ kg/cm² = 98 psi parallel to optical axis.

Between −23.3°C and −1.1°C (−10°F and 30°F), no variation in shear strength of ice has been observed.

The ultimate shear strength τ of ice was calculated by the author as $\tau = (\sigma_1/2)(\sin 120°) = 6.9$ kg/cm².

Approximate values of shear strength of ice from 6.7 kg/cm² to 7.8 kg/cm² (95 to 110 psi) are reported by SIPRE.[26]

10-8. Strength Properties of Frozen Soil

Modulus of Elasticity E. A survey of the literature reveals the values of modulus of elasticity of frozen soil given in Table 10-2.

Table 10-2
Modulus of Elasticity of Frozen Soil

Soil Type	Moisture Content (%)	Modulus of Elasticity E (kg/cm²) −1°C	−4°C	−7°C
1	2	3	4	5
Sand	22	26,500	92,000	–
Silt	23	140,000	35,000	58,000
Clay	29	134,400	20,000	28,000

This information shows that the modulus of elasticity of frozen soil increases with the increase in moisture content and decreases with temperature.

Ultimate Compressive Strength of Frozen Soil. The values of ultimate compressive strength of some types of frozen soil at various temperatures are compiled in Table 10-3. As seen from this table, the compressive strength of frozen soil increases with moisture content as well as with decreasing freezing temperatures.

Table 10-3

Ultimate Compressive Strength of Frozen Soil

Soil Type	Ultimate Compressive Strength (kg/cm²)				References
	−10°C	−15°C	−20°C	−25°C	
1	2	3	4	5	6
Quartz sand, saturated	120	–	–	200	Rogge, Brennecke [18]
	87	133	141	–	
Medium and fine sand, saturated	–	138	–	200	Rogge, Brennecke [18]
Fine-particled sand, saturated	120	–	–	200	Rogge, Brennecke [18]
Fine sand and water, degree of saturation, $S = 75\%$	77	106	136	147	Rogge, Brennecke [18]
Fine sand, degree of saturation, $S = 50\%$	52	62	109	130	Rogge, Brennecke [18]
Silty sand, A-2-4, at −18°C, moisture content,					
$w = 8.8\%$	–	–	5.0	–	Author †
9.7%	–	–	6.0	–	Author †
13.0%	–	–	8.1	–	Author †
16.3%	–	–	8.9	–	Author †
Pure clay, saturated	55	133	–	153	Rogge, Brennecke [18]
	–	72	–	–	Rogge, Brennecke [18]
Pure clay, Emden locks	24	37	50	–	Rogge, Brennecke [18]

† Size of frozen soil samples: 3.3 cm in diameter and 7.20 cm high.

A graph showing relationship between ultimate compressive strength of frozen soils as a function of temperature is shown after Tsytovich [30] in Fig. 10-4.

According to Hetzell and Wundram,[15] the compressive strength of a saturated, mobile sand at −15°C is 14 kg/cm², a strength which increases up to 200 kg/cm² at a temperature of −20°C.

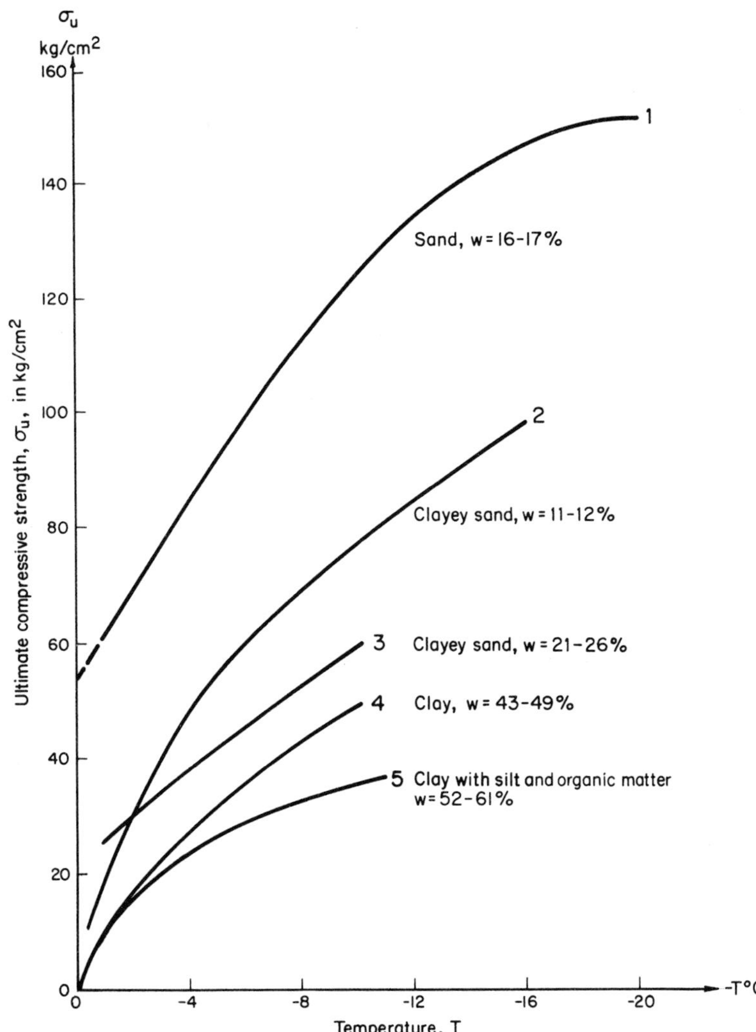

FIG. 10-4 Relationship between ultimate compressive strength of various types of frozen soils as a function of temperature (after Tsytovich [30]).

From Table 10-3 it is seen that pure frozen clays have strengths about one half of the strength of frozen sand. Sandy clays and clayey sands give average strength values between those of clay and sand.

The results of the author's studies of ultimate compressive and shear strengths of frozen and unfrozen soils as a function of compacted moisture contents are shown in Fig. 10-5. These tests were performed in the Soil Mechanics and Foundation Engineering and

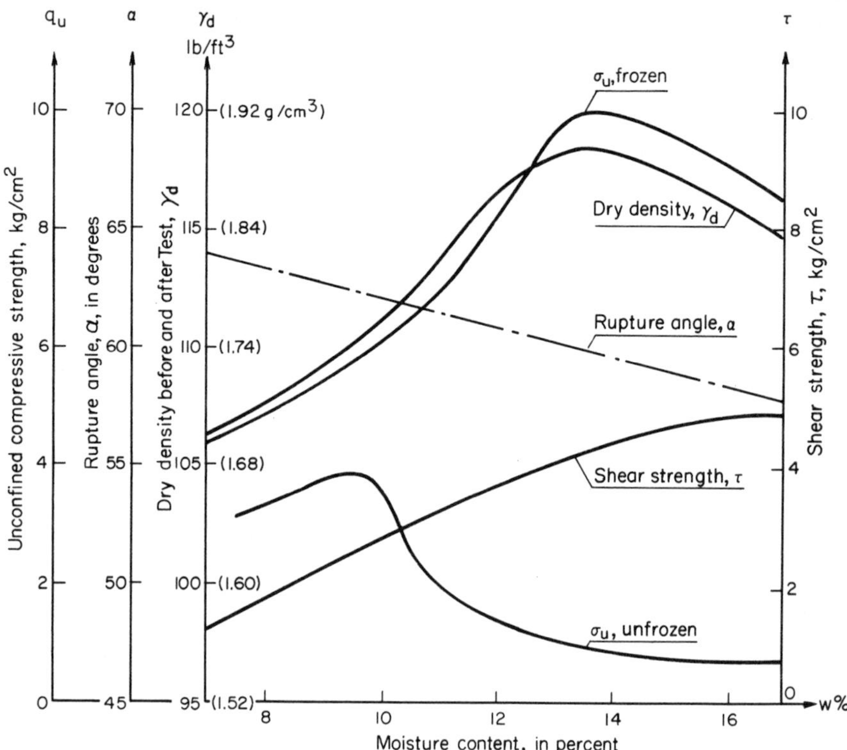

FIG. 10-5 Ultimate unconfined compressive strength of unfrozen and frozen soil and its shear strength.

Frost Action in Soils Research Laboratory at Rutgers—The State University, New Brunswick, New Jersey.

The results of tests on frozen "fine sand and water" made in 1960 in the laboratory of the Board of Water Supply (owner of the Richmond water supply tunnel at Brooklyn)[23] are as follows:

On a sample $3\frac{5}{16}$ in. in diameter and $4\frac{5}{8}$ in. high, the ultimate compressive strength was $\sigma_u = 731$ psi ≈ 48.7 kg/cm²; on a sample $3\frac{3}{8}$ in. in diameter and $4\frac{1}{16}$ in. high, $\sigma_u = 936$ psi $= 62.4$ kg/cm².

Reference (23) does not say anything about the shape of the soil samples tested (whether square or circular) nor at what temperatures these tests were performed.

According to Reference (18), the ultimate tensile strengths of frozen soil (Emden locks) are:

−10°C	−15°C	−20°C
22 kg/cm²	33 kg/cm²	39 kg/cm².

The tensile strength of frozen soil increases as its freezing temperature decreases.

Shear Strength of Frozen Soil. Tsytovich[30] writes that "frozen soils may be considered as overconsolidated soils (in the process of freezing)" and that "within certain limits, they are subject to proportionality between shear strength and normal pressure:"

$$\tau = \sigma_n \cdot \tan \phi_f + c_f, \qquad (10\text{-}3)$$

where τ = shear strength of the frozen soil,
$\tan \phi_f$ = coefficient of internal friction of frozen soil,
σ_n = normal stress on the rupture plane of the frozen soil, and
c_f = cohesion of frozen soil.

Figure 10-6 illustrates some of Tsytovich's shear test results of frozen clays at various temperatures. Table 10-4 presents allowable bearing capacity design values of frozen soil of the Permafrost Institute of the Academy of Sciences of the U.S.S.R. (1956). These values are valid if it is certain that the temperature in the soil underneath the structure remains below 0°C.

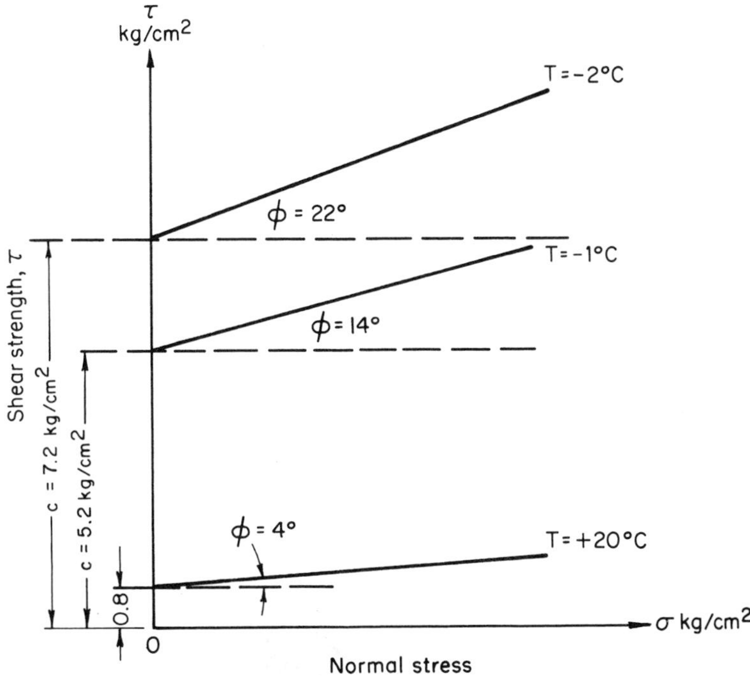

FIG. 10-6 Tsytovich's shear test results of clays at various temperatures.

Table 10-4

Allowable Design-Bearing Capacity Values of Frozen Soil (30)

Soil Types	Capacity (kg/cm²) Highest Temperature of Soil Within Contact Surface Between Soil and Base of Foundation Footing During Time of Use of the Structure		
	−0.4°C(= 31.3°F)	−1.2°C(= 29.8°F)	−4.0°C(= 24.8°F)
1	2	3	4
Sand, medium and fine	6.0	10.0	14.0
Clay sand with silt, moisture content ⩽ 35%	3.5	7.0	10.0
Clayey silt, moisture content ⩽ 45%	3.0	5.0	8.0
Ice-filled silty soils † (clayey sand, clayey silt with sand, and clays), with large amount of ice laminae thicker than 5 mm	2.5	4.0	6.0

† Applies where there is no direct contact between ice and base of foundation footing. This is achieved by placing on the soil at the bottom of excavation a layer of moist sand 5 to 10 cm thick. The sand must then be cooled to the corresponding temperature below freezing.

10-9. Effective Thickness of Wall of Frozen Soil. The wall of frozen soil should be thick enough to keep water and unfrozen soil from flowing into the foundation pit during excavation and to resist lateral earth pressure and the hydrostatic pressure of groundwater.

A wall of frozen soil from 10 to 15 cm thick may be considered impermeable to water. This requirement, in turn, depends upon the effectiveness of the single columns of frozen soil.

The required thickness of the wall depends upon the amount of heat received from the groundwater. Because of groundwater heat, the thickness of the ice wall on the outside (towards the flowing groundwater), measured from the center line of the freezer points, is usually less (≈ 1.5 ft or 0.5 m) than that towards the inside of the unexcavated foundation pit (≈ 3 ft or 1 m), where the inflow of groundwater is gradually cut off with the progressive thickness of the ice wall.

No formulas are available for the calculation of the thickness of the wall of frozen soil. For orientation purposes in foundation engineering, the following minimum values for the design of thickness, d_{min}, of a wall of frozen soil are used as a guide:[2]

$d_{min} \approx$ 1.1 m to 2.5 m at depths to 100 m and at a spacing of ice walls to $\approx$15 m;

$d_{min} \approx$ 2.5 m to 5.0 m at depths to 100 m and spacing of walls to $\approx$30 m.

With no definite strength theories available on frozen soil walls, a straight wall may be subjected to earth pressure theory. The frozen soil walls of a circular shaft may be proportioned by the theory applied to a thick-walled cylinder or by any other theory suitable for such calculation.

In designing the thickness of a wall of frozen soil, waterproofness is often more decisive than the compressive and tensile strengths of the frozen soil if water is to be kept out of the foundation pit effectively. The strength of the wall of frozen soil, however, cannot be ignored.

The strength of cylindrical walls of frozen soil may be approximately calculated according to Lamé's equation:[18]

$$\delta = \frac{d}{2}\left(-1 + \sqrt{\frac{\sigma_{adm}}{\sigma_{adm} - 2p}}\right), \qquad (10\text{-}4)$$

where δ = thickness of cylinder of frozen soil, in centimeters,
d = inside diameter of shaft,
σ_{adm} = allowable compressive stress on frozen soil, in kg/cm^2, and
p = external pressure on cylindrical wall of frozen soil, in kg/cm^2.

Lamé's formula is good only for uniform pressure. If the soil profile consists of a system of several layers, i.e., nonuniform soil, then the pressures are nonuniform, and Lamé's equation is not applicable.

10-10. Advantages of Artificial Soil Freezing for Foundation Engineering. Some of the advantages of artificial soil freezing for foundation engineering purposes are listed here.

1. Water is kept out of the excavation when digging is done in water-bearing soil. Freezing is practicable for a wide range of soils provided that they are saturated.
2. Artificial freezing may be applied during any season of the year.
3. The wall of frozen soil has a relatively great mechanical strength.
4. The walls of frozen soil can be made so strong that no sheeting, bracing, or strutting of the excavation walls is necessary, with the attendant savings in cost of materials.

5. The method of artificial soil freezing can be used in combination with other foundation engineering systems, such as sheet piling or lowering of the groundwater table.
6. The soil freezing is particularly applicable where nearby structures would be damaged by vibrations from pile driving.
7. The freezing method is applicable where quick conditions of sand are present.
8. The method is most applicable to saturated sandy soils, and less effective in clayey soils.
9. Artificial soil freezing can be successfully carried out when the velocity of groundwater flow is as much as 2.0 m/day (6 ft/day).
10. Artificial freezing of soil is equally useful for pits of small cross section and for pits of great depth.
11. This method may also be justified for large projects over long periods of construction when special freezing equipment is available.

10-11. Disadvantages of Artificial Soil Freezing

1. The first cost of installation of the refrigeration plant is relatively high. Because of its high cost, this method of stabilizing foundation excavations is justified or applicable in highly mobile, water-saturated soil only when no other method would lead to an efficient and economic result.
2. Artificial soil freezing takes a long time.
3. It is of a temporary nature.
4. It requires large, complex freezing installation facilities.
5. If the various layers of soil have different thermal properties, the soil freezing work, i.e., the design and the formation of the ice wall, is very difficult.
6. Freezing and subsequent thawing may destroy the natural structure of soil and reduce its strength properties. This is of particular significance in clayey soils, but less so in sandy soils.
7. Artificial freezing of soil is difficult when the velocity of the groundwater flow is approximately 2 m/day ($\approx$ 6 ft/day).

Chapter 11

Thermal Calculations

11-1. Amount of Heat Abstracted from Soil Upon Freezing. Frost penetration in soil is a physical process that can be treated mathematically with some degree of accuracy. A comprehensive theoretical treatment of the frost penetration problem in soil may be found in the author's book *The Frost Penetration Problem in Highway Engineering.*[31] Because the freezing process in moist soil is very complex, theoretical calculations are most accurately made in a natural, uniform soil.

The amount of heat to be removed from the soil for the formation of the ice wall can only be approximated. It corresponds to the amount of heat that must be abstracted from the groundwater-bearing layers and transferred to the cold brine. This amount depends upon the nature of the soil to be frozen, its physical and thermal properties, on the desired thickness of the ice wall, the strength of the various soil strata when frozen and unfrozen, the desired freezing temperatures in the soil, the depth of the ice wall below ground surface, and the degree of salinity of the groundwater.

The required thickness of the ice wall depends on the strength of frozen clayey and sandy soils and the order of their stratification (clay underneath sand or vice versa).

The amount of heat to be removed from the soil by freezing is determined by the volume of the frozen soil mass plus some safety factor to allow for losses.

11-2. Total Amount of Heat. The total amount of heat Q_t to be removed from the soil in freezing operations consists of a sum of various heat components,

$$Q_t = \Sigma q = q_s + q_w + q_L + q_i, \qquad (11\text{-}1)$$

where q_s = heat removed for cooling of solids of soil from average initial soil temperature T_1 before freezing to average final temperature of frozen soil T_2, where $T_1 > T_2$.

Depending upon the intensity of freezing, the value of T_2 may be taken as −10°C or −20°C, whichever temperature is maintained in the soil;

q_w = heat removed for cooling of soil water from average initial soil temperature T_1 to temperature of T_f = 0°C, where $T_1 > T_f$;

q_L = heat removed for freezing of soil water at T_f = 0°C (release of latent heat of fusion, L = 80 cal/g = 80 Cal/kg for conversion of water to ice), and

q_i = freezing of ice from T_f = 0°C to average final temperature T_2 of frozen soil, where T_f = 0°C > T_2.

The heat components Σq are calculated as follows.

Heat Removed for Cooling of Solids of Soil:

$$q_s = V_s \cdot \gamma_s \cdot C_{Ws}(T_1 - T_2), \qquad (11\text{-}2)$$

where Cal = large calories = kilocalories = 1000 small (or gram-) calories;

$V_s = V - V_w$ = volume of solid particles in soil, in cubic meters;

V = total volume of soil to be frozen, in cubic meters;

$V_w = nVS$ = volume of water in voids of soil, in cubic meters;

n = porosity of soil, in decimal fractions; porosity of soil may vary from n = 0.28 to about n = 0.42;

S = degree of saturation of soil by water. When all voids of soil are fully saturated, S = 1.00;

$\gamma_s = G\gamma_w$ = unit weight of solid particles, in kg/m^3;

G = specific gravity of solid particles of soil (dimensionless);

γ_w = 1000 kg/m^3 = unit weight of water, and

C_{Ws} = mass heat capacity of solids of soil.

The average value of C_{Ws} for soil solids (mineralogical matter) may be taken as 0.2 Cal/(kg)(°C) = 0.2 cal/(g)(°C).

Heat Removed from Cooling of Water:

$$q_w = V_w \gamma_w C_{Ww}(T_1 - T_f) \qquad \text{(Cal)}, \qquad (11\text{-}3)$$

where C_{Ww} = 1.00 Cal/(kg)(°C) = mass heat capacity ofwater.

Latent Heat of Fusion Removed for Converting Water to Ice:

$$q_L = V_w \cdot \gamma_w \cdot L \qquad \text{(Cal)}, \qquad (11\text{-}4)$$

where L = 80 Cal/(kg) = latent heat of fusion of water (ice).

Heat Removed from Freezing of Ice:

$$q_i = V_w \gamma_w C_{Wi}(T_f - T_2) \qquad \text{(Cal)}, \tag{11-5}$$

where $C_{Wi} = 0.5$ Cal/(kg)(°C) = mass heat capacity of ice.

The total amount of heat removed from the freezing soil, based on the absolute volume of soil to be frozen, may now be written as

$$Q_t = \Sigma q = V_s \gamma_s C_{Ws}(T_1 - T_2) + V_w \gamma_w C_{Ww}(T_1 - T_f) + V_w \gamma_w L + V_w \gamma_w C_{Wi}(T_f - T_2) \qquad \text{(Cal)}, \tag{11-6}$$

or, based on relative volume of soil,

$$Q_{t1} = \Sigma q_1 = (1 - n)\gamma_s C_{Ws}(T_1 - T_2) + n\gamma_w[C_{Ww}(T_1 - T_f) + L + C_{Wi}(T_f - T_2)], \tag{11-7}$$

where n = porosity of soil, in decimal fractions.

Unavoidable Losses. For unavoidable thermal losses in soil, about 100% is added to the calculated amount of heat Q_t. The heat supplied by groundwater is a decisive factor for calculating the necessary cold quantities. Radiation losses in refrigeration plants are assessed as 25% of Q_t.

11-3. Capacity of Refrigeration Plant. In order to freeze soil, the refrigeration plant must remove from it

$$Q = (2.25)(Q_t) \qquad \text{(Cal)}, \tag{11-8}$$

where 2.25 = increase-coefficient for losses of heat; or, based on one unit of volume of soil,

$$Q_V = (2.25)(Q_{t1}/V) \qquad \text{(Cal/m}^3\text{)}. \tag{11-9}$$

For extensive soil freezing in foundation engineering, preliminary or pilot freezing tests are made.

Knowing the necessary amount of heat to be removed from the freezing soil Q_t and the capacity of the refrigeration plant N, one can calculate the approximate time t of soil freezing as

$$t = Q_t/N \qquad \text{(hours or days)}. \tag{11-10}$$

11-4. Heat Abstracted by Freezer Pipes. If the outside diameter d_o of the freezer pipe, its depth H, and the amount of heat q_o to be abstracted from the soil in 1 hour per 1 m² of pipe mantle area are known, then the amount of heat removed from soil by one freezer pipe in 1 hour may be calculated as

$$q_{\text{pipe}} = q_o \pi d_o H \qquad \text{(Cal/hr)}. \tag{11-11}$$

In preliminary calculations for smooth steel pipes, an approximative value of $q_o \approx 210$ Cal/hr may be used.

If there are n freezer pipes installed, the freezing operation may be accomplished in

$$t = \frac{Q_t}{n q_{\text{pipe}}} \qquad \text{(hours)}, \tag{11-12}$$

where Q_t = total amount of heat abstracted from soil, including safety margins.

After the diameter of the freezer pipes and the number of freezer pipes are satisfactorily selected, the capacity of the refrigeration equipment is calculated as

$$N = (1.15) n q_{\text{pipe}} = (1.15) \frac{Q_t}{t} \qquad \text{(Cal/hr)}. \tag{11-13}$$

The equipment (compressors) can now be chosen from a manufacturer's catalog.

11-5. Frost Penetration Distance (= Thickness of Ice Wall). The distance ξ that the 0°C-isotherm penetrates soil after a lapse of time t may be calculated from the following equation:[31]

$$\xi = m\sqrt{t} \qquad \text{(m)}, \qquad \text{(6-1), (11-14)}$$

where ξ is in meters, t in hours, and m is a coefficient of proportionality.

Determination of m. The coefficient m is determined by means of Neumann's thermophysical solution of two Fourier's partial differential equations of heat transfer for the frozen and unfrozen parts of soil [Ref. (31), p. 81]:

$$\underbrace{\frac{Q_s \rho_2 \sqrt{\pi}}{2} m}_{Y_1 = Cm} = \underbrace{b_1 (T_f - T_s) \frac{e^{-m^2/(4\cdot\alpha_1)}}{G[m/(2\sqrt{\alpha_1})]} - b_2 (T_0 - T_f) \frac{e^{-m^2/(4\cdot\alpha_2)}}{1 - G[m/(2\sqrt{\alpha_2})]}}_{Y_2 = F(m)}, \tag{11-15}$$

where Q_s = amount of heat in Cal/kg to be abstracted from the water-bearing layer of soil;

ρ_1 = unit weight in kg/m³ of frozen soil;

ρ_2 = unit weight of moist, unfrozen soil, in kg/m³;

$b_1 = K_1/\sqrt{\alpha_1} = \sqrt{K_1 C_1 \rho_1}$ = heat flow coefficient for the frozen soil, in (m² $\sqrt{\text{hr}}$ °C;

$b_2 = K_2/\sqrt{\alpha_2} = \sqrt{K_2 C_2 \rho_2}$ = heat flow coefficient for the unfrozen soil, in (m² · $\sqrt{\text{hr}}$ · °C);

K_1, K_2 = coefficients of thermal conductivity of frozen and unfrozen soils, respectively, in Cal/(m)(hr)(°C);

α_1, α_2 = coefficients of thermal diffusivity of frozen and unfrozen soil, respectively, in (m²/hr);

C_1, C_2 = heat capacity of frozen and unfrozen soil with moisture content, in Cal/(kg)(°C);

$T_f = 0°C$ = freezing temperature of water;

T_s = surface (outside mantle) temperature of the freezer pipe (cold source) in contact with soil, in °C;

T_0 = initial, natural temperature of soil before freezing, in °C, or the temperature of the groundwater;

$G[m/(2\sqrt{\alpha_1})]$ = Gauss' error integral for the frozen soil for $\beta = x\eta = m/(2\sqrt{\alpha_1})$;

$G[m/(2\sqrt{\alpha_2})]$ = Gauss' error integral for the unfrozen soil for $\beta = x\eta = m/(2\sqrt{\alpha_2})$;

$$G[m/(2\sqrt{\alpha})] = G(\beta) = G(x\eta) = (2/\sqrt{\pi}) \int_{\beta=0}^{\beta=x\eta} e^{-\beta^2} \cdot d\beta. \tag{11-16}$$

For values of Gauss' error function (probability integral) see the Appendix.

The temperature conditions in soil pertaining to the frost penetration distance are illustrated in Fig. 11-1.

The transcendental function, Eq. (11-15), $Y_1 = Y_2$, with one unknown m, can be solved best graphically:

$$Y_1 = Cm = f(m) - \text{a straight line through } 0, 0 \tag{11-17}$$
$$Y_2 = F(m) - \text{a transcendental curve} \tag{11-18}$$

The intersection of these two Y functions gives an abscissa m, which is the only root possible in order that both sides of Eq. (11-15) be equal. By means of this value of m, the frost penetration distance ξ can be calculated, Eq. (11-14).

Problem. A vertical freezer point is installed in a uniform soil for the purpose of making a wall of frozen soil. Determine the radial, horizontal distance of frost penetration in soil, i.e., the thickness of the ice wall, and plot the temperature profile (tautochrone) in soil after 60 days = 1440 hours of freezing.

The temperatures:

initial soil temperature (groundwater temperature),	$T_0 =$	8°C
freezing temperature,	$T_f =$	0°C
surface freezing temperature at the outside mantle surface of the freezer pipe,	$T_s =$	−20°C.

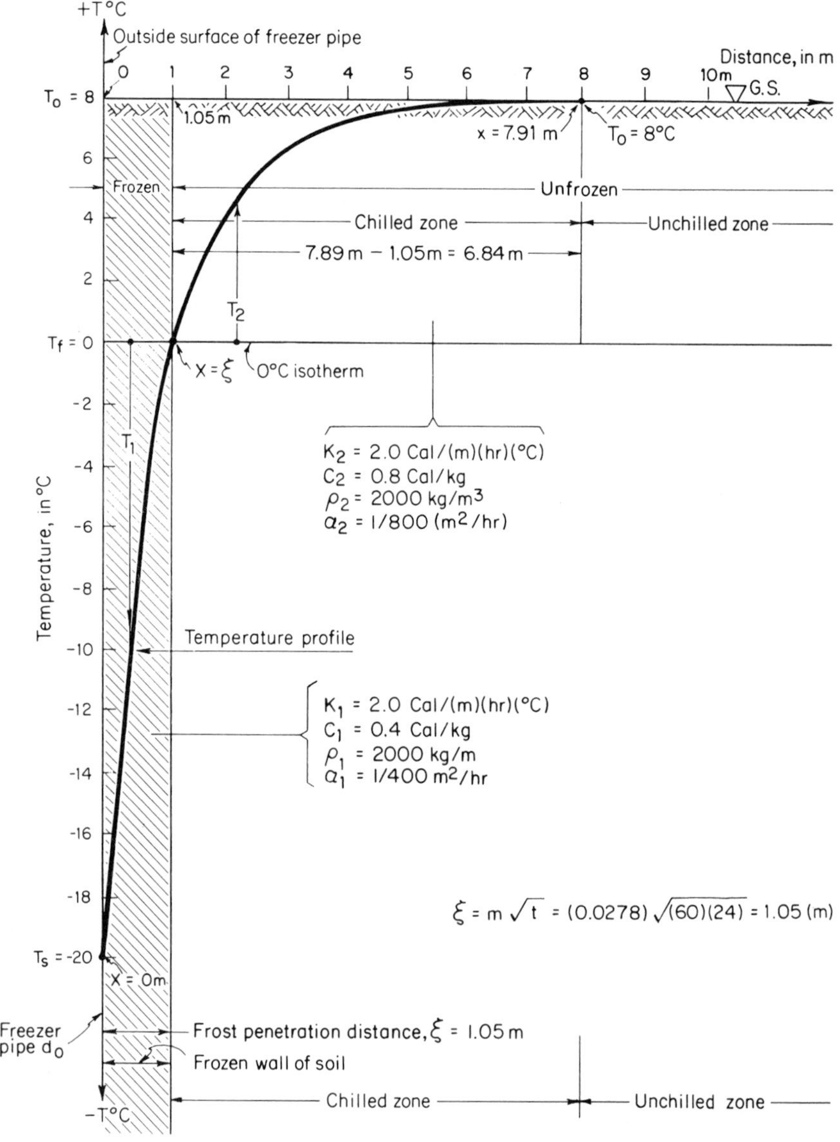

FIG. 11-1 Frost penetration distance ξ in soil after 60 days.

Physical constants of soil:

$\rho_1 = \rho_2 = 2000$ kg/m^3 = wet unit weight of soil. The soil moisture content is given as 20% for each kilogram of soil.

$K_1 = K_2 = 2.0$ Cal/(m)(hr)(°C).

$C_1 = 0.4$ Cal/(kg)(°C).

$C_2 = 0.8$ Cal/(kg)(°C).

$$\alpha_1 = \frac{K_1}{C_1\rho_1} = \frac{2.0}{(0.4)(2000)} = \frac{1}{400} = 0.00250 \text{ (m}^2\text{/hr)}.$$

$$\alpha_2 = \frac{K_2}{C_2\rho_2} = \frac{2.0}{(0.8)(2000)} = \frac{1}{800} = 0.00125 \text{ (m}^2\text{/hr)}.$$

In the above quantities, index 1 pertains to the frozen zone of soil, and index 2 pertains to the unfrozen zone of the soil.

Auxiliary values:

$$b_1 = \frac{K_1}{\sqrt{\alpha_1}} = \frac{2.0}{\sqrt{0.00250}} = 40.00 \text{ Cal/(m}^2\text{)(}\sqrt{\text{hr}}\text{)(°C)}.$$

$$b_2 = \frac{K_2}{\sqrt{\alpha_2}} = \frac{2.0}{\sqrt{0.00125}} = 56.56 \text{ Cal/(m}^2\text{)(}\sqrt{\text{hr}}\text{)(°C)}.$$

$$\sqrt{\alpha_1} = \sqrt{1/400} = 0.050; \qquad 2\sqrt{\alpha_1} = 0.10.$$

$$\sqrt{\alpha_2} = \sqrt{1/800} = 0.035; \qquad 2\sqrt{\alpha_2} = 0.07.$$

$$4\alpha_1 = 0.200; \qquad 4\alpha_2 = 0.140.$$

$$T_f - T_s = 0° - (-20°) = 20°\text{C}.$$

$$T_0 - T_f = 8° - 0° = 8°\text{C}.$$

$$b_1(T_f - T_s) = (40.00)(20) = 800.$$

$$b_2(T_0 - T_f) = (56.56)(8) = 452.48 \approx 452.5.$$

Solution. This problem is similar to the problem of frost penetration depth presented in Chapter 6, Eq. (6-2). In this problem, however, the penetration of frost, i.e., the distance of frost penetration, is lateral to the freezer pipe.

Calculation of Q_s in Eq. (11-15). In the calculation of the frozen depth of soil by means of Neumann's theory in Chapter 6, the amount of heat set free upon freezing was taken as only $Q_L = 80$ Cal/kg (latent heat of fusion of water), ignoring the other heats. Actually, when the temperature of the soil is lowered from T_0 to T_s, much more heat than latent heat has to be removed. Therefore, instead of Q_L as in Eq. (6-2), a new term, Q_s, as shown in Eq. (11-15), must be used. The value of Q_s is determined by adding all the heat components removed while freezing the soil from temperature T_0 to T_s.

In this particular problem, Q_s is calculated as follows.

Heat, Q_s, *that must be removed from* 1 kg *of soil when the soil temperature is lowered from* $T_0 = 8°C$ *to* $T_s = -20°C$.

For 1 kg soil, from 8°C to −20°C = | 28°C | :

$$(T_0 - T_f)C_2 = (8° - 0°)(0.8) = \qquad 6.4 \text{ Cal/kg}$$
$$(T_f - T_s)C_1 = [0° - (-20°)][0.4] = \qquad 8.0 \text{ Cal/kg}$$

Because the moisture content is given as 20% for each kilogram of soil, there is 1/5 = 0.20 kg of water in each kilogram of soil.

0.20 kg of water from $T_0 = 8°C$ to $T_f = 0°C$:

$$(0.20)(T_0 - T_f)C_{Ww} = (0.20)(8)(1.0) = \qquad 1.6 \text{ Cal/kg}$$

0.20 kg *of water from* $T_f = 0°C$ *to* $T_f = 0°C$ (*temperature is constant during the time of release of latent heat of fusion*):

$$(0.20)(Q_L) = (0.20)(80) = \qquad 16.0 \text{ Cal/kg}$$

Lowering of temperature of 0.20 kg *of ice from* $T_f = 0°C$ *to* $T_s = -20°C$:

$$(0.20)(T_f - T_s)C_{Wi} = (0.20)(20)(0.5) = \qquad 2.0 \text{ Cal/kg}$$

$$\text{Total: } Q_s = 34.0 \text{ Cal/kg}$$

The Y_1*-function.* By Eq. (11-15), the Y_1-function is

$$Y_1 = Cm = 0.5Q_s\rho_2\sqrt{\pi}\, m =$$
$$= (0.5)(34.0)(2000)(\sqrt{\pi})(m) = (60{,}265)(m). \quad (11\text{-}17)$$

Note that in this Y_1-equation the moisture content w of the soil does not appear as was the case when Q_L instead of Q_s was considered (Chapter 6).

The Y_2*-function.* By Eq. (11-15),

$$Y_2 = F(m) = (800)\frac{e^{-m^2/(4\cdot 1/400)}}{G\left[\dfrac{m}{2(1/\sqrt{400})}\right]} - (452.5)\frac{e^{-m^2/(4\cdot 1/800)}}{1 - G\left[\dfrac{m}{2(1/\sqrt{800})}\right]} =$$

$$= (800)\frac{e^{-(100)m^2}}{G[(10)(m)]} - (452.5)\frac{e^{-(200)m^2}}{1 - G[(14.28)(m)]}. \quad (11\text{-}18)$$

With the values as given in Eqs. (11-17) and (11-18), Eq. (11-15) can now be written as

$$\underbrace{(60{,}520)(m)}_{Y_1} = \underbrace{\overbrace{(800)\frac{e^{-100m^2}}{G[(10)(m)]}}^{Y_2'} - \overbrace{(452.5)\frac{e^{-200m^2}}{1 - G[(14.28)(m)]}}^{Y_2''}}_{Y_2}. \quad (11\text{-}19)$$

The transcendental equation (11-19) is most readily solved for m grapho-analytically (Fig. 11-2). With $Y_1 = Y_2 = 1720$, the value of $m = 0.0278$ is scaled off the graph. This m value is the only possible solution of Eq. (11-19).

The Frost Penetration Distance ξ. The frost penetration distance ξ in $t = 60$ days (1440 hours) can now be calculated by Eq. (11-14) as

$$\xi = m\sqrt{t} = (0.0278)\sqrt{(60)(24)} = \underline{1.05 \text{ (meters)} = 4.14 \text{ ft.}}$$

This frost penetration distance (ice wall thickness) is shown in Fig. 11-1.

Temperature Profile in the Frozen Zone After $t = 60$ *days* $= 1440$ *hours of Freezing*. The temperature T at any horizontal distance $x < \xi$ from the outside wall of the vertical freezer pipe is calculated by Eq. (6-5):

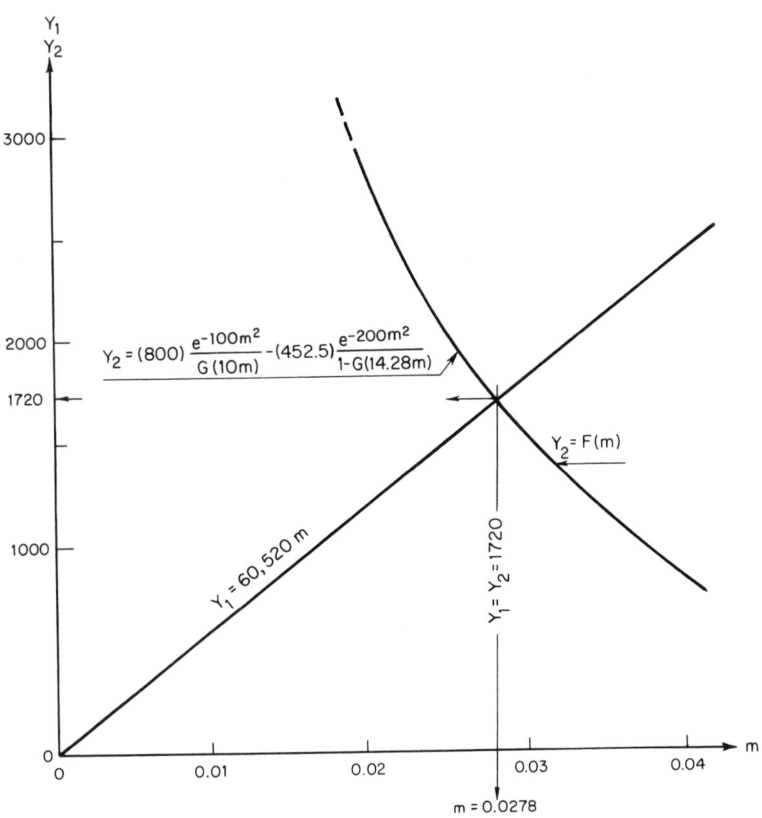

FIG. 11-2 Grapho-analytical solution of the transcendental equation (11-19).

$$T_1 = T_s + (T_f - T_s) \cdot \frac{G[x/(2\sqrt{\alpha_1 \cdot t})]}{G[m/(2\sqrt{\alpha_1})]}. \tag{6-5}$$

Here $T_s = -20°C$; $T_f = 0°C$; $T_f - T_s = 20°C$.
$m = 0.0278$ (from Fig. 11-2).
$2\sqrt{\alpha_1} = 0.10$; $\frac{1}{2}\sqrt{\alpha_1} = 10$; $\sqrt{t} = \sqrt{(60)(24)} = 37.92$.
$2\sqrt{\alpha_1 \cdot t} = (0.10)(37.92) = 3.792$; $1/(2\sqrt{\alpha_1 \cdot t}) = 1/3.792 =$
$= 0.264$.
$G[m/(2\sqrt{\alpha_1})] = G(0.0278/0.10) = G(0.278) = 0.3053$.

With these values, Eq. (6-5) is now rewritten as

$$T_1 = (-20) + (20)\frac{G(0.264x)}{0.3053} = (20)\left[\frac{G(0.264x)}{0.3053} - 1\right]. \tag{11-20}$$

Temperature Profile in the Unfrozen Zone After 60 *days* (1440 *hours*) *of Freezing.* The temperatures T_2 in the unfrozen zone, where $x > \xi$, are calculated by Eq. (6-7):

$$T_2 = T_0 - (T_0 - T_f) \cdot \frac{1 - G[x/(2\sqrt{\alpha_2 \cdot t})]}{1 - G[m/(2\sqrt{\alpha_2})]}. \tag{6-7}$$

Here $T_0 = 8°C$; $T_0 - T_f = 8°C$.
$m = 0.0278$ (from Fig. 11-2).
$2\sqrt{\alpha_2} = 2\sqrt{1/800} = 0.07$; $1/(2\sqrt{\alpha_2} = 1/0.07 = 14.28$.
$(m)(14.28) = (0.0278)(14.28) = 0.3969$.

$$G\left(\frac{m}{2\sqrt{\alpha_2}}\right) = G\left(\frac{0.0278}{0.07}\right) = G(0.3969) = 0.4253.$$

$$1 - G[m/(2\sqrt{\alpha_2})] = 1 - G(0.3969) = 1 - 0.4253 = 0.5747 \approx 0.575.$$

$$2\sqrt{\alpha_2 \cdot 1440} = (0.07)(37.92) = 2.6544 \approx 2.65.$$

$$\frac{1}{(2\sqrt{\alpha_2 \cdot t})} = \frac{1}{2.65} = 0.378.$$

$$G[x/(2\sqrt{\alpha_2 \cdot t})] = G(0.378x).$$

With these values, Eq. (6-7) is now written as

$$T_2 = 8 - 8\frac{1 - G(0.378x)}{0.575} = 8\left\{1 - \frac{1 - G[(0.378)(x)]}{0.575}\right\}. \tag{11-21}$$

The calculated temperatures are compiled as follows.

Temperature in Frozen Zone

Distance x (m)	*Temperature* T_1 (°C)
$x = 0.00$	$T_s = T_{0.00} = -20.00$
$x = 0.10$	$T_{0.10} = -18.05$
$x = 0.25$	$T_{0.25} = -15.10$
$x = 0.50$	$T_{0.50} = -10.32$
$x = 0.75$	$T_{0.75} = -\ 5.12$
$x = 1.00$	$T_{1.00} = -\ 0.94$
$\xi = x = 1.05$	$T_f = T_{1.05} = \ 0.00$

Temperature in Unfrozen Zone

(Distance x is measured from the outside wall of the freezer pipe.)

Distance x (m)	*Temperature* T_2 (°C)
1.05	$T_2 = T_{0.00} = T_{1.05} = 0.00 = T_f$
1.25	$T_{1.25} = 0.98$
1.50	$T_{1.50} = 2.12$
1.75	$T_{1.75} = 3.11$
2.00	$T_{2.00} = 4.02$
2.50	$T_{2.50} = 5.45$
3.00	$T_{3.00} = 6.54$
5.00	$T_{5.00} = 7.89$
7.91	$T_{7.91} = 8.00 = T_0$.

The plot of the temperature profile is shown in Fig. 11-1.

Chapter 12

Artificial Thawing of Soil

To facilitate excavation in frozen soil, and thereby reduce costs, the soil can be loosened up by mechanical tools, by blasting, or by natural or artificial thawing. Artificial thawing is accomplished with steam points, water points, or electrical points, or with a heated shack on the foundation site.

According to the direction of heat distribution, soil thawing methods may be broadly classed as either (1) radial or (2) vertical.

12-1. Radial Thawing. In the radial thawing method, heat is distributed horizontally, and the isothermal surfaces may be imagined as representing vertical, concentric surfaces, their longitudinal axes coinciding with the vertical source of heat: steam, water, or electrical points or "needles."

12-2. Vertical Thawing. In one vertical thawing method heat is distributed from the ground surface downward into the soil. The source of heat, local heaters or horizontal electrodes, can be moved about on the ground surface. In another method heat is distributed vertically from the lower frost boundary (0°C isothermal surface) in the soil up to the ground surface by deep electrodes.

12-3. Thawing Points

A *steam point,* or steam needle, is a steel pipe 3 to 4.5 ft long and 1 to 2 in. in diameter, the lower end of which is closed. The steam points are inserted into predrilled bore holes spaced about 3 ft apart in the frozen soil. The wall of the pipe has at its lower end 4 or 5 holes, about 3 to 5 mm in diameter, through which steam is forced into the soil. The upper end of the steam point is connected to the steam supply. Steam is supplied at a pressure of from 6 to 7 atm.

A *water point* is designed like the freezer point, except that warm water is circulated instead of cold brine. It is about the same length as the steam point.

An *electrical point*, or electrode, consists of a metal pipe 2.5 in. in diameter, inside which is a spiral resistance wire in a clean, fine sand (Fig. 12-1). Heat is transferred from the resistor through the sand and the metal wall of the electrical point to the frozen soil, thawing the latter upwards. Electrodes are usually spaced about 3 ft apart.

On the average, it requires from 40 to 60 minutes and 15 to 25 kilowatt-hours to thaw a cubic meter of soil.

12-4. Thawing from Heated Shack. Soil may also be thawed from a heated shack placed on the frozen ground. The air in the shack is

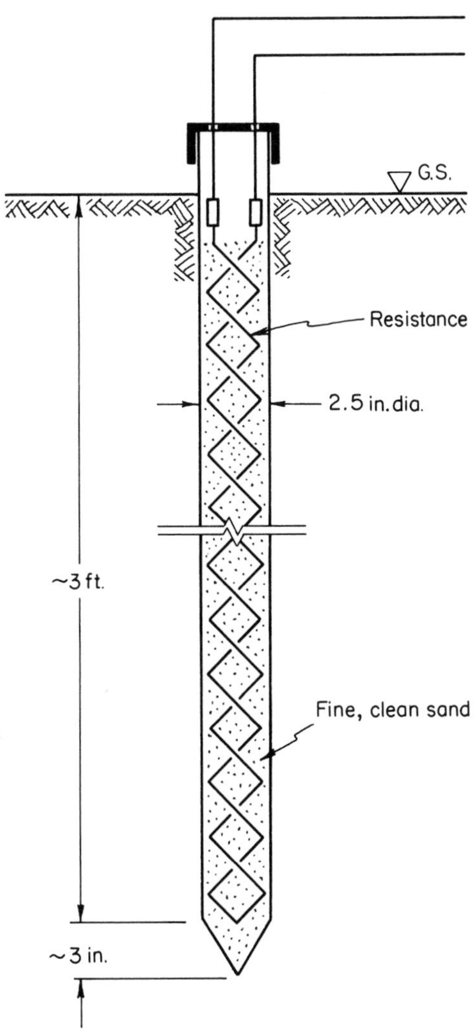

FIG. 12-1 Electrical point.

warmed electrically, by steam, or by any other means. The most intensive thawing of soil takes place during the first 24 hours of heating. After this time, the rate of thawing decreases until, after about 100 hours, thawing practically ceases. The average rate of thawing of soil is about 1 to 1.2 cm/hr vertically and about 0.1 to 0.2 cm/hr laterally.

12-5. Calculation of Thawing Rate. In calculating the rate of thawing soil, the following assumptions are usually made:

1) the temperature of the heat source is constant;
2) heat distributes perpendicularly to ground surface;
3) the soil is uniform.

The thawing time depends upon the ice content and temperature of the soil, as well as upon the electric potential (in volts) applied.

If the thawed soil contains much water and is a fine-particled soil such as silt, it may be profitable to install two types of electrodes, plus and minus. The minus electrode is a pipe that collects the water migrating in the electrical field. The water is pumped from the water-collecting electrodes, thus dehydrating the soil. The process of dewatering soil by means of electricity is *electro-osmosis.*

Wellpoints may also be used in combination with electrical thawing and dewatering of soil.

The temperature T of the soil to be thawed at a point a distance x from the source of heat is calculated from the theory of sudden change in temperature by means of the following equation:[31]

$$T = T_s + (T_0 - T_s)\frac{2}{\sqrt{\pi}}\int_{\beta=0}^{\beta=x\eta} e^{-\beta^2}\, d\beta, \tag{12-1}$$

where T_s = surface temperature at $x = 0$,
T_0 = initial temperature of soil, and

$$\frac{2}{\sqrt{\pi}}\int_{\beta=0}^{\beta=x\eta} e^{-\beta^2}\, d\beta = G(x\eta), \tag{12-2}$$

which is Gauss' error function, or the probability integral;

$$\beta = x\eta = \frac{x}{2\sqrt{\alpha t}} \tag{12-4}$$

$$\eta = \frac{1}{2\sqrt{\alpha \cdot t}}, \tag{12-3}$$

where α = coefficient of diffusivity of soil, and
t = thawing time.

Example. Determine the depth x of thawing of soil underneath a heating shack.

Given: $T_0 = -4°C$ = average initial temperature of frozen soil;
$T_s = +80°C$ = temperature of heat source = surface temperature of electrodes;
$\alpha = 0.0009$ m²/hr = diffusivity of frozen soil, and
$t = 100$ hr = thawing time.

Solution. The temperature T upon thawing is $T = 0°C$. By Eq. (12-1),

$$-\frac{T_s}{T_0 - T_s} = G(x\eta), \tag{12-5}$$

or

$$0 = 80 + (-4 - 80)\, G\left(\frac{x}{2\sqrt{\alpha t}}\right); \tag{12-6}$$

$$\frac{-80}{-84} = G\left[\frac{x}{(2)\sqrt{(0.0009)(100)}}\right] = G\left(\frac{x}{0.600}\right), \tag{12-7}$$

or with

$$G(x/0.600) = 0.954, \tag{12-8}$$

$$x/0.600 = x\eta = 1.412,$$

and

$$x = (1.412)(0.600) = 0.8472 \approx \underline{0.85 \text{ (m)}}.$$

Example. Calculate the time necessary for thawing a layer of a frozen soil $x = 10$ cm thick by means of vertical electrodes if

a) the temperature of the heat source is $T_s = +20°C$,
b) the initial temperature of the frozen soil is $T_0 = -10°C$, and
c) the coefficient of thermal diffusivity of the frozen soil is $\alpha = 0.0009$ m²/hr.

Solution.
By Eq. (12-1) or Eq. (12-5),

$$-\frac{T_s}{T_0 - T_s} = G(x\eta),$$

or

$$-\frac{20}{-10 - 20} = 20/30 = 0.667 = G(x\eta).$$

$$G[(0.1)\eta] = 0.667.$$

Therefore, from tables,

$$\beta = (0.1)\eta = 0.685.$$

$$\eta = 6.85;$$

$$\eta = 6.85 = \frac{1}{2\sqrt{\alpha t}};$$

$$1/\sqrt{t} = (13.7)\sqrt{0.0009} = 0.411;$$

$$\sqrt{t} = 1/0.411;\ t = 1/(0.411)^2 = 1/0.1689 = \underline{5.91\ (\text{hr})}.$$

REFERENCES

1. A. D. Dumont-Villares, "The Underpinning of the 26-storey Companhia Paulista de Seguros Building, São Paulo, Brazil," *Géotechnique*, **6**, 1, 1956.
2. K. H. Seydel, "Grundsätzliches über die Baugrundvereisung und deren Bedeutung für Grundbautechnische Zwecke," *Bautechnik*, 1953, H.5, 131–137; H.7, pp. 199–202.
3. G. Gordon, "Arch Dam of Ice Stops Slide," *Engineering News-Record*, **118**, 1937, p. 211.
4. T. B. Lightfoot, *Proceedings, Inst. of Mechanical Engineers* (London), May 1886, p. 238.
5. F. H. Pötsch, *Das Gefrierverfahren*, Freiberg, 1886.
6. F. H. Pötsch, "Das Gefrierverfahren," *Zentralblatt der Bauverwaltung*, 1883, p. 461; 1884, p. 287; 1888, p. 279.
7. F. Heise and F. Herbst, *Lehrbuch der Bergbaukunde*, Julius Springer, Berlin, **2**, 1923, p. 245.
8. De Loverdo, "La congélation du sols dans les travaux du Métropolitain de Paris," Monographie sur l'état actuel de l'industrie du Froid en France, published by Association Française du Froid, II. Intern. Kältekongress, Vienna, 1910.
9. S. A. Thoresen, *Engineering News-Record*, **110**, 827, 1933.
10. *Refrigeration Engineering*, February, No. 2, 1955, p. 34.
11. D. E. Moran, *Ice and Refrigeration*, Vol. 1, 1891, p. 264.
12. *Engineering News*, **73**, 1915, p. 778.
13. G. R. Smith, "Freezing Solidifies Tunnel Shaft Site," *Construction Methods and Equipment*, **44**, 10, October 1962, pp. 104–108.
14. A. R. Jumikis, *Soil Mechanics*, D. Van Nostrand Company, Inc., Princeton, N.J., 1962, pp. 75–76.
15. G. Hetzell and O. Wundram, *Die Grundbautechnik und ihre maschinellen Hilfsmittel*, Springer-Verlag, Berlin, 1929, p. 395.
16. A. Schoklitsch, *Der Grundbau*, Springer-Verlag, Vienna, 1952, pp. 250.
17. Heise-Herbst-Fritsche, *Lehrbuch der Bergbaukunde*, 7th ed., Vol. 2, Springer-Verlag, Berlin, 1950.
18. L. Brennecke and E. Lohmeyer, *Der Grundbau*, Berlin, Julius Springer, 4th ed., **3**, 1930, pp. 356–357.
19. M. Bäckström, *Kältetechnik*, G. Braun, Karlsruhe, 1953, p. 153.
20. J. Stini, *Tunnelbaugeologie*, Springer-Verlag, Vienna, 1950.
21. Taunton, "Dry Ice Creates Frozen Cofferdams for Bridge Pier Repair," *Civil Engineering*, **20**, 1950, p. 508.

22. A. R. Jumikis, "The Soil Freezing Experiment," *Highway Research Board Bulletin*, No. 135, on Factors Influencing Ground Freezing, National Academy of Sciences–National Research Council Publication No. 425, Washington, D.C., 1956.
23. G. C. Stewart, W. K. Gildersleeve, S. Jampole, and J. E. Connolly, "Freezing Aids Shaft Sinking for a Water Tunnel Under New York Harbor," *Civil Engineering*, **33**, 4, April 1963, pp. 52–54.
24. A. R. Jumikis, *Mechanics of Soils—Fundamentals for Advanced Study*. D. Van Nostrand Company, Inc., Princeton, N.J., 1964, pp. 219–232.
25. A. R. Jumikis, *Active and Passive Earth Pressure Coefficient Tables*, Bureau of Engineering Research, College of Engineering, Rutgers—The State University, New Brunswick, N.J., *Engineering Research Publication* No. 43, 1962.
26. Snow, Ice and Permafrost Research Establishment, Corps of Engineers, U.S. Army, *SIPRE Report*, No. 4, July 1951, by University of Minnesota, Review of the Properties of Snow and Ice, Minneapolis, Minn., March 1951.
27. N. E. Dorsey, *Properties of Ordinary Water-Substance*, Reinhold Publishing Corporation, New York, 1940.
28. H. T. Barnes, *Ice Engineering*, Renouf Publishing Co., Montreal, 1928.
29. J. N. Finlayson, *Canadian Engineer*, **53**, 1927, pp. 101–103.
30. N. A. Tsytovich (translated from the Russian by L. Drashevska), "Bases and Foundations on Frozen Soils," *Highway Research Board Special Report*, No. 58, National Academy of Sciences–National Research Council Publication 804, Washington, D.C., 1960, p. 28.
31. A. R. Jumikis, *The Frost Penetration Problem in Highway Engineering*, Rutgers University Press, New Brunswick, N.J., 1955.

Part IV

Various Topics

Chapter 13

Soil Freezing Under Cold Storage Warehouses

13-1. General Notes. Cold storage plants are susceptible to the condition of having the soil freeze underneath them. The resulting frost heaves can cause heavy damage to the structure above.

If over a period of years a freezing temperature prevails in the lowest floor (particularly the basement) of a cold storage plant, warehouse, or any refrigerated structure, the soil may be cooled, despite the best insulation, until the water in the soil freezes. This means that the 0°C isotherm underneath the cold room is forced several feet into the soil (Fig. 13-1). If the annual average temperature of the cold storage plant is −20°C, then there is an "eternal winter" over an area of soil equal to the extent of the cold storage area.

The 0°C isotherm penetrates deeper at the center of the cold storage plant (heat sink) than along its perimeter. This is so because of the outside climatic warmth around the building and the insulating effect of the soil. The variation in soil temperature due to changing seasons is not significant.

Frost penetration into the soil under the plant is usually very slow and heaving may not occur for several years after construction of the plant has been completed.

The heaving of the floor of a cold storage plant is very similar to soil heaving on roads.

The freezing of the soil water, particularly that supplied from groundwater by upward migration because of the temperature difference between the groundwater and the basement slab in contact with the soil, brings about an increase in the volume of the soil, resulting in the heaving of the frozen soil. Besides damaging the basement

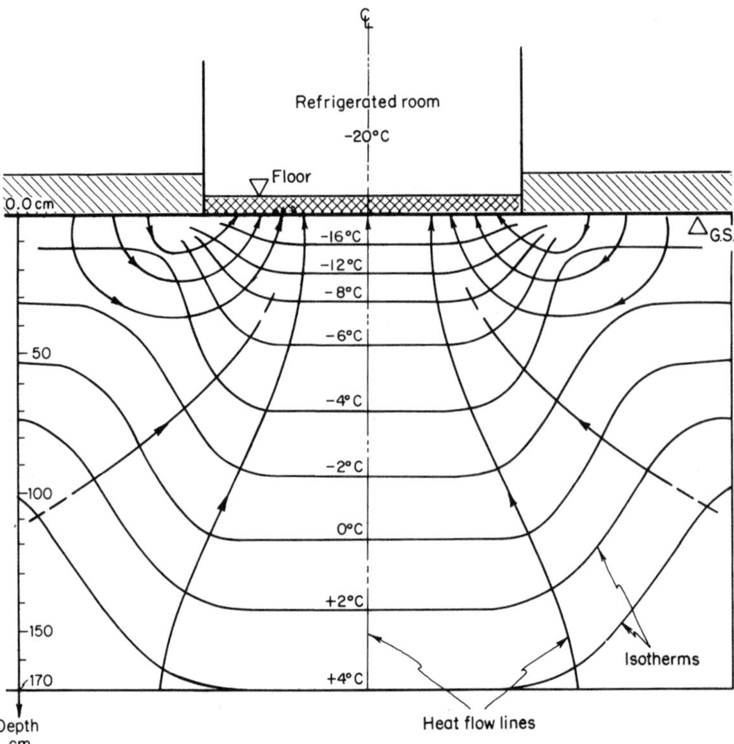

FIG. 13-1 Illustrating isotherms in soil underneath a cold room.

floor, heaving may affect the foundation and distort the entire structure.

Pearce and Hutcheson[1] observe that damage to a slab-on-grade construction of a 50 x 50 ft cold storage warehouse was caused by frost action in the underlying soil. With a temperature of $-23.3°C$ ($= -10°F$) in the cold room, the center of the floor heaved one foot after seven years of freezing operations. The distortion of the building (cracks in the walls and tilting) was so extensive that serious consideration was given to abandoning it.

13-2. Frost Penetration Depth. The frost penetration depth ξ below the contact-to-soil surface of the basement floor may be calculated by means of Fourier's differential equation of the unsteady heat flow, using the solution containing Gauss' probability integral,[2] Eq. (11-14):

$$\xi = m\sqrt{t}, \tag{11-14}$$

where $t =$ time in hours, and m is to be determined from the transcendental equation (11-15).

13-3. Amount of Heat Removed from Soil. The amount of heat Q removed from the soil underneath the cold storage plant may be calculated as

$$Q = \frac{T_c - T_0}{\frac{1}{\alpha_c} + \frac{h_1}{K_1} + \frac{h_2}{K_2} + \frac{h_3}{K_3} + \cdots + \frac{z}{K_z}}, \tag{13-1}$$

where Q = heat abstracted in the middle of the floor of the cold storage plant in contact with soil, in Cal/(m)(hr);
T_c = temperature in the cold storage room, in °C;
T_0 = temperature of groundwater, i.e., initial temperature of soil at a depth unaffected by the low temperature in the cold storage room, in °C;
α_c = heat transfer coefficient from the air of the cold storage room to the surface of the floor of that room, in Cal/(m²)(hr)(°C);
$h_1, h_2, h_3, \ldots$ = thicknesses of layers of material in the floor construction, in meters;
$K_1, K_2, K_3, \ldots$ = coefficients of thermal conductivity of the floor courses $h_1, h_2, h_3, \ldots$, respectively, in Cal/(m)(hr)(°C);
z = depth of groundwater table, i.e., constant temperature of soil underneath the floor construction of the cold storage plant, in meters;
K_z = coefficient of thermal conductivity of soil, in Cal/(m)(hr)(°C).

Upon dividing the total temperature difference $(T_c - T_0)$ in proportion to the singular quotients in the denominator to the total denominator, one can calculate whether the temperature at the contact surface between the soil and the base of the floor of the cold storage room is above or below 0°C.

13-4. Time of Protection Against Freezing. The time t that an insulated floor ξ units thick can protect soil against freezing from the cold storage plant may be calculated from Eq. (11-14):

$$\xi = m\sqrt{t}, \tag{13-2}$$

and

$$t = \xi^2/m^2, \tag{13-3}$$

where m is to be determined from Eq. (11-15).

Since with insulation there is no heat flow, $Q = 0$. Then Eq. (11-15) transforms into

$$0=\frac{K_1}{\sqrt{\alpha_1}}(T_f-T_s)\frac{e^{-m^2/(4\alpha_1)}}{G[m/(2\sqrt{\alpha_1})]}-\frac{K_2}{\sqrt{\alpha_2}}(T_0-T_f)\frac{e^{-m^2/(4\alpha_2)}}{1-G[m/(2\sqrt{\alpha_2})]} \tag{13-4}$$

resulting in

$$\frac{K_2}{K_1}\frac{\sqrt{\alpha_1}}{\sqrt{\alpha_2}}\frac{(T_0-T_f)}{(T_f-T_s)}=1-G[m/(2\sqrt{\alpha_2})]\cdot e^{m^2/(4\alpha_2)-m^2/(4\alpha_1)}, \tag{13-5}$$

where T_0 = initial temperature of soil before being refrigerated;
T_f = 0°C = 32°F = freezing temperature of soil;
T_s = surface temperature above insulating course, i.e., temperature of the refrigerated room;
K_1, K_2 = thermal conductivity;
α_1, α_2 = thermal diffusivity.

Subscript 1 pertains to the insulation ξ units thick. Subscript 2 refers to the soil underneath the insulation course.

$$G(\beta)=G\left(\frac{m}{2\sqrt{\alpha_2}}\right)$$

is the Gauss' error integral.

In spite of the best insulation, frost eventually penetrates into the soil and freezes the soil moisture.

13-5. Remedial Measures Against Frost Penetration. There are four methods of preventing or minimizing frost penetration:

1. designing the low-temperature rooms for floors higher than the one directly on or in the soil;
2. increasing the thickness of insulation;
3. providing space under the floor of the cold room through which air can circulate at a temperature above 0°C;
4. constructing an auxiliary heating system under the floor.

13-6. Thawing of Soil Under Cold Storage Plant. If the freezing in the.cold storage plant should be discontinued, the temperature should be raised very gradually. Otherwise the soil, which would contain in its voids a large percentage of ice, would thaw suddenly from the top because of the sudden rise in temperature, which would quickly release the excess soil moisture. This moisture would have accumulated from an upward flow from the groundwater over the years because of the prevailing freezing temperature gradient, and the soil would have become saturated, being converted from a plastic to a quasi-liquid consistency. The thawed, saturated soil would lose its bearing capacity, both soil and cold storage plant would settle, and damage to the structure would occur.

Chapter 14

Icing on Pavements

14-1. General Notes. An analysis of pavement icing[3] is presented here because of its practical importance and academic interest and to promote a better understanding of the icing phenomenon. The physical conditions for ice formation on roads and landing fields and the temperature regime below the surface are described and illustrated graphically with tautochrones. There is also a discussion of the effect of rain falling on a road surface that is below freezing. The icing theory is demonstrated by conditions as they prevailed in the general metropolitan area of New York in January 1956.

Snow, sleet, and rain cause a variety of conditions on paved surfaces which offer special difficulties to pedestrians and to highway and landing field traffic. Upon the formation of ice, traffic first reduces speed, then moves at a crawl, and finally in many sections stops completely for many hours, forcing motorists to abandon their vehicles, thus prolonging the traffic jam.

Such traffic conditions prevailed on January 8–9, 1956, in the general metropolitan area of New York. This area, with a radius from Manhattan of more than 75 miles, includes, besides all of metropolitan New York, most of Long Island, New Haven, Conn.; Suffern, N.Y.; northeastern New Jersey and the Newark district; and south to the vicinity of New Brunswick and Trenton, New Jersey. This is the most heavily traveled section of the eastern seaboard (Fig. 14-1). One can imagine the large-scale confusion that resulted on the many major arteries and side roads when, on the dates mentioned, roads and windshields became covered with ice (Fig. 14-2). Because of the slippery pavement conditions it was particularly difficult to operate in hilly country, and on curves and bridges.

14-2. Icing Theory. Formation of Ice. Ice can form on pavements under several conditions. For brevity, however, the discussion will be

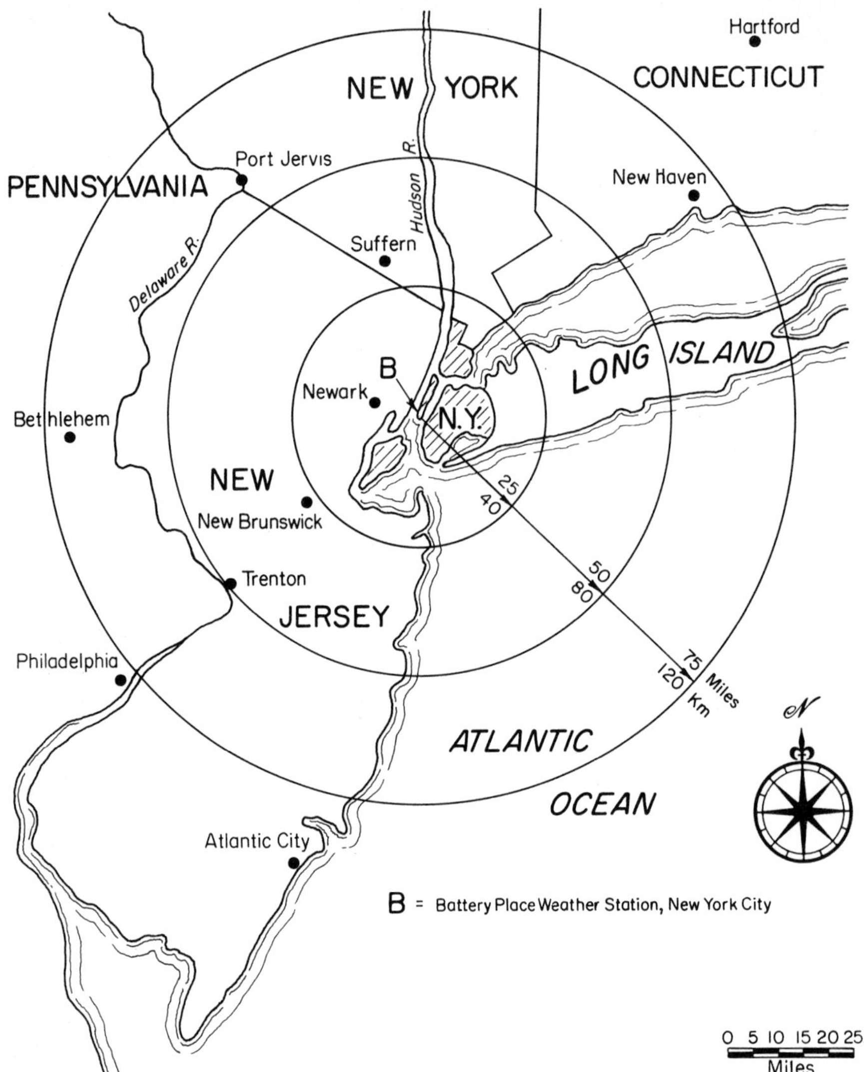

FIG. 14-1 Sketch-map of the general metropolitan area of New York.

confined to that special form of icing known by the meteorological term "glaze," which occurs under the special conditions to be described. The term "surface" will apply equally to any paved surface or to the ground surface, because the same reasoning applies.

Let us assume that the air adjacent to the frozen pavement or soil is cold, and that fine drops of rain fall through the cold zone. When these fine drops, at a temperature above but near freezing, fall and strike a

FIG. 14-1a Traffic arteries of part of the New York metropolitan area (by permission of Aero Service Corporation, Philadelphia, Pa.).

frozen surface, they freeze, coating the surface with a smooth, clear film of ice. After impact, the droplets freeze on the surface, sometimes within a very few minutes. The icing affects vehicle braking distance adversely by reducing traction. The coefficient of friction between the tires and iced pavement, according to Hewes and Oglesby,[(4)] can be as low as approximately $\mu = 0.05$, which makes proper vehicle control almost impossible. It is the quick freezing of ice on pavements, according to some authors, which causes the low coefficient of friction. The ice crystals so produced are very fine, hard, and smooth. The thickness of the ice varies from about 1 to 2 mm, although this depends upon the amount and duration of precipitation, evaporation, and run-off.

(a)

(b)

FIG. 14-2 Icing on pavement.

The size of the droplets, according to Shaw,[5] is about 0.5 mm, but spherical raindrops vary from 1 to 4.5 mm in diameter, while rice-shaped droplets are about 6 mm long.

14-3. Latent Heat. One gram of water upon freezing releases 80 gram-calories of latent heat, and a certain amount of the rain remains liquid at about 0°C. This latent heat of fusion of rain droplets is thus more than sufficient to raise the surface temperature for a certain time from below freezing to 0°C, at which temperature the rain droplets start to freeze. Hence during freezing the droplet itself gives off heat, and the released heat raises the pavement surface temperature until the temperatures of both droplet and pavement become equal, i.e., 0°C.

Latent heat of fusion can be liberated and dissipated by

1) evaporation of water,
2) convection,
3) conduction to the air, and
4) conduction to the pavement or soil.

Factors 1), 2), and 3) are small compared with the dissipation of heat by conduction to the pavement or soil. This discussion will therefore be confined to the formation of ice on pavements when liberated heat is dissipated principally in this manner.

According to Geiger,[6] glaze can form in two ways: 1) through the solidification of supercooled precipitation on warm ground and 2) through the freezing of raindrops (above 0°C) on very cold ground.

In the first case, assume that the temperature of a one-gram supercooled raindrop striking the warm pavement is −5°C. Upon contact, the drop starts to freeze, and its temperature rises to 0°C. Five gram-calories are thereby consumed, and 75 more calories must be liberated to freeze the one-gram drop. Because the value of latent heat of evaporation is 540 calories, only a small amount of the one-gram drop—i.e., $(75 \times 1)/540 = 0.138$ gram—must evaporate in order to liberate the remaining $80 - 5 = 75$ calories and start the freezing. This small amount of evaporation takes place within a short time, and the freezing starts soon also. In this respect the evaporation in the freezing process is very significant.

In the second case, assume that the temperature of the rain is +4°C. Falling through the cold air adjacent to the cold surface, the rain cools to 0°C. Each one-gram drop striking the pavement at this temperature liberates 80 gram-calories of latent heat. Only after this amount of heat is liberated does the water start to freeze.

The main factor in the process of ice formation is thus the dissipation of latent heat into the air and the ground.

14-4. Conditions Favorable for Icing. From the discussion of ice formation, it can be summarized that there are two conditions governing the process – A) meteorological conditions and B) thermal properties of air, water, pavement and soil.

A. *Meteorological Conditions.* The chief prerequisite for the formation of ice, of course, is

1) the rapid approach at higher altitudes of a warm, humid air flow preceded by a period of cold.

Other factors are

2) the intensity and duration of precipitation, which determine the thickness of icing and its rate of formation;
3) the temperature of the rain falling through the cold air zone adjacent to the ground; and
4) the temperature of the pavement (usually below freezing).

B. *Thermal Properties.* The processes of heat absorption by radiation and conduction through soil and pavement depend upon the composition of the surface properties, heat capacities, thermal conductivities and densities of the materials. These influence

1) the storage of heat in water, soil, and pavement;
2) the dissipation into the surrounding media of the latent heat liberated upon cooling and freezing of the rain droplets;
3) the temperature regime in pavement and soil; and
4) the heat absorption by radiation.

14-5. Analytical Treatment. Assume that the cold temperature distribution at a given time below the pavement or ground surface within the frozen zone is linear, i.e., dT/dx (Fig. 14-3), where dT ($= T_f - T_s$) is the temperature difference between the freezing ($273°K = 0°C$) and surface temperatures, respectively, and x is the depth below the surface. The temperature system in the figure is Kelvin. Assume also that there is no lateral heat flow or horizontal temperature difference. Upon freezing, the liberated calories ($q_L = 80$) of latent heat are transmitted by conduction into the soil.

Amount of Latent Heat. The amount of latent heat liberated during the time dt of rainfall when the rain strikes the surface at an intensity of h_r cm/sec through one square centimeter of surface area is

$$q_L \gamma_w h_r \, dt \qquad (\text{cal/cm}^2), \tag{14-1}$$

where $q_L = 80$ calories per gram = latent heat, and
γ_w = unit weight of water, in g/cm^3.

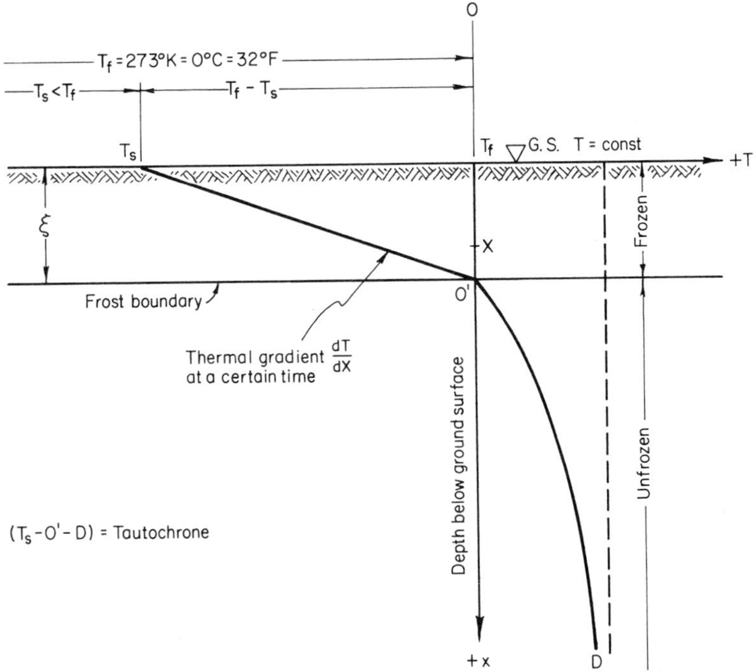

FIG. 14-3 Tautochrone at a certain time.

It is difficult to determine the proportions of liberated heat that are dissipated into the air and into the ground. However, for simplicity, assume as before that all the liberated heat is conducted into the ground. This assumption can be made because the thermal conductivity of air is approximately one thousand times less than that of frozen soil, i.e., $K_{air}/K_{fs} = 0.000055/0.055 = 1/1000$.

The amount of heat conducted into the ground or pavement is

$$K \frac{\partial T}{\partial x} \, dt = q_L \gamma_w h_r \, dt, \tag{14-2}$$

where K = coefficient of thermal conductivity of the frozen ground or pavement, in cal/(cm)(sec)(°C);

x = depth coordinate;

dt = time differential;

$\frac{\partial T}{\partial x}$ = temperature gradient at any point at time t = const. Here the partial derivative $\partial T/\partial x$ is chosen instead of dT/dx to indicate that the temperature T varies not only with depth x below the surface but also with time.

Warming Gradient. While the pavement is being warmed by the liberated latent heat, the temperature gradient within the frozen zone below the surface bends around and moves towards the freezing point, $T_f = 273°K$ (= 0°C) at the surface (Fig. 14-4). Ruckli[7] suggests replacing the curved part (a-b-a') of the temperature gradient bend in the frozen zone by a straight line (Fig. 14-5). Then from Fig. 14-5 and Eq. (14-2), for a uniform rate of warming of the frozen zone from the surface down, the thermal gradient is

$$\frac{\partial T}{\partial x} = \tan \beta = \frac{q_L \gamma_w h_r}{K}. \tag{14-3}$$

Freezing Time. The time t_0 required to freeze the rain can be calculated from the heat balance:

$$\left\{\begin{matrix}\text{Latent heat liberated during} \\ \text{time } t_0 \text{ of the fallen rain drop-} \\ \text{lets}\end{matrix}\right\} = \left\{\begin{matrix}\text{Heat received by the warmed} \\ \text{zone during same time } t_0\end{matrix}\right\},$$

or

$$q_L \gamma_w h_r t_0 = c \gamma x_0 \frac{(T_f - T_s)}{2}. \tag{14-4}$$

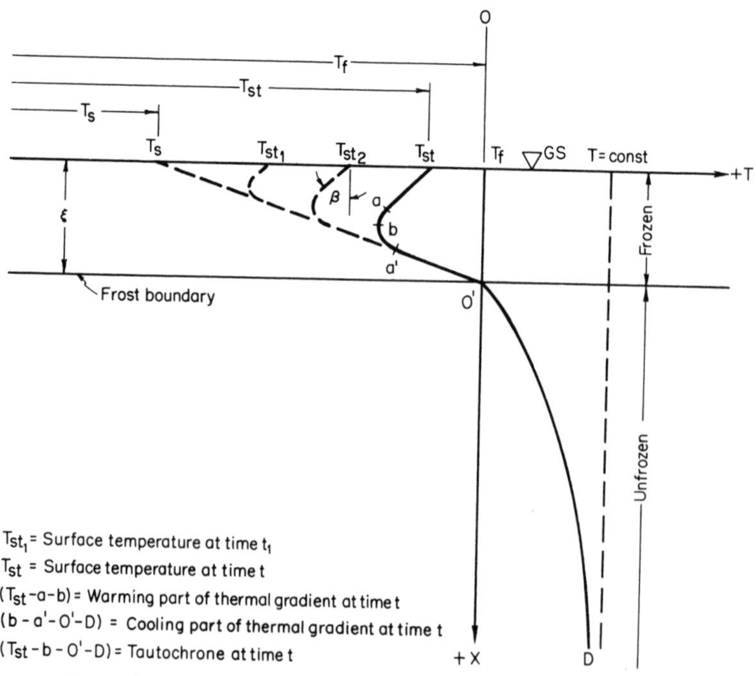

FIG. 14-4 Tautochrone during liberation of latent heat.

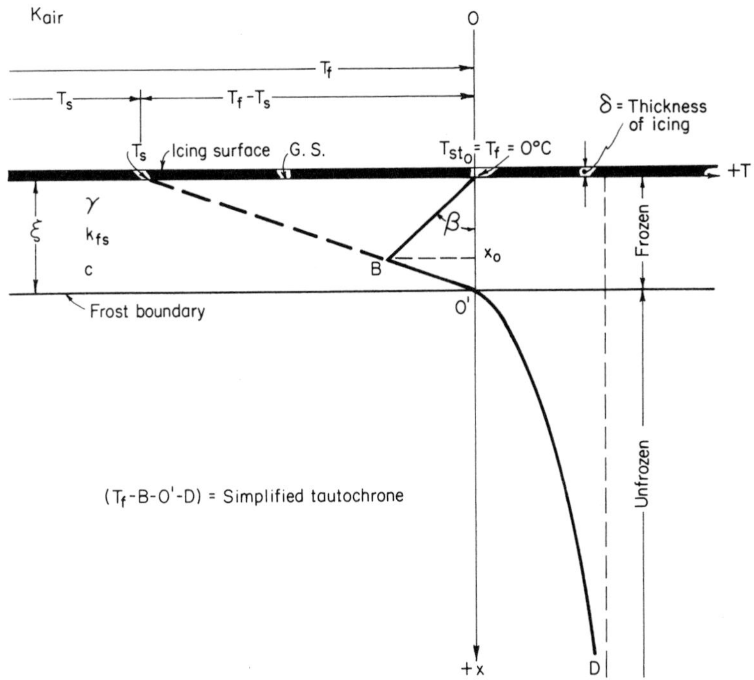

FIG. 14-5 Simplified tautochrone at time t_0 when the surface temperature is 0°C.

With

$$x_0 = \frac{\xi}{1 + \xi[\tan \beta/(T_f - T_s)]}, \tag{14-5}$$

refer to Fig. 14-5 and to Ruckli,[7]

$$t_0 = \frac{c\gamma(T_f - T_s)}{2\gamma_w q_L h_r} x_0, \tag{14-6}$$

where c = heat capacity;
γ = unit weight of the soil or pavement material, in g/cm³;
ξ = frost penetration depth, in cm;
x_0 = depth coordinate when the warming tautochrone at its upper end passes through the 0°C-point.

Thickness of Icing. During the time t_0 all of the rain is frozen and the ice has grown to a thickness of

$$\delta = (1.09)h_r t_0 \quad \text{(cm)}. \tag{14-7}$$

Because ice forms rapidly, it can be assumed that the run-off coefficient is unity. The coefficient 1.09 allows for the expansion of ice by 9% by volume.

After all the rain has frozen on the surface, the warmed zone gradually cools again, and with the air still at freezing temperatures the surface temperature drops. The ice remains until the weather becomes warmer.

14-6. Icing in Metropolitan New York January 8–9, 1956. Temperature records[8] show that after the period above freezing ending January 5, the temperature on January 6, 7, and 8 dropped below freezing, reaching a low in the morning of January 8, when the readings at several weather record stations were 15°F to 18°F. The course of the air temperature regime can be followed from Tables 14-1, 14-2, and Figs. 14-6, 14-7, and 14-8. The glaze began at 8:20 p.m. on January 8 and ended at 6:15 p.m. the next day.

Variations of air and soil temperature are illustrated in Figs. 14-6, 14-7, and 14-8. Soil temperatures[9] are tabulated in Table 14-2.

Soil Properties. These are some of the properties of the Nixon Loam soil used for this study:

SOIL: NIXON LOAM

Depth Below Surface, in inches	*Sand*	*Silt*	*Clay*
0– 8	38%	40%	22%
8–12	30%	44%	26%
12–32	28%	44%	28%

Average void ratio: $e = 0.71$
Average unit weight: $\gamma = 96.14$ lb/ft^3 $= 1.54$ g/cm^3.

Tautochrone Movement. From Fig. 14-8 it can be seen that while the rain froze on the ground on January 8, the soil tautochrone moved to the warm side of the vertical line 0–0′, i.e., from position No. 1 to position No. 2. Then, about midnight of that day, the tautochrone moved back to the cold side (position No. 3), and during the next day, January 9, it moved into position No. 4. That is, because of the rise in air temperature above freezing, icing was over.

14-7. Calculated Freezing Time and Thickness of Icing During Glaze, January 8–9, 1956. Figure 14-8 shows that the surface temperature at 4:00 a.m. on January 8 was

$$T_s = 21°\text{F} = -6.11°\text{C} \approx 267°\text{K}$$

and

$$T_f = 32°\text{F} = 0°\text{C} = 273°\text{K}.$$

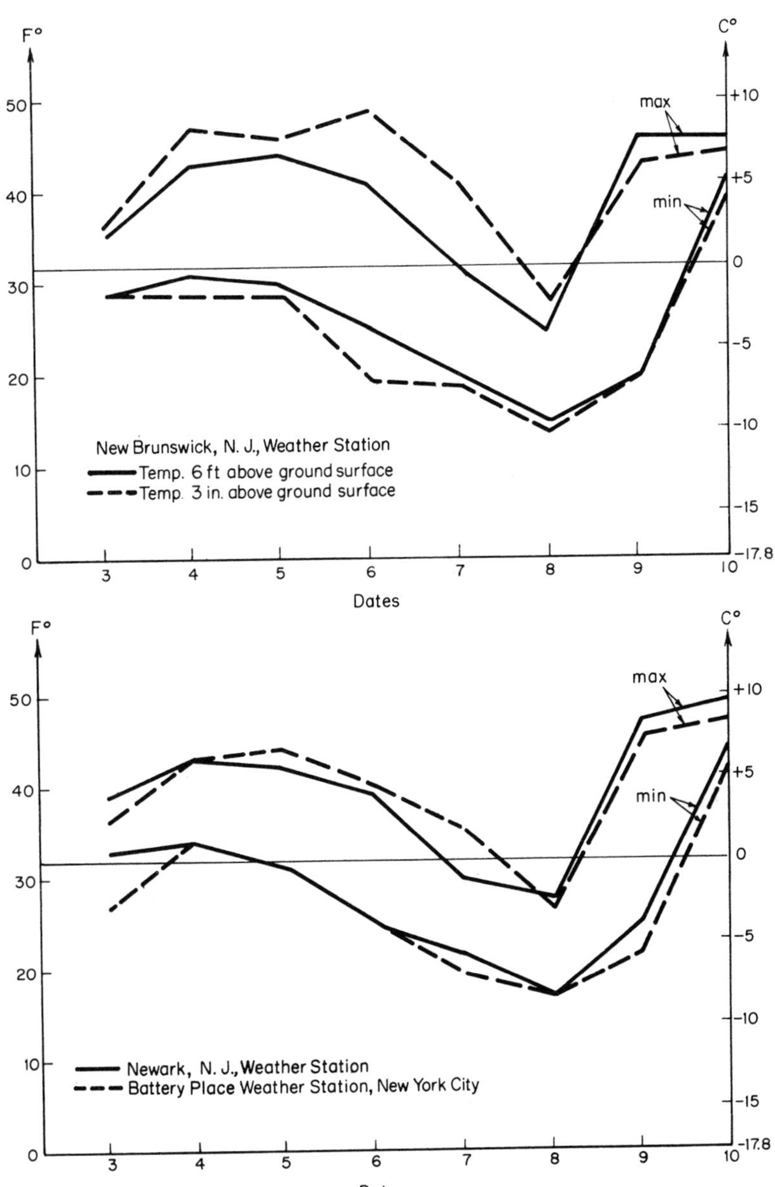

FIG. 14-6 Maximum and minimum air temperature, New York metropolitan area, January 3–10, 1956.

Table 14-1

Hourly Air Temperatures in the General Metropolitan Area of New York, January 5 Through 10, 1956

Reporting Weather Station	Date	2	4	6 a.m.	8	10	12 noon	2	4	6	8 p.m.	10	12
		Temperature (°F)											
U.S. Dept. of Commerce[5]	5	36	36	34	35	39	42	44	42	37	35	33	31
NEWARK, N.J.	6	30	29	29	30	34	38	39	36	32	29	27	25
(Newark Airport)	7	24	25	25	26	27	31	32	30	27	26	23	20
Ground elevation 11 ft.	8	18	18	18	18	21	24	27	26	20	19	19	23
Freezing drizzle and rain	Prec.†											T	0.01/T
fell during the evening of Jan. 8, continued over	9	28	31	35	39	41	43	44	44	44	44	45	45
night, ended following	Prec.	T	T	T/0.01	0.01/0.01	T/0.01	0.01/0.01	T/0	0.01/0	T/T	0.01/T	T/0	
morning.	10	46	46	45	46	46	46	46	47	45	44	43	43
Rutgers University	5	35	35	34.5	33	32	41.5	43.5	41	35	33.5	32	31
College of Agriculture	6	29	28.5	28	29	37	38	40	36	31	28	26	24
Dept. of Meteorology	7	23	24	25.5	25	33	24	32	30	28	26	23.5	20
NEW BRUNSWICK, N.J.	8	17	15	16	16	19	22.5	24	22.5	18.5	18	18	20
(College Farm)	9	25.5	29	33.5	36	39	41	43	43	44	43	46	45.5
Ground elevation 80 ft.	10	46	46	45.5	45	46	45	46	45	45	44	43	42
Height of measured temperatures: 4′6″		Total precipitation Jan. 8, 0 in. Total precipitation Jan. 9, 0.08 in.											

U.S. Dept. of Commerce	5	35	35	34	34	36	37	39	41	39	36	33	31
NEW YORK, N.Y.	6	31	30	29	28	29	32	36	37	33	31	29	25
City Office	7	25	26	25	24	25	28	28	28	25	25	23	22
(Battery Place)	8	19	18	18	19	19	22	25	25	22	20	17	20
Ground elevation 10 ft.	Prec.											T/T	T/T
	9	24	28	31	35	37	40	42	43	45	46	46	46
	Prec.	0.02/0.02	0.02/0.02	0.02/0.01	0.03/0.07	0.04/0.10	0.05/0.01	0.01/0.02	0.03/0.02	0.03/0.01	T/T	0.02/T	
	10	46	46	46	48	48	48	48	48	47	46	46	45

† Precipitation in inches: T = trace. Numerator in precipitation line indicates amount during odd hours; denominator indicates amount during even hours.

Table 14-2

Maximum and Minimum Soil Temperatures at the College Farm,† Rutgers University, College of Agriculture,[9] January 5 Through 10, 1956

Date	Temperature (°F)											
	Depth Below Ground Surface (in.)											
	1		2		4		8		16		32	
	Max.	Min.	Max.	Min.	Max.	Min.	Max.	Min.	Max.	Min.	Max.	Min.
5	33	32	32	32	32	31	33	32	35	34	38	38
6	33	31	32	31	32	31	33	32	35	34	38	38
7	32	30	32	31	32	31	33	32	35	34	38	38
8	31	28	31	30	31	30	33	32	35	34	38	38
‡9	33	29	32	30	32	30	33	32	35	34	38	38
10	34	33	32	32	32	32	33	32	35	34	38	38

† Soil covered with blue-green turf.
‡ Ground covered with ice. Freezing rain.

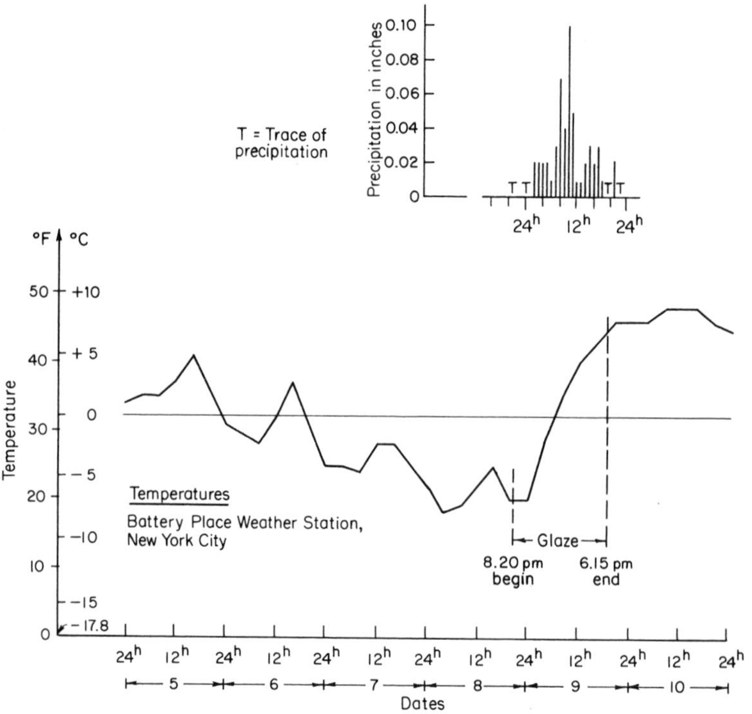

FIG. 14-7 Hourly air temperature, New York metropolitan area, January 5–10, 1956.

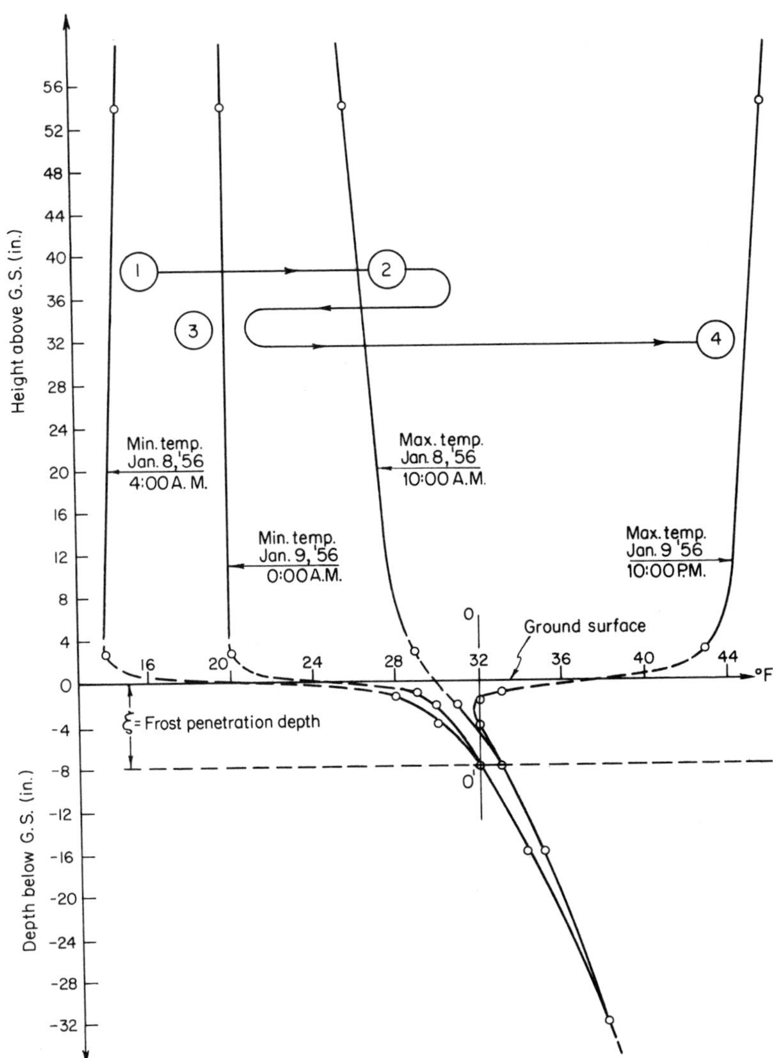

FIG. 14-8 Maximum and minimum tautochrone, January 8–9, 1956.

The frost penetration depth at that time, just before or about the time of raining, was 8 in. (= 20 cm). The average precipitation at Newark Airport can be assumed as $h_r = 0.01$ in./hr $= 0.000007$ cm/sec, and at Battery Place, New York City, $h_r \approx 0.03$ in./hr $= 0.000021$ cm/sec.

With a coefficient of thermal conductivity of a frozen soil of $K = 0.0075$ cal/(cm)(sec)(°C), and heat capacity of $c = 0.20$ cal/(g)(°C), the warming thermal gradient by Eq. (14-3) is

$\partial T/\partial x = \tan \beta = (80)(1.0)(0.000007)/0.0075 = 0.0746$ (°C/cm) for $h_r = 0.01$ in./hr, and $\tan \beta = 0.224$ for $h_r = 0.03$ in./hr.

By Eq. (14-5) the depth coordinate x_0 at time t_0 when the surface temperature reaches 0°C is

$$x_0 = \frac{20}{1 + 20(0.0746/6)} = 16 \text{ (cm)} = 6.3 \text{ (in.) for } h_r = 0.01 \text{ in./hr,}$$

and $x_0 = 11.6$ (cm) = 4.56 (in.) for $h_r = 0.03$ in./hr.

The time t_0 during which the fallen rain freezes is, by Eq. (14-6),

$$t_0 = \frac{(0.20)(1.54)(6)(16.0)}{(2)(1.0)(80)(0.000007)} = 26{,}400 \text{ (sec)} = 7 \text{ hr } 20 \text{ min}$$

for $h_r = 0.01$ in./hr, and $t_0 = 6439.5$ (sec) = 1 hr 47 min for $h_r = 0.03$ in./hr, respectively.

By Eq. (14-7), the thickness of icing is $\delta = 0.201$ cm ≈ 2 mm, and $\delta = 0.147$ cm ≈ 1.5 mm, respectively.

This analysis shows that thermal and meteorological conditions, soil properties, amount of latent heat, and time t_0 required to warm the pavement to 0°C and freeze the rain are very significant. The greater the rain intensity, the less is the time t_0, and the thinner the ice. This discussion also indicates that the rain does not freeze quickly, as indicated earlier, but, depending upon the intensity of the rain, takes several hours to freeze.

REFERENCES

1. D. C. Pearce and N. B. Hutcheson, "Frost Action Under Cold Storage Plants," *Refrigeration Engineering*, **66**, 10, October 1958.
2. A. R. Jumikis, *The Frost Penetration Problem in Highway Engineering*, Rutgers University Press, New Brunswick, N.J., 1955.
3. A. R. Jumikis, "Icing on Pavements," *Highway Research Board Bulletin*, No. 218, on Frost Effects in Soils and on Pavement Surfaces, National Academy of Sciences–National Research Council Publication No. 671. Washington, D.C., 1959, pp. 24–33.
4. L. I. Hewes and C. H. Oglesby, *Highway Engineering*, John Wiley and Sons, New York, 1954, p. 598.
5. N. Shaw, *Manual of Meteorology*, Vol. 3, Cambridge, at the University Press, London, 1930, p. 326.
6. R. Geiger, *The Climate Near the Ground*, Harvard University Press, Cambridge, Mass., 1950, p. 152.
7. R. Ruckli, *Der Frost im Baugrund*, Springer, Vienna, 1950, p. 13.
8. U.S. Department of Commerce, Weather Bureau, "Local Climatological Data," 1955–56, Ashville, N.C.
9. Department of Meteorology, College of Agriculture, Rutgers—The State University, "Temperature Data," New Brunswick, N.J., 1956.

Appendixes

Appendix 1

A. Greek Alphabet

A	α	Alpha	N	ν	Nu
B	β	Beta	Ξ	ξ	Xi
Γ	γ	Gamma	O	o	Omicron
Δ	δ	Delta	Π	π	Pi
E	ϵ	Epsilon	P	ρ	Rho
Z	ζ	Zeta	Σ	$\sigma\varsigma$	Sigma
H	η	Eta	T	τ	Tau
Θ	θ	Theta	Υ	υ	Upsilon
I	ι	Iota	Φ	ϕ	Phi
K	κ	Kappa	X	χ	Chi
Λ	λ	Lambda	Ψ	ψ	Psi
M	μ	Mu	Ω	ω	Omega

B. Symbols and Abbreviations

Symbol	*Description*
A	Area
A_{av}	Average area
a	Coefficient of blackness
atm	Atmosphere; atmospheric pressure
b	A coefficient
b_1; b_2	Coefficients (Eq. 11-15)
Btu	British thermal unit

Symbol	*Description*
C	Centigrade (or Celcius) temperature scale (0° = 32°F, 100° = 212°F)
C	A constant; a coefficient; coefficient of radiation of a body
℄	Center line
C_W	Heat capacity
$C_{W\mathrm{i}}$	Heat capacity of ice
$C_{W\mathrm{s}}$	Mass heat capacity of solids of soil
$C_{W\mathrm{w}}$	Heat capacity of water
C_n	Reciprocal coefficient of radiation
C_0	Coefficient of radiation of an absolute black body
C_1	Heat capacity of frozen part of soil; radiation coefficient
C_2	Heat capacity of unfrozen part of soil; radiation coefficient
c	A coefficient; a constant; cohesion; specific heat; heat capacity
c_m	Mass heat capacity
$c_{m\mathrm{i}}$	Mass heat capacity of ice
$c_{m\mathrm{s}}$	Mass heat capacity of dry soil
$c_{m\mathrm{w}}$	Mass heat capacity of water
c_{s}	Heat capacity of solids
c_{sp}	Specific heat
c_v	Volumetric heat capacity
$c_{v\mathrm{f}}$	Volumetric heat capacity of frozen soil
$c_{v\mathrm{u}}$	Volumetric heat capacity of unfrozen soil
c_{w}	Heat capacity of water
Cal	Large calorie (or kilocalorie)
cal	Small calorie
cm	Centimeter
const	Constant
D	Diameter
d	Diameter; thickness; depth; a coefficient
d_i	Inside diameter
d_o	Outside diameter
dQ; dq	Differential of heat
dT	Differential of temperature
dT/dx	First derivative; change in temperature
dt	Differential of time
dx	Differential of length
$d\xi$	Differential of frost penetration depth
E	Modulus of elasticity; radiant energy from a real body; earth pressure

Symbol	*Description*
E_0	Radiant energy
e	Base of the natural logarithm system (= 2.7182 . . .); void ratio
emf	Electromotive force
F	Fahrenheit temperature scale
F	Force; a function
f	Index for frozen soil; index for a freezing temperature
$f(m)$	Function (of m)
ft	Foot
ft-lb	Foot-pound
G	Specific gravity
G.S.	Ground surface
G.W.T.	Groundwater table
$G(X) = G(x\eta) = G(\beta)$	Gauss' probability integral (or error function), (Eq. 6-2)
g	Gram
g	Acceleration of gravity = 981 cm/sec^2 = 32.2 ft/sec^2
H; h	Height; depth
h; h_1; h_2; . . . h_n	Thickness of soil layers
h_r	Intensity of precipitation
hr	Hour
i	Gradient
i_{sn}	Temperature gradient in snow
i_ξ	Temperature gradient in frozen soil
in.	Inch
K	Kelvin, absolute temperature scale (0° ≅ −273.1°C)
K	Coefficient of heat conduction
K; K_1; K_2; . . . K_n	Coefficients of thermal conductivity
K_1; K_2	Coefficient of thermal conductivity of frozen and unfrozen soil, respectively
K_f	Coefficient of thermal conductivity of frozen soil
K_i	Coefficient of thermal conductivity of ice
K_{ins}	Coefficient of thermal conductivity of insulation
K_{oi}	Coefficient of thermal conductivity between outside and inside of wall
K_r	Equivalent linear coefficient of heat transfer
K_{sn}	Coefficient of thermal conductivity of snow
K_{ss}	Coefficient of thermal conductivity of sandstone
K_u	Coefficient of thermal conductivity of unfrozen soil

Symbol	*Description*
K_w	Coefficient of heat transfer for water
k	Coefficient of permeability of soil
kg	Kilogram
kg-m	Kilogram-meter
km	Kilometer
L	Length; latent heat of fusion
L_s	Latent heat of sublimation
L_v	Latent heat of vaporization
l	Liter
log	Common (Brigg's) logarithm to the base 10
ln	Natural logarithm of, or logarithm to the base of $e = 2.7182\ldots$
M	Mass; a moment; bending moment
mv	Millivolts
m	Meter
m	Mass; coefficient of proportionality (Eq. 6-1)
mm	Millimeter
max	Maximum
min	Minimum; minute
N	Capacity of refrigeration plant; number of degree-days (Eq. 6-13)
$N_1, N_2 \ldots N_n$	Number of degree-days
N_{ca}	Climatologically available number of degree-days
n	Number of courses in a soil system; porosity of soil; number of freezer pipes
p; p_1; p_2	Pressure; stress
p_a	Atmospheric pressure
p_c	Critical pressure
p_v	Vapor pressure
Q	Amount of soil moisture transferred; heat energy; amount of heat transferred
Q_s; Q_w	Heat components
Q_t	Total amount of heat
Q_{t1}; Q_V	Amount of heat pertaining to relative volume (one unit) of soil
q	Unit flow of heat
$q_{general}$	General amount of heat flow
q_i	Heat removed from ice
q_{ins}	Heat removed from insulation
q_L	Heat flow for length L of pipe; amount of latent heat

Symbol	*Description*
q_s	Heat removed from solids of soil
q_w	Heat removed from water
q_1; q_2	Heat components; unit flow of heat
R; R_1; R_2; . . . R_n	Thermal resistances; a point
R_{ins}	Thermal resistance of pipe insulation
R_r	Reciprocal heat transfer coefficient
r; r_1; r_2	Radius
r_i	Inside radius
r_o	Outside radius
S	Degree of saturation
T	Temperature
T_a	Ambient temperature
T_b	Boiling temperature
T_{air}	Air temperature
T_c	Temperature of cold storage room
T_{cr}	Critical temperature
T_f	Freezing temperature
T_g	Groundwater temperature
T_i	Initial temperature
T_n	Temperature at exit of nth layer
T_0	Initial temperature
T_s	Surface temperature; skin temperature; temperature of sublimation
T_{st}	Temperature at surface at time t
T_v	Temperature of vaporization
T_{wall}	Temperature of wall
T_{wool}	Temperature of wool
T_1	Temperature of frozen zone of soil
T_2	Temperature of unfrozen zone of soil
T_{11}	Temperature
T_{1w}; T_{2w}	Temperature at wall surface
t	Time; time interval; depth
t_0	Time
$\tan \phi$	Coefficient of internal friction of soil
$\tan \phi_f$	Coefficient of internal friction of frozen soil
V	Volt
V	Volume; specific volume
V_s	Volume of solids in soil
V_w	Volume of water in soil
v	Specific volume

Symbol	*Description*
W	Weight; work
W_w	Weight of water
w	Moisture content (in percent) by dry weight of soil; optimum moisture content
X	Argument in Gauss' error function ($= x\eta = \beta$)
x	An unknown quantity; abscissa; coordinate; length; depth of frost
$x_1; x_2; \ldots x_n$	Coordinates; length; depth; thickness
x_0	Depth
$Y_1; Y_2$	Symbols for abbreviated equations
y	An unknown quantity; a coordinate
z	An unknown quantity; a coordinate; depth; depth to groundwater table
α	Coefficient of thermal diffusivity; coefficient of heat convection; angle of rupture
α_1	Coefficient of thermal diffusivity of frozen part of soil
α_2	Coefficient of thermal diffusivity of unfrozen part of soil
α_c	Coefficient of heat convection
α_i	Inside coefficient of heat convection; internal heat transfer coefficient
α_o	External heat transfer coefficient
β	Argument in Gauss' error function ($= x\eta$)
γ	Unit weight; unit weight of soil
γ_d	Dry unit weight of soil
γ_s	Unit weight of solids of soil
γ_{Hg}	Unit weight of mercury
γ_{sat}	Unit weight of saturated soil
γ_{sub}	Submerged (buoyant) unit weight of soil
γ_w	Unit weight of water
Δ	Difference; increment; decrement
ΔT	Temperature difference
Δh	Amount of frost heave
Δp	Pressure correction
δ	Thickness of frozen wall of soil (or of ice wall); thickness of ice
∂Q	Partial differential (of Q)
$\partial^2 T/\partial t^2$	Second partial derivative

Symbol	*Description*
ϵ	Strain
ϵ_y; ϵ_z	Strain components
η	Dynamic viscosity of water; factor of safety; a variable in Gauss' error function
η/η_0	Relative dynamic viscosity
μ	Micron (= 0.001 mm); Poisson's ratio
ξ	Frost penetration depth; thickness of insulation course
π	Pi, ratio of circumference of a circle to its diameter (= 3.14159 . . .)
ρ_i	Density of ice
ρ_s	Density of snow; density of soil
ρ_1	Density of frozen zone of soil
ρ_2	Density of unfrozen zone of soil
$\sum_1^n R$	Summation of R from 1 to n
σ_n	Normal stress
σ_u	Ultimate stress
σ_{adm}	Admissible (allowable) compressive strength of soil
σ_1	Major (or principal) stress
τ	Temperature interval; shear strength of ice; shear strength of soil
τ_1	A temperature term for frozen part of soil
τ_2	A temperature term for unfrozen parts of soil
$\tau_\perp$	Shear strength of ice perpendicular to optical axis
$\tau_{\parallel}$	Shear strength of ice parallel to optical axis
ϕ	Angle of internal friction of soil
ϕ_f	Angle of internal friction of frozen soil

Appendix 2

Conversion Tables for Units of Measurement

Because the metric system is increasingly being used in preference to the inch-pound-second system in science and engineering, conversion tables of the most common units in both systems are included here. Most of the data are from "Units and Systems of Weights and Measures—Their Origin, Development, and Present Status," by Lewis V. Judson, National Bureau of Standards Circular 570, United States Department of Commerce, issued May 21, 1956. The compound units were derived from this source.

MASS AND WEIGHT

1 g = 0.001 kg = 0.03527 oz = 2.205×10^{-3} lb
1 kg = 2.20462 lb 1 lb = 0.45359 kg
1 metric ton = 1000 kg = 2205 lb = 1.102 short ton
1 short ton = 2000 lb = 9.072×10^{5} g = 907.2 kg

LENGTH

1 mm = 0.03937 in. 1 cm = 10 mm = 0.39370 in.
1 m = 1000 mm = 100 cm = 39.37 in. = 3.280833 ft
1 in. = 2.54 cm 1 ft = 0.304801 m 1 yd = 0.914403 m

AREA

1 cm^2 = 0.15500 in.^{2}
1 m^2 = 10.76387 ft^2 = 1 centiare (ca) = 10^{-2} are = 10^{-4} hectare (ha)
1 ha = 2.4710624 acres = 10,000 m^2 = 100 square ares
1 in.^{2} = 6.45164 cm^2 = 6.4564×10^{-4} m^2
1 ft^2 = 0.0929 m^2 = 2.296×10^{-5} acre

1 acre = 43,560 ft^2 = 40.468420 ares = 0.4046842 ha
1 mi^2 = 640 acres

VOLUME

1 cm^3 = 10^{-6} m^3 = 0.06102 in.^{3} = 3.531×10^{-5} ft^3
1 m^3 = 10^6 cm^3 = 6.102×10^4 in.^{3} = 35.31445 ft^3
1 in.^{3} = 5.787×10^{-4} ft^3 = 16.38716 cm^3 = 1.6387×10^{-5} m^3
1 ft^3 = 1728 in.^{3} = 2.832×10^4 cm^3 = 0.02832 m^3

CAPACITY

1 liter = 1000 cm^3 = 0.001 m^3 = 61.02 in.^{3} = 3.551×10^{-2} ft^3 = 0.26417 gallons
1 (U.S.) gallon = 231 in.^{3} = 0.1337 ft^3 = 3785 cm^3 = 3.78543 liters = 0.00379 m^3
1 cm^3 = 0.001 liters = 2.642×10^{-4} gallons
1 m^3 = 1000 liters = 264.17047 gallons
1 ft^3 = 7.481 gallons = 28.32 liters

PRESSURE

1 kg/cm^2 = 14.22340 psi ≈ 1.024 ton/ft^2 = 9.76489 metric tons/m^2 =
= 0.967841 atm
1 kg/m^2 = 0.20482 lb/ft^2
1 g/cm^2 = 10 kg/m^2
1 metric ton/m^2 = 0.1 kg/cm^2 = 0.102408 short tons/ft^2
1 psi = 0.07031 kg/cm^2 = 6.804×10^{-2} atm
1 lb/ft^2 = 4.88241 kg/m^2 = 4.725×10^{-4} atm
1 short ton/ft^2 = 9.76489 t/m^2
1 atm = 76.0 cm Hg at 0°C = 29.92 in. Hg at 0°C = 406.8 in. H_2O at +4°C =
= 2117 lb/ft^2 = 14.70 psi = 1.058 short tons/ft^2 = 1.033228 kg/cm^2

UNIT WEIGHT

1 g/cm^3 = 1000 kg/m^3 = 62.43 lb/ft^3
1 kg/m^3 = 0.06243 lb/ft^3 = 0.001 g/cm^3
1 lb/ft^3 = 16.01837 kg/m^3 = 1.602×10^{-2} g/cm^3

VELOCITY

1 cm/sec = 1.969 ft/min = 3.281×10^{-2} ft/sec = 0.036 km/hr =
= 0.0006 km/min = 0.6 m/min = 0.01 m/sec = 2.237×10^{-2} mph
1 m/sec = 100 cm/sec = 196.8 ft/min = 3.281 ft/sec = 3.6 km/hr =
= 0.06 km/hr = 60 m/min = 2.237 mph
1 m/min = 1.667 cm/sec = 3.281 ft/sec = 5.468×10^{-2} ft/sec = 0.06 km/hr =
= 0.001 km/min = 1.667×10^{-2} m/sec = 3.728×10^{-2} mph
1 km/hr = 27.78 cm/sec = 54.68 ft/min = 0.9113 ft/sec = 1.667×10^{-2} km/min =

= 16.67 m/min = 0.2778 m/sec = 0.6214 mph
1 mph = 44.70 cm/sec = 88 ft/min = 1.467 ft/sec = 1.609 km/hr = = 0.4470 m/sec
1 ft/sec = 30.48 cm/sec = 18.29 m/min = 0.3048 m/sec = 60 ft/min = = 1.097 km/hr = 1.829×10^{-2} km/min
1 ft/min = 0.5080 cm/sec = 1.667×10^{-2} ft/sec = 1.829×10^{-2} km/hr = = 3.048×10^{-4} km/min = 0.3048 m/min = 5.080×10^{-3} m/sec
1 in./sec = 2.54 cm/sec

TEMPERATURE

$°C = (5/9)(°F - 32°)$
$°F = (9/5)(°C) + 32°$

HEAT

1 Cal = 3.968 B
1 cal = 0.003968 B
1 Cal/m^2 = 0.369 B/ft^2 = 0.00256 B/in.^{2}
1 Cal/kg = 1.8 B/lb

$$1\ \text{B} = \left(\frac{\text{lb}}{\text{kg}} \cdot \frac{°\text{F}}{°\text{C}}\right) = (0.4535924)\left(\frac{5}{9}\right)\ \text{Cal} = 0.252\ \text{Cal} = 252\ \text{cal}$$

1 B/in. = 9.92112 Cal/m
1 B/ft^2 = 2.713 Cal/m^2
1 B/in.^{2} = 290.6 Cal/m^2
1 B/lb = 0.556 Cal/kg
1 B/(ft^3)(°F) = 160×10^{-4} cal/(cm^3)(°C) = 16 Cal/(m^3)(°C)
1 B/(in.^{2})(hr)(°F) = 703.07 Cal/(m^2)(hr)(°C)
1 B/(in.)(hr)(°F) = 17.858 Cal/(m)(hr)(°C)
1 B/(ft^2)(hr)(°F) = 4.88244 Cal/(m^2)(hr)(°C) = 0.488244 cal/(cm^2)(hr)(°C)
1 B/(ft)(hr)(°F) = 1.48817 Cal/(m)(hr)(°C)
1 B/(lb)(°F) = 1 Cal/(kg)(°C)
1 ft^2/hr = 0.0929 m^2/hr
1 Cal(m^2)(hr)(°C) = 0.0014223 B/(in.^{2})(hr)(°F) = 0.20482 B/(ft^2)(hr)(°F)
1 Cal/(m)(hr)(°C) = 0.055997 B/(in.)(hr)(°F) = 0.67197 B/(ft)(hr)(°F)
1 Cal/m = 0.100795 B/in.
1 Cal/(kg)(°C) = 1.00 B/(lb)(°F)
1 m^2/hr = 10.76387 ft^2/hr

$$1\ \frac{\text{cal}}{\text{cm}^2\text{sec}}\ \frac{\text{cm}}{°\text{C}} = 360\ \frac{\text{Cal}}{\text{m}^2\text{hr}}\ \frac{\text{m}}{°\text{C}} = 241.9\ \frac{\text{B}}{\text{ft}^2\text{hr}}\ \frac{\text{ft}}{°\text{F}} = 4.185\ \frac{\text{watts}}{\text{cm}^2}\ \frac{\text{cm}}{°\text{C}}$$

$$1\ \frac{\text{Cal}}{\text{m}^2\text{hr}}\ \frac{\text{m}}{°\text{C}} = (2.778)(10^{-3})\ \frac{\text{cal}}{\text{cm}^2\text{sec}}\ \frac{\text{cm}}{°\text{C}} = (6.720)(10^{-1})\ \frac{\text{B}}{\text{ft}^2\text{hr}}\ \frac{\text{ft}}{°\text{F}} =$$

$$= (1.163)(10^{-2})\ \frac{\text{watts}}{\text{cm}^2}\ \frac{\text{cm}}{°\text{C}}$$

$$1 \frac{\text{B}}{\text{ft}^2\text{hr}} \frac{\text{ft}}{°\text{F}} = (4.134)(10^{-3}) \frac{\text{cal}}{\text{cm}^2\text{sec}} \frac{\text{cm}}{°\text{C}} = (1.488) \frac{\text{Cal}}{\text{m}^2\text{hr}} \frac{\text{m}}{°\text{F}} =$$

$$= (1.730)(10^{-2}) \frac{\text{watts}}{\text{cm}^2} \frac{\text{cm}}{°\text{C}}$$

$$1 \frac{\text{watts}}{\text{cm}^2} \frac{\text{cm}}{°\text{C}} = (0.2390) \frac{\text{cal}}{\text{cm}^2\text{sec}} \frac{\text{cm}}{°\text{C}} = (86.02) \frac{\text{Cal}}{\text{m}^2\text{hr}} \frac{\text{m}}{°\text{C}} = (57.81) \frac{\text{B}}{\text{ft}^2\text{hr}} \frac{\text{ft}}{°\text{F}}$$

Appendix 3

Specific Gravity of Soils

Soil Types	Specific Gravity G
1	2
Quartzic sand	2.64–2.66
Silts	2.64–2.69
Loess	2.66–2.70
Silty clay	2.69–2.72
Clay	2.44–2.53–2.70–2.85–2.90
Bentonite clay	2.34
Chalk	2.63–2.73–2.81
Humus	1.37
Kaolin	2.47–2.50–2.58
Lime	2.70
Peat	1.26–1.50–1.80
Peat, sphagnum, 25% decomposed	0.50–0.70–0.80
Silt with organic admixtures	2.40–2.50

Appendix 4

Unit Weight of Soil

Unit Weight Formulas

Soil Condition	Degree of Saturation	Unit Weight, Symbol	Unit Weight Formulas $\gamma = f(n)$	$\gamma = f(e)$
1	2	3	4	5
General equation	S	γ	$(1-n)G\gamma_w + nS\gamma_w$	$\frac{eS+G}{1+e} \cdot \gamma_w$
Dry soil	$S = 0$	γ_d	$(1-n)G\gamma_w$	$\frac{G}{1+e} \cdot \gamma_w$
Moist soil	$1 > S > 0$	γ	$(1-n)G\gamma_w + nS\gamma_w$	$\frac{(1+w)G \cdot \gamma_w}{1+e} = \frac{eS+G}{1+e} \cdot \gamma_w$
Saturated soil	$S = 1$	γ_{sat}	$(1-n)G\gamma_w + n\gamma_w$	$\frac{G+e}{1+e} \cdot \gamma_w$
Buoyant (submerged)	–	γ_{sub}	$(1-n)(G-1)\gamma_w$	$\frac{G-1}{1+e} \cdot \gamma_w$

w = moisture content of soil, by dry weight
n = porosity of soil
e = void ratio of soil
G = specific gravity of soil
S = degree of saturation of soil

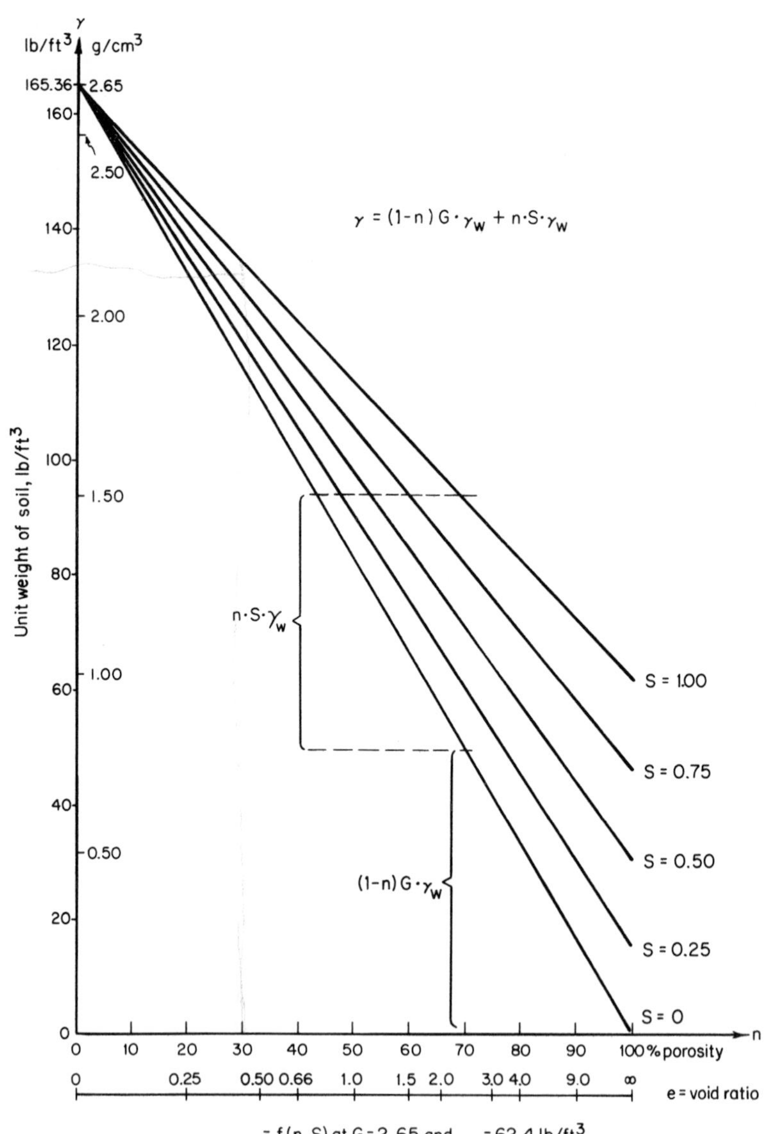

$\gamma = f(n, S)$ at $G = 2.65$ and $\gamma_w = 62.4$ lb/ft^3

Graph for unit weight of soil.

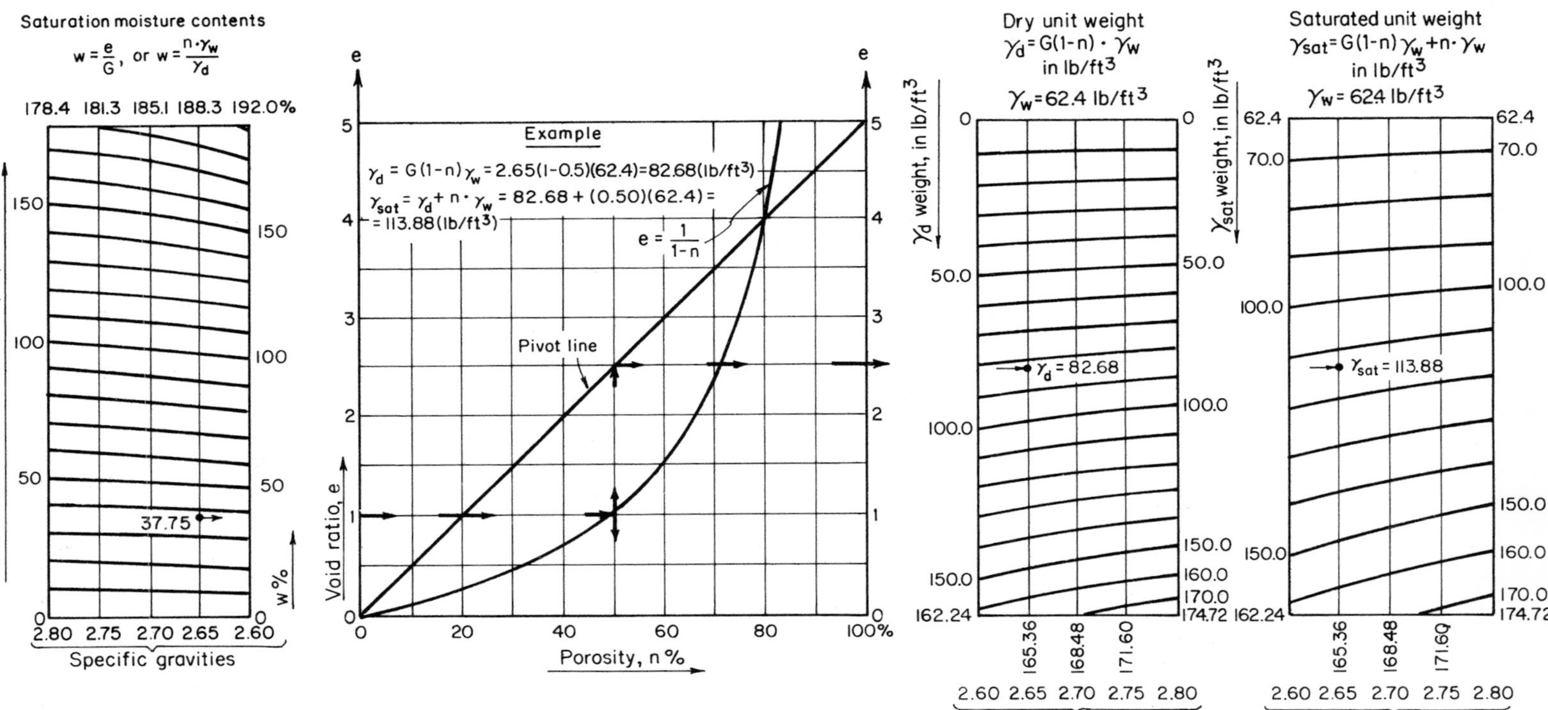

Moisture, porosity, and density relationships of soils (British system of units).

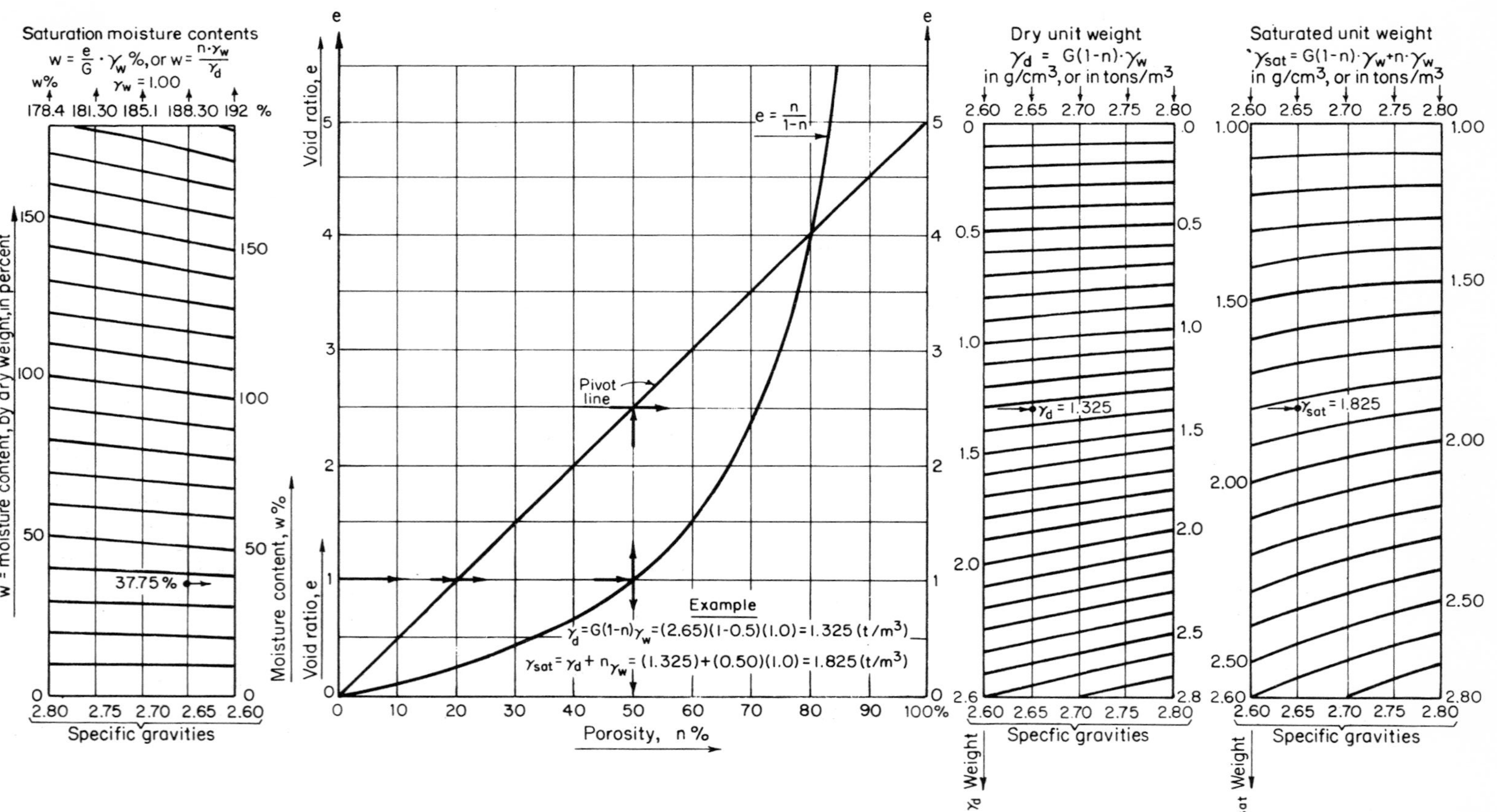

Moisture, porosity, and density relationships of soils (metric system of units).

Values of Unit Weight of Soil and Rock

Soils and Rocks	Unit Weight kg/m^3	Unit Weight lb/ft^3
1	2	3
Asphalt	1100–1500	69–94
Basalt	2400–3100	150–194
Brick, common	1700	105
Brick, fire	2200–2400	135–150
Brick, hard	2000	125
Building wreckage and debris	1400	85
Clay	1800–2600	112–162
Clay, very dense	2000	125
Clay, loose	1800	112
Clay, silty, dry	1600	100
Clay, wet	1800	112
Earth, dry, loose	1200	75
Earth, dense	1500	94
Earth, moist, loose	1300	80
Earth, moist, dense	1600	100
Earth, flowing mud	1700	105
Gneiss	2400–2700	150–168
Granite	2600–2700	162–168
Gravel, dry, loose	1400–1700	87–105
Gravel, dense	1600–1900	100–119
Gravel, dry	1700	105
Gravel, wet	1900–2000	119–125
Gravel and coarse sand, dense	2000	125
Lava, basaltic	2800–3000	174–187
Limestone	2000–2900	125–181
Limy soil, dry	1700	105
Limy soil, wet	2000	125
Loam	1600	100
Loess	1600	100
Peat	1100	68
Sand, fine, clean, dry	1600	100
Sand, dry	1400–1700	87–105
Sand, wet	1900–2000	119–125
Shale	2600–2900	162–181
Silt	1800	112
Slag, furnace	2000–3900	125–243
Slate	2600–3300	162–206
Stone, crushed	1600	100
Traprock	2700–3400	168–212

Appendix 5

Angle ϕ of Internal Friction of Soil

Soil Type	Angle ϕ	tan ϕ
1	2	3
Sand	30°	0.577
Silt and moist clay	25°	0.466
Silty clay, moisture content less than 15%	20°	0.364
Plastic clay	14°	0.249
Coarse soils	24°–35°	0.460–0.700
Clayey soils	12°–40°	0.200–0.850

Appendix 6

Thermal Coefficients of Linear Expansion of Ice

Temperature (°C)	Coefficient α
1	2
0	52.7×10^{-6} [a]
−10	51.7×10^{-6}
−20	50.5×10^{-6}
−30	49.0×10^{-6}
−40	47.4×10^{-6}
−50	45.6×10^{-6}
−60	43.7×10^{-6}
−20 to −1	51.0×10^{-6} [b]

[a] From N. E. Dorsey, *Properties of Ordinary Water-Substance,* Reinhold Publishing Corporation, New York, 1940, p. 473.

[b] From *Handbook of Chemistry,* 3rd ed., edited by N. A. Lange, McGraw-Hill Book Co., Inc., New York, 1961, p. 1678.

Appendix 7

Isopiestic Coefficients of Cubic Expansion of Ice I

Temperature Range (°C)	Coefficient of Thermal Cubical Expansion β per 1°C at 1 atm
1	2
0 to −19.5	155×10^{-6} [a]
− 0.8 to −24	122×10^{-6} [a]
< (−3)	170×10^{-6} [a]
− 0.7 to − 4.7	77×10^{-6} [a]
− 0.4 to −10	152×10^{-6} [a]
−20 to − 1	112.5×10^{-6} [b]
−20 to 0	153×10^{-6} [c]

[a] From N. E. Dorsey, *Properties of Ordinary Water-Substance,* Reinhold Publishing Corporation, New York, 1940, p. 468.

[b] From *Handbook of Chemistry,* 3rd ed., edited by N. A. Lange, McGraw-Hill Book Co., Inc., New York, 1961, p. 1677.

[c] Value of choice.

Appendix 8

Density and Specific Volume of Ice I and Ice III at Melting Points[a]

Type of Ice	Melting Point (°C)	Pressure (atm)	ICE Density (g/cm³)	ICE Spec. Vol. (cm³/g)	WATER Density (g/cm³)	WATER Spec. Vol. (cm³/g)
1	2	3	4	5	6	7
Ice I	0.0	1	0.9168	1.0908	0.9921	1.0008
	−5.0	590	0.9297	1.0756	1.0267	0.9740
	−10.0	1090	0.9397	1.0642	1.0504	0.9520
	−15.0	1540	0.9444	1.0589	1.0671	0.9371
	−20.0	1910	0.9481	1.0547	1.0830	0.9234
	−22.0[b]	2045	0.9483	1.0545	1.0878	0.9193
Ice III	−17.0	3420	1.1595	0.8624	1.1293	0.8855
	−17.0	3420	1.1609	0.8624	1.1293	0.8855
	−18.5	2820	1.1513	0.8686	1.1127	0.8987
	−20.0	2430	1.1476	0.8714	1.1101	0.9085
	−22.0[b]	2045	1.1459	0.8727	1.0878	0.9193

[a] From N. E. Dorsey, *Properties of Ordinary Water-Substance*, Reinhold Publishing Corporation, New York, 1940, p. 467.

[b] Triple point, water and two ices.

Appendix 9

Latent Heat of Fusion of Ice and Other Common Substances

Substance	Melting Point T_m (°C)	Latent Heat of Fusion L (cal/g)
1	2	3
Ice [a]	− 6.5	76.03
Ice [a]	0	79.67
Ice [b]	0	79.69
Ice	0	80 [c]
Ice from sea-water	− 8.0	54 [c]
Carbon dioxide, solid	− 78.5	45.3 Cal/kg
Mercury [d]	− 38.85	3
Paraffin	52	35
Salt, NaCl [e]	804	124
Sulphur	119	13
Ammonia	− 75	108.0
Ether	−116.2	
Helium	−272.2	

[a] From G. W. C. Kaye and T. H. Laby, *Tables of Physical and Chemical Constants*, Longmans, Green and Co., London, 10th ed., 1948, p. 75.

[b] From *International Critical Tables*, McGraw-Hill Book Co., Inc., New York, 1929. Published for the National Research Council of the U.S.A., vol. 5, p. 131.

[c] Value of choice. [d] Specific gravity, 13.59. [e] Specific gravity, 2.161.

Appendix 10

Specific Heat of Various Substances

Substance	Temperature (°C)	Specific Heat c_{sp}
1	2	3
Kaolin	20 to 98	0.224
Quartz sand	20 to 98	0.191
Mica	20 to 98	0.2061
Granite	12 to 100	0.192
Sandstone	–	0.220
Limestone	15 to 100	0.216
Quartz	12 to 100	0.188
Glass, flint	10 to 50	0.117
Air	0 to 200	0.2375
Water	3.5	1.000
Ice	–18 to –78	0.463
Asbestos	20 to 98	0.195
Wood	20	0.327
Paraffin	–	0.481
Asphalt cement	–	0.400

Appendix 11

Specific Heat of Ice

Temperature (°C)	Specific Heat c_{sp}
1	2
0	0.4873 [a]
−10	0.4770
−20	0.4647 [b]
−30	0.4504 [c]
−40	0.4340
−50	0.4160

[a] Specific heat 0.502 at −1°C to −21°C, according to G. W. C. Kaye and T. H. Laby, *Tables of Physical and Chemical Constants,* Longmans, Green and Co., London, 1948, p. 75.

[b] Specific heat 0.462 at −20°C, according to *International Critical Tables,* McGraw-Hill Book Co., Inc. (published for the National Research Council of the U.S.A.), 1929, vol. 5, p. 95.

[c] H. T. Barnes, *Ice Engineering,* Renouf Publishing Co., Montreal, 1928, p. 38.

Appendix 12

Freezing Temperatures of Calcium Chloride and Sodium Chloride Brine at Various Concentrations

Concentration (%)	FREEZING TEMPERATURE (°F)	
	Calcium Chloride Brine	Sodium Chloride Brine
1	2	3
5	29.0	27.0
10	23.0	20.0
15	12.5	12.0
20	–3.0	1.8
21	–5.5	–0.8
22	–10.5	–3.0
23	–15.5	–6.0
24	–20.5	+3.8
25	–25.0	+16.1

Appendix 13

Thermal Conductivity of Ice

Temperature (°C)	Conductivity K	
	cal/(cm)(sec)(°C)	milliwatts/(cm)(°C)
1	2	3
0	5.258×10^{-3} [a]	22.4 [a]
−10	5.54×10^{-3} [b]	23.2 [b]
−20	5.81×10^{-3}	24.3
−30	6.09×10^{-3}	25.5
−40	6.36×10^{-3}	26.6

[a] Source: *International Critical Tables,* McGraw-Hill Book Co., Inc., New York, 1927. Published for the National Research Council of the U.S.A., 1st ed.. Vol. 2, p. 315.

[b] From N. E. Dorsey, *Properties of Ordinary Water-Substance,* Reinhold Publishing Corporation, New York, 1940, p. 482.

Appendix 14

Thermal Conductivity of Various Substances

Comparison of Various Substances

Material	Unit Weight (kg/m³)	Thermal Conductivity K [Cal/(m)(hr)(°C)]	Heat Capacity C (Cal/kg)
1	2	3	4
Asbestos sheets, 1 to 5 mm thick	900	0.15	0.20
Asphalt	1800	0.65	–
Basalt, at 20°C	2400–3100	1.44	0.20
Ash, timber, air-dry	450–500	0.1–0.13	0.18
Cinder, dry	700–1000	0.06–0.25	0.18
Clay, at 0°C	1800–2600	2.83	0.224
Concrete, $T = 70°C$	–	0.77	0.156
Cork plates, natural	250	0.06	0.50
Felt, technical	150–250	0.04–0.05	0.45
Glass wool	200	0.05	–
Granite, $T = 20°C$ to 100°C	2650–2700	7.32	0.20
Ice	900	1.90	0.50
Ice, –20°C	900	2.00	0.505
Mineral wool	200	0.06	–
Moss, sphagnum, air-dry	135	0.04	0.40
Peat moss plates, air-dry	170–250	0.05–0.06	0.50
air-dry	800–1000	0.26–0.40	0.39–0.87
Peat, pressed, moist	1140	0.59	0.39
Plywood	600	0.15	0.65
Sawdust, air-dry	150–250	0.05–0.08	0.60
Sand	1600–1800	1.70–2.10	0.20
Snow, loose	300	0.20	0.50
Snow, dense	500	0.50	0.50
Tarpaper	600	0.15–0.20	0.36
Topsoil	1800	1.00	–
Water	1000	0.50	1.00

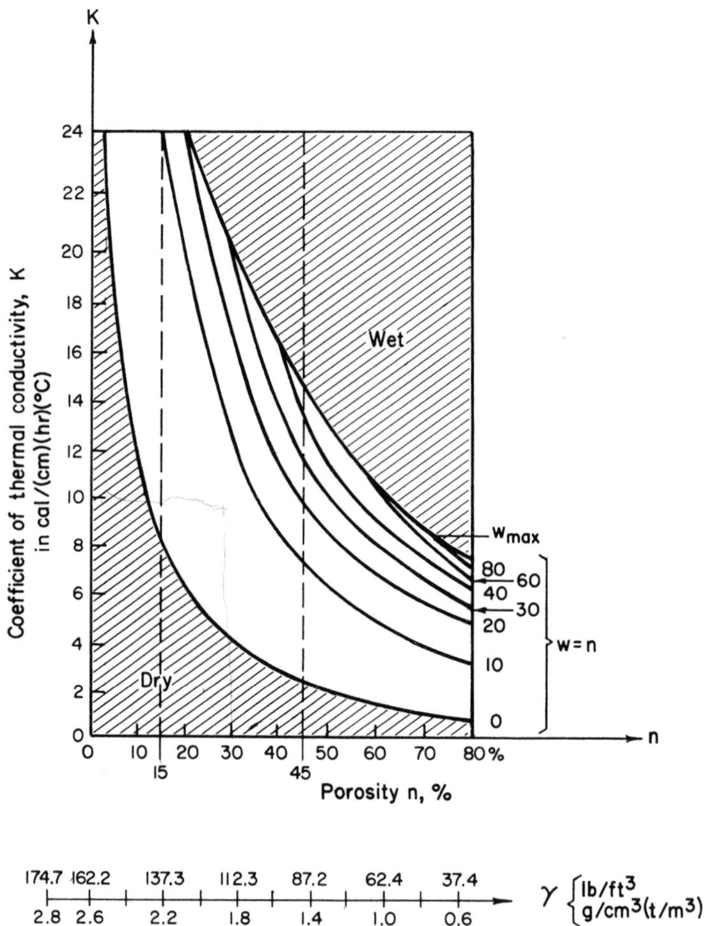

Dependence of coefficient of thermal conductivity K of soil upon porosity n, unit weight γ_s, and moisture content w of soil after Krischer (see K. H. Seydel, Ref. 2 in Part III).

Appendix 15

Values of Gauss' Error Function or Probability Integral*

$$G(\beta) = G(x\eta) = \frac{2}{\sqrt{\pi}} \int_{\beta=0}^{\beta=x\eta} e^{-\beta^2}\, d\beta$$

$\beta = x\eta = \dfrac{x}{2\sqrt{\alpha t}}$	$G(\beta) = G(x\eta)$	$\beta = x\eta = \dfrac{x}{2\sqrt{\alpha t}}$	$G(\beta) = G(x\eta)$
1	2	1	2
0.00	0.0000		
0.01	0.0113	0.16	0.1790
0.02	0.0226	0.17	0.1900
0.03	0.0338	0.18	0.2009
0.04	0.0451	0.19	0.2118
0.05	0.0564	0.20	0.2227
0.06	0.0676	0.21	0.2335
0.07	0.0789	0.22	0.2443
0.08	0.0901	0.23	0.2550
0.09	0.1013	0.24	0.2657
0.10	0.1125	0.25	0.2763
0.11	0.1236	0.26	0.2869
0.12	0.1348	0.27	0.2974
0.13	0.1459	0.28	0.3079
0.14	0.1569	0.29	0.3183
0.15	0.1680	0.30	0.3286

$\beta = x\eta = \dfrac{x}{2\sqrt{\alpha t}}$	$G(\beta) = G(x\eta)$	$\beta = x\eta = \dfrac{x}{2\sqrt{\alpha t}}$	$G(\beta) = G(x\eta)$
1	2	1	2
0.31	0.3389	0.71	0.6847
0.32	0.3491	0.72	0.6914
0.33	0.3593	0.73	0.6981
0.34	0.3694	0.74	0.7047
0.35	0.3794	0.75	0.7112
0.36	0.3893	0.76	0.7115
0.37	0.3992	0.77	0.7238
0.38	0.4090	0.78	0.7300
0.39	0.4187	0.79	0.7361
0.40	0.4284	0.80	0.7421
0.41	0.4380	0.81	0.7480
0.42	0.4475	0.82	0.7538
0.43	0.4569	0.83	0.7595
0.44	0.4662	0.84	0.7651
0.45	0.4755	0.85	0.7707
0.46	0.4847	0.86	0.7761
0.47	0.4937	0.87	0.7814
0.48	0.5027	0.88	0.7867
0.49	0.5117	0.89	0.7918
0.50	0.5205	0.90	0.7969
0.51	0.5292	0.91	0.8019
0.52	0.5379	0.92	0.8068
0.53	0.5465	0.93	0.8116
0.54	0.5549	0.94	0.8163
0.55	0.5563	0.95	0.8209
0.56	0.5716	0.96	0.8254
0.57	0.5798	0.97	0.8299
0.58	0.5879	0.98	0.8342
0.59	0.5959	0.99	0.8385
0.60	0.6039	1.00	0.8427
0.61	0.6117	1.01	0.8468
0.62	0.6194	1.02	0.8508
0.63	0.6270	1.03	0.8548
0.64	0.6346	1.04	0.8586
0.65	0.6420	1.05	0.8624
0.66	0.6494	1.06	0.8661
0.67	0.6566	1.07	0.8698
0.68	0.6638	1.08	0.8733
0.69	0.6808	1.09	0.8768
0.70	0.6778	1.10	0.8802

$\beta = x\eta = \dfrac{x}{2\sqrt{\alpha t}}$	$G(\beta) = G(x\eta)$	$\beta = x\eta = \dfrac{x}{2\sqrt{\alpha t}}$	$G(\beta) = G(x\eta)$
1	2	1	2
1.12	0.8868	1.72	0.9850
1.14	0.8931	1.74	0.9861
1.16	0.8991	1.76	0.9872
1.18	0.9048	1.78	0.9882
1.20	0.9103	1.80	0.9891
1.22	0.9155	1.82	0.9899
1.24	0.9205	1.84	0.9907
1.26	0.9252	1.86	0.9915
1.28	0.9297	1.88	0.9922
1.30	0.9340	1.90	0.9928
1.32	0.9381	1.92	0.9934
1.34	0.9419	1.94	0.9939
1.36	0.9456	1.96	0.9944
1.38	0.9490	1.98	0.9949
1.40	0.9523	2.00	0.99532
1.42	0.9554	2.10	0.99702
1.44	0.9583	2.20	0.99814
1.46	0.9611	2.30	0.99886
1.48	0.9624	2.40	0.99931
1.50	0.9661	2.50	0.99959
1.52	0.9684	2.60	0.99976
1.54	0.9706	2.70	0.99987
1.56	0.9726	2.80	0.999925
1.58	0.9745	2.90	0.999959
1.60	0.9763	3.00	1.000000
1.62	0.9780		
1.64	0.9796		
1.66	0.9811		
1.68	0.9825		
1.70	0.9838		

* Reprinted by permission of the publisher, from B. O. Pierce and R. M. Foster, *A Short Table of Integrals*, 4th edition, Blaisdell Publishing Company (New York, 1956), pp. 128–32.

Appendix 16

F. Neumann's Theory

Originally, Franz Neumann developed his theory to study the formation of ice upon freezing of still water (*1*, *2*, *3*). However, by properly fitting geotechnical soil constants into this theory, it can be applied also to the frost penetration problem in soils.

EQUATIONS

Neumann gives two partial differential equations for ice and water, or, in terms of soils, for a moist, isotropic, semi-infinite body. It is assumed that the initial temperature, T_o, of such a soil is positive and constant. Then, by a sudden lowering of the surface temperature, T_s, to a new constant and freezing value, the cooling process is inaugurated. In the formulas below, index figure "1" refers to the frozen part of the soil. Index "2" refers to the unfrozen part of the soil.

The two partial differential equations are:

1) for the frozen part of the soil ($0 < x < \xi$):

$$\frac{\partial T_1}{\partial t} = \alpha_1 \cdot \frac{\partial^2 T_1}{\partial x^2} \tag{16-1}$$

and

2) for the unfrozen part ($x > \xi$):

$$\frac{\partial T_2}{\partial t} = \alpha_2 \cdot \frac{\partial^2 T_2}{\partial x^2}. \tag{16-2}$$

Here the symbols used are the same as in previous chapters.

BOUNDARY CONDITIONS

The following are the boundary conditions:

1) The initial conditions: at $x > 0$, $t = 0$, $T_1 = T_o = \text{const.}$ (16-3)

2) The fixed boundary conditions:

a) At $x = 0$, $t \geqslant 0$, $T_1 = T_s$. (16-4)

b) When $x \to \infty$, $t \geqslant 0$, $T_2 \to T_o = \text{const}$. (16-5)

c) The condition at the advancing isothermal surface of the frozen layer downwards: at $x = \xi$, $t > 0$, $T_1 = T_2 = \text{const} = T_f = 32°\text{F}$, where T_f = freezing temperature. (16-6)

The course of the temperature distribution can be pursued from Fig. 16-1.

HEAT BALANCE

The heat balance at the frost boundary, where $x = \xi$, is determined by reasoning as follows: at $x = \xi$, the temperature is 32°F. On advancing the frost boundary an amount of $d\xi$ in time dt, a frozen volume, $dv = A \cdot d\xi$, results. If the moisture content of the soil is $w\%$ by dry weight, then the quantity of

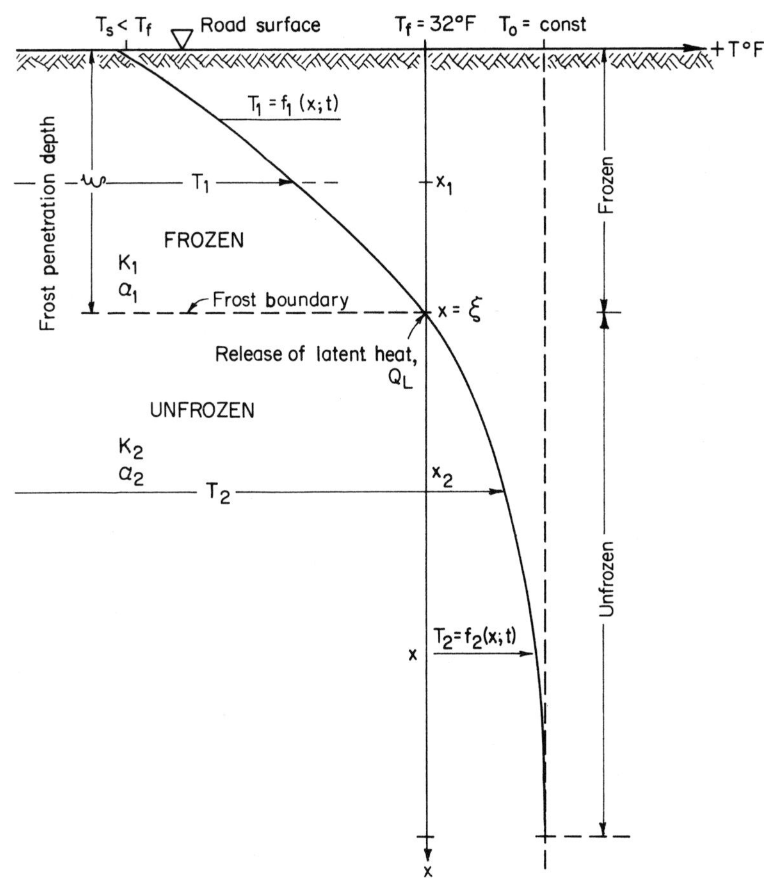

FIG. 16-1 Temperature profile (tautochrone).

moisture in the soil per unit of volume is

$$\rho_s \cdot w,$$

where ρ_s is the density of ice, viz., frozen soil.

The latent heat of fusion, Q_L, of ice is

$$Q_L \cdot \rho_s \cdot w,$$

where

$$Q_L = 144 \left[\frac{\mathrm{B}}{\mathrm{lb}}\right].$$

The amount of heat set free during an increase in thickness of ice by an amount of $d\xi$ in time dt through the area A is

$$Q = Q_L \cdot \rho_s \cdot w \cdot A \cdot d\xi. \tag{16-7}$$

Because of the continuity of heat flow, this amount of heat together with the heat from the unfrozen soil must be conducted upward through the isothermal surface of the road through the frozen layer of soil:

$$\overbrace{-K_1 \cdot \left[\left(\frac{\partial T_1}{\partial x}\right)_{x=\xi} \cdot A \cdot dt\right]}^{\text{heat flowing upward through the frozen soil}} =$$

$$= \overbrace{-Q_L \cdot \rho_s \cdot w \cdot A \cdot d\xi}^{\text{heat set free}} \overbrace{-K_2 \left[\left(\frac{\partial T_2}{\partial x}\right)_{x=\xi} \cdot A \cdot dt\right]}^{\text{heat from unfrozen soil}}. \tag{16-8}$$

Because no other heat sources are considered here, the algebraic sum of the three kinds of heat must be in balance, i.e., zero. Equation (16-8) represents a double surface condition.

RATE OF FROST PENETRATION

From Equation (16-8), the rate of frost penetration is

$$\frac{d\xi}{dt} = \frac{1}{Q_L \cdot \rho_s \cdot w} \cdot \left[K_1 \cdot \left(\frac{\partial T}{\partial x}\right)_{x=\xi} - K_2 \cdot \left(\frac{\partial T}{\partial x}\right)_{x=\xi}\right]. \tag{16-9}$$

Solution, The Gauss's error integral, of the form

$$G(X) = G(x\eta) = \frac{2}{\sqrt{\pi}} \cdot \int_0^{x\eta} (e^{-\beta^2}) \cdot d\beta,$$

is a solution of the differential Equations (16-1), (16-2) and (16-9) (3). It should be noted that for $x = 0$, $G(x \cdot \eta) = 0$, and for $x = \infty$, $G(x \cdot \eta) = 1$.

If

$$\eta_1 = \frac{1}{2\sqrt{\alpha_1 \cdot t}} \text{ and } \eta_2 = \frac{1}{2 \cdot \sqrt{\alpha_2 \cdot t}},$$

then the solutions of the partial differential Equations (16-1) and (16-2) are

$$T_1 = B_1 + D_1 \cdot G(x\eta_1) \quad (0 < x \leqslant \xi) \tag{16-10}$$

and

$$T_2 = B_2 + D_2 \cdot G(x\eta_2) \quad (x \geqslant \xi), \tag{16-11}$$

respectively.

Here B_1, D_1, B_2 and D_2 are constants.

The boundary condition (2c), Equation (16-6), implies that when $x = \xi$, $G(x \cdot \eta_1)$ and $G(x \cdot \eta_2)$ must each be constant. This is possible only when $x = 0$, $x = \infty$ or when the frost penetration depth, $x = \xi$ (= thickness of the frozen soil layer), is proportional to $\sqrt{t}$:

$$\xi = m \cdot \sqrt{t}, \tag{16-12}$$

where m = a constant.

So that the solutions (16-10) and (16-11) may satisfy Equations (16-4), (16-6) and (16-8), adjust the boundary conditions, Equations (16-3) to (16-6), to Equations (16-10) and (16-11), and using Equation (16-12), obtain

$$B_1 = T_1 = T_s, \tag{16-13}$$

$$B_1 + D_1 \cdot G\left(\frac{m}{2 \cdot \sqrt{\alpha_1}}\right) = T_f = 32°\text{F}, \tag{16-14}$$

$$B_2 + D_2 \cdot G\left(\frac{m}{2 \cdot \sqrt{\alpha_2}}\right) = T_f = 32°\text{F}, \tag{16-15}$$

where T_f = freezing temperature.

If $x = \infty$, then $G(x \cdot \eta) = 1$, and

$$B_2 + D_2 = T_2 = T_o. \tag{16-16}$$

For the purpose of developing Equation (16-9), combine it with Equations (16-10), (16-11) and (16-12). Differentiation of the latter three equations gives:

1) from Equation (16-12),

$$\frac{d\xi}{dt} = \frac{m}{2 \cdot \sqrt{t}}; \tag{16-17}$$

2) differentiating Equation (16-10):

$$\left(\frac{\partial T_1}{\partial x}\right)_{x=\xi} = \frac{\partial}{\partial x}\{B_1 + [D_1 \cdot G(x \cdot \eta_1)]\} =$$

$$= D_1 \cdot \left[\frac{\partial\left(\frac{2}{\sqrt{\pi}}\int_o^{\beta = x \cdot \eta_1}(e^{-\beta^2}) \cdot d\beta\right)}{\partial(x \cdot \eta_1)} \cdot \frac{\partial(x \cdot \eta_1)}{\partial(x)}\right] =$$

$$= \frac{D_1}{\sqrt{\alpha_1 \cdot \pi \cdot t}} \cdot \left(e^{-\frac{m^2}{4 \cdot \alpha_1}}\right); \tag{16-18}$$

3) differentiating Equation (16-11):

$$\left(\frac{\partial T_2}{\partial x}\right)_{x=\xi} = \frac{\partial}{\partial x}\{B_2 + [D_2 \cdot G(x \cdot \eta_2)]\} =$$

$$= \frac{D_2}{\sqrt{\alpha_2 \cdot \pi \cdot t}} \cdot \left(e^{-\frac{m^2}{4 \cdot \alpha_2}}\right). \tag{16-19}$$

Substituting Equations (16-17), (16-18) and (16-19) into Equation (16-9), we obtain

$$\frac{Q_L \cdot \rho_s \cdot \sqrt{\pi} \cdot w \cdot m}{2 \cdot \sqrt{t}} = \frac{K_1 \cdot D_1}{\sqrt{\alpha_1 \cdot t}} \cdot \left(e^{-\frac{m^2}{4 \cdot \alpha_1}}\right) - \frac{K_2 \cdot D_2}{\sqrt{\alpha_2 \cdot t}} \cdot \left(e^{-\frac{m^2}{4 \cdot \alpha_2}}\right). \tag{16-20}$$

The solution of Equations (16-13) to (16-16) for D_1 and D_2 gives

$$D_1 = \frac{T_f - B_1}{G\left(\frac{m}{2 \cdot \sqrt{\alpha_1}}\right)} = \frac{T_f - T_s}{G\left(\frac{m}{2 \cdot \sqrt{\alpha_1}}\right)}, \tag{16-21}$$

and

$$D_2 = \frac{T_o - T_f}{1 - G\left(\frac{m}{2 \cdot \sqrt{\alpha_2}}\right)}. \tag{16-22}$$

Substituting Equations (16-21) and (16-22) into Equation (16-20), we obtain

$$\frac{Q_L \cdot \rho_s \cdot \sqrt{\pi} \cdot w \cdot m}{2} =$$

$$= b_1 \cdot (T_f - T_s) \cdot \frac{e^{-\frac{m^2}{4 \cdot \alpha_1}}}{G\left(\frac{m}{2 \cdot \sqrt{\alpha_1}}\right)} - b_2 \cdot (T_o - T_f) \cdot \frac{e^{-\frac{m^2}{4 \cdot \alpha_2}}}{1 - G\left(\frac{m}{2 \cdot \sqrt{\alpha_2}}\right)}, \tag{16-23}$$

where

$$b_1 = \frac{K_1}{\sqrt{\alpha_1}} = \sqrt{K_1 \cdot c_1 \cdot \rho_1}, \tag{16-24}$$

and

$$b_2 = \frac{K_2}{\sqrt{\alpha_2}} = \sqrt{K_2 \cdot c_2 \cdot \rho_2}. \tag{16-25}$$

SOLUTION OF TRANSCENDENTAL FUNCTION

Equation (16-23) is a transcendental function with one unknown, m. It can be solved best graphically. We designate this equation as follows:

$$C \cdot m = f(m),$$

where C is a constant.

$$Y_1 = C \cdot m \text{ [a straight line through (0;0)].} \tag{16-26}$$

$$Y_2 = F(m) \text{ (a transcendental curve).} \tag{16-27}$$

Then,

$$Y_1 = Y_2. \tag{16-28}$$

Plot the line, $Y_1 = C \cdot m$, and the curve, $Y_2 = F(m)$. The intersection of these two Y-functions gives an abscissa, m, which is the only root possible in order that both sides of Equation (16-23) be equal.

By means of this value of m, the frost penetration depth, ξ, can be calculated (Equation 16-12). From this equation, it follows that the penetration of the frozen layer (viz., ice) increases in direct proportion to the square root of the time, and that the process of ice formation takes place more slowly with the increase in depth. Also, the coefficients B_1 (Equation 16-13), D_1 (Equation 16-21), B_2 (Equation 16-14) and D_2 (Equation 16-22) can be calculated, which, upon substitution into Equations (16-10) and (16-11), allow the temperature to be calculated at any point below the surface and at any time, and to plot the temperature profile or tautochrone * as indicated in Fig. 16-1.

TEMPERATURE EQUATIONS

Now the temperature (Equations 16-10 and 16-11) can be expressed as follows:

For the frozen zone:

$$T_1 = T_s + (T_f - T_s) \cdot \frac{G\left(\dfrac{x}{2\sqrt{\alpha_1 \cdot t}}\right)}{G\left(\dfrac{m}{2\sqrt{\alpha_1}}\right)}. \tag{16-29}$$

Check:

1) for $x = 0$, $t > 0$, $G(x\eta_1) = 0$, and $T_1 = T_s$;

2) for $x = \xi$, $t > 0$, $G(x\eta_1) = G\left(\dfrac{m}{2\sqrt{\alpha_1}}\right)$, and $T_1 = T_f = 32°$ F.

---

* In this work the term "tautochrone" is used to denote a curve showing the vertical distribution of temperature in the ground at a given moment of time.

For the unfrozen zone:

$$\overbrace{B_2 = T_o - D_2}^{\text{Eq. 16-16}} = T_o - \frac{\overbrace{(T_o - T_f)}^{\text{Eq. 16-22}}}{1 - G\left(\frac{m}{2\sqrt{\alpha_2}}\right)},$$

and

$$T_2 = T_o - \overbrace{\frac{T_o - T_f}{1 - G\left(\frac{m}{2\sqrt{\alpha_2}}\right)}}^{B_2} + \overbrace{\frac{T_o - T_f}{1 - G\left(\frac{m}{2\sqrt{\alpha_2}}\right)}}^{D_2} \cdot G\left(\frac{x}{2\sqrt{\alpha_2 \cdot t}}\right), \qquad (16\text{-}11)$$

or

$$T_2 = T_o - (T_o - T_f) \cdot \frac{\left[1 - G\left(\frac{x}{2\sqrt{\alpha_2 \cdot t}}\right)\right]}{\left[1 - G\left(\frac{m}{2\sqrt{\alpha_2}}\right)\right]}. \qquad (16\text{-}30)$$

Check:

1) for $x = \xi$, $G(x\eta_2) = G\left(\frac{m}{2\sqrt{\alpha_2}}\right)$, and $T_2 = T_1 = T_f = 32°\text{F}$;
2) for $x = \infty$, $G(x\eta_2) = 1$, and $T_2 = T_o$;
3) for $t = 0$, $G(x\eta_2) = 1$, and $T_2 = T_o$.

If we take $T_s > t_f = 32°\text{F}$ and $T_o < T_f = 32°\text{F}$, the theory then represents the laws of fusion of ice, viz., thawing. In the case of thawing, quantities K_1, α_1, c_1 apply to the unfrozen zone, while K_2, α_2 and c_2 apply to the frozen zone.

Sample Problem

Physical constants: Voids ratio, $e = 0.50$; specific gravity of the soil (sand), $\gamma_s = 2.65$.

Unit weight of dry soil, $\rho_{dr\,s} = (2.65) \cdot (62.4) \cdot \left(1 - \frac{0.50}{1.50}\right) = 110.45 \left(\frac{\text{lb}}{\text{ft}^3}\right).$

Moisture content: $W_w = \gamma_{w \cdot n} = (62.4) \cdot (0.33) \qquad = \;\; 20.60 \left(\frac{\text{lb}}{\text{ft}^3}\right).$

$$\rho_s = 131.05 \left(\frac{\text{lb}}{\text{ft}^3}\right).$$

20.6 lb of moisture $= \left(\frac{20.60}{110.45}\right)(100) = 18.7\%$ by dry weight, or 15.75% by wet weight.

Thermal constants: Assume prior to freezing:

Coefficient of thermal conductivity,

$$K_2 = (1.07)[(\mathrm{B}) \cdot (\mathrm{ft}^{-2}) \cdot (\mathrm{hr})^{-1} \cdot (\mathrm{F})^{-1}/\mathrm{ft}].$$

Volumetric heat capacity:

$$C_2 = \rho_{drs} \cdot c_s + w \cdot c_w = (110.45) \cdot (0.20) + (20.60) \cdot (1.0) = 42.7 \left[\frac{\mathrm{B}}{(\mathrm{ft}^3) \cdot (\mathrm{F})}\right],$$

where $c_s = 0.20$ and $c_w = 1.0$ are heat capacities of unfrozen soil and water, respectively.

Thermal diffusivity:

$$\alpha_2 = \frac{K_2}{C_2} = \frac{1.067}{42.70} = 0.025\ [(\mathrm{ft})^2 \cdot (\mathrm{h})^{-1}].$$

Coefficient b_2 for Equation (16-23):

$$b_2 = \sqrt{K_2 \cdot \rho_s \cdot c_s} = \sqrt{K_2 \cdot C_2} = \sqrt{(1.07) \cdot (42.7)} = 6.80 \qquad (16\text{-}25a)$$

Assume after freezing: Coefficient of thermal conductivity (25% greater than before freezing),

$$K_1 = (1.25) \cdot K_2 = (1.25) \cdot (1.07) = 1.34\ [(\mathrm{B}) \cdot (\mathrm{ft})^{-2} \cdot (\mathrm{F})^{-1} \cdot (\mathrm{hr})^{-1}/\mathrm{ft}].$$

Volumetric heat capacity:

$$C_1 = (110.45) \cdot (0.20) + (20.60) \cdot (0.35) = 29.30 \left[\frac{\mathrm{B}}{(\mathrm{ft}^3) \cdot (\mathrm{F})}\right],$$

where $c = 0.35$ is the assumed value for the heat capacity of ice.

Thermal diffusivity:

$$\alpha_1 = \frac{K_1}{C_1} = \frac{1.34}{29.30} = 0.046\ [(\mathrm{ft})^2 \cdot (\mathrm{hr})^{-1}].$$

Coefficient b_1 for Equation (16-23):

$$b_1 = \sqrt{K_1 \cdot C_1} = \sqrt{(1.34) \cdot (29.30)} = 6.30. \qquad (16\text{-}24a)$$

Temperatures:

Before freezing, $T_o = 36°\mathrm{F}$

Temperature of the frozen ground surface, $T_s = 14.0°\mathrm{F}$

The coefficient of proportionality, m:

$$Y_1 = \frac{\sqrt{\pi} \cdot Q_L \cdot \rho_s \cdot w \cdot m}{2} = \frac{(1.7725) \cdot (144) \cdot (131.1) \cdot (0.1575)}{2} \cdot m =$$

$$= (2635.13) \cdot (m). \qquad (16\text{-}26a)$$

Graphically, this equation represents a straight line through the origin of the coordinates.

$$Y_2 = F(m) = (6.30) \cdot (32-14) \cdot \frac{e^{-\frac{m^2}{4(0.046)}}}{G\left(\frac{m}{2\sqrt{0.046}}\right)} - (6.80) \cdot (36-32) \cdot \frac{e^{-\frac{m^2}{4(0.025)}}}{1 - G\left(\frac{m}{2\sqrt{0.025}}\right)}$$

$$= (113.4) \cdot \frac{e^{-\frac{m^2}{0.184}}}{G\left(\frac{m}{0.428}\right)} - (27.2) \cdot \frac{e^{-\frac{m^2}{0.100}}}{1 - G\left(\frac{m}{0.316}\right)}. \qquad (16\text{-}27a)$$

The graphical solution by plotting $Y_1 = Y_2$ furnishes $m = 0.1174$ (see Fig. 16-2).

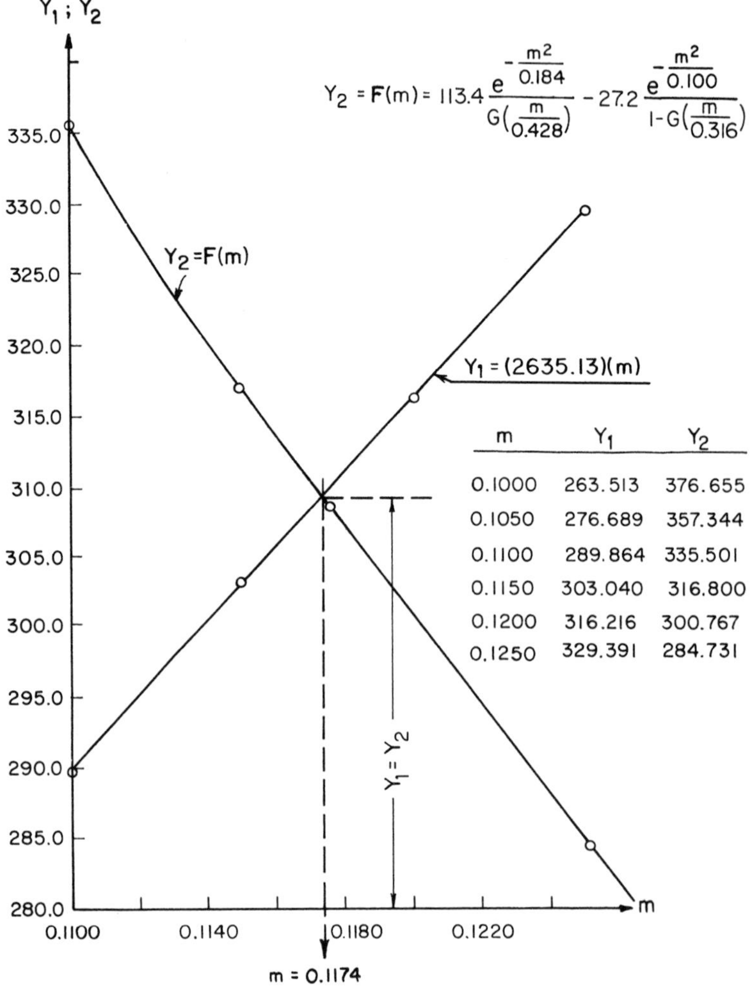

m	Y_1	Y_2
0.1000	263.513	376.655
0.1050	276.689	357.344
0.1100	289.864	335.501
0.1150	303.040	316.800
0.1200	316.216	300.767
0.1250	329.391	284.731

FIG. 16-2 Graphic solution of the transcendental equation (16-23).

The frost penetration depth:

$$\xi = m \cdot \sqrt{t} = (0.1174) \cdot \sqrt{t}. \tag{16-12a}$$

In 7 days = 168 hr the frost penetration depth is

$$\xi_{168} = (0.1174) \cdot \sqrt{168} = (0.1174) \cdot (12.965) = 1.520\ [\text{ft}] = 18.24\ [\text{in.}].$$

The temperature profile (tautochrone) for t = 168 hr:

1) For the frozen zone (Eq. 16-29):

$$T_1 = T_s + (T_f - T_s) \cdot \frac{G\left(\dfrac{x}{2\sqrt{\alpha_1 \cdot t}}\right)}{G\left(\dfrac{m}{2\sqrt{\alpha_1}}\right)} = 14 + (32 - 14) \cdot \frac{G\left(\dfrac{x}{2\sqrt{(0.046) \cdot (168)}}\right)}{G\left(\dfrac{0.1174}{2\sqrt{0.046}}\right)} =$$

$$= 14 + (18) \cdot \frac{G\left(\dfrac{x}{5.560}\right)}{0.3008} \tag{16-29a}$$

2) For the unfrozen zone:

$$T_2 = T_o - (T_o - T_f) \cdot \frac{\left[1 - G\left(\dfrac{x}{2\sqrt{\alpha_2 \cdot t}}\right)\right]}{\left[1 - G\left(\dfrac{m}{2\sqrt{\alpha_2}}\right)\right]} =$$

$$= 36 - (36 - 32) \cdot \frac{\left[1 - G\left(\dfrac{x}{2\sqrt{(0.025) \cdot (168)}}\right)\right]}{\left[1 - G\left(\dfrac{0.1174}{2\sqrt{0.025}}\right)\right]} = 36 - (4) \cdot \frac{\left[1 - G\left(\dfrac{x}{4.098}\right)\right]}{0.6002}. \tag{16-30a}$$

This illustrative problem is shown graphically by Fig. 16-3.

TABLE 16-1. Temperature Profile Ordinates After Seven Days.

Depth x, ft	T_1 °F	T_2 °F	Remarks
0	$14.0 = T_s$	...	Frozen Zone
0.5	20.1	...	
1.0	26.0	...	
1.5	31.8	...	
1.52	$32.0 = T_f$	$32 = T_f$	
2.0	...	32.8	Cooled Zone
3.0	...	34.0	
4.0	...	34.9	
5.0	...	35.4	
8.0	...	35.9	
10.0	...	35.997	

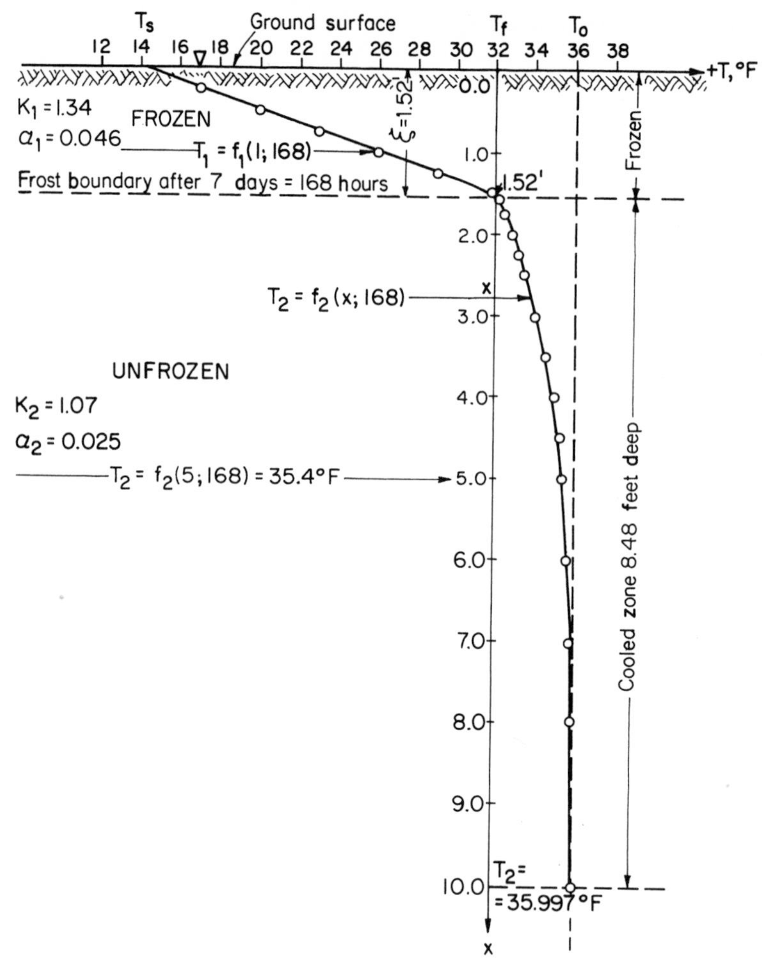

FIG. 16-3 Temperature profile after 7 days; $\xi = 1.52$ ft.

REFERENCES

1. H. M. Weber, *Die Partiellen Differential-Gleichungen der mathematischen Physik nach Riemanns Vorlesungen*, Braunschweig, 1901, Friedrich Vieweg, Vol. 2, §49, pp. 118–122.
2. S. Tetsu Tamura, "Mathem cal Theory of Ice Formation," *Monthly Weather Review and Annual Summary*, Washington, D.C., U.S. Department of Agriculture, Weather Bureau, 1906, Vol. 33, February 1905, pp. 55–57.
3. A. R. Jumikis, *The Frost Penetration Problem in Highway Engineering*, New Brunswick, New Jersey, 1955, Rutgers University Press, pp. 77–87.

Appendix 17

Stefan's Solution

GENERAL CASE

J. Stefan (*1, 2, 3, 4*) gives a simple formula for the formation of ice which can be applied for computing the frost penetration depth as a function of time. He assumed that

1) the temperature, T_o, of the water at the isothermal boundary surface, between the frozen and the unfrozen zone, is 32°F, and that this is also so below the frost boundary;
2) the surface temperature = air temperature, T_s, is constant;
3) the temperature in the frozen zone varies linearly; and
4) the density of ice is the same as that of water.

Then, similarly as in the Neumann theory, the principal differential equation for the frozen soil ($o < x < \xi$) is

$$\frac{\partial T_1}{\partial t} = \alpha_1 \cdot \frac{\partial^2 T_1}{\partial x^2}. \tag{17-1}$$

There is no second equation as in the Neumann theory.
The boundary conditions in this case are

1) at $x = 0$, $T_1 = T_s$, (17-2a)
2) at $x = \xi$, $T_1 = T_f = 32°\text{F}$, and (17-2b)
3) the continuity condition for the flow of heat reduces to

$$\frac{d\xi}{dt} = \frac{1}{Q_L \cdot \rho_s \cdot w} \cdot \left[K_1 \cdot \frac{\partial T}{\partial x}\right]_{x=\xi} \tag{17-2c}$$

as compared with Equation (16-9). Here, again, the quantity ($\rho_s \cdot w$) is the amount of moisture in the soil. The following equation

$$T_1 = T_f + C \int_X^{\delta} (e^{-\beta^2}) \cdot d\beta \tag{17-3}$$

is a particular solution of the general differential Equation (17-1) (5, 6, 7) for the boundary conditions (17-2a), (17-2b) and (17-2c). Here $X = x \cdot \eta$, and C and δ are two constants.

The boundary condition (17-2a) requires that

$$T_s = T_f + C \int_0^\delta (e^{-\beta^2}) \cdot d\beta \tag{17-3a}$$

(for $x = 0$). From here, the relationship between C and δ is established. The physical nature of the problem implies that C must be negative.

The boundary condition at $x = \xi$ (17-2b) indicates that the upper and lower limits (δ and $x \cdot \eta$, respectively) of the integral in Equation (17-3) must be equal, i.e.,

$$\delta = x \cdot \eta = \xi \cdot \eta = \frac{\xi}{2 \cdot \sqrt{\alpha_1 \cdot t}}. \tag{17-4}$$

Hence, the frost penetration depth, ξ, is

$$\xi = 2 \cdot \delta \cdot \sqrt{\alpha_1 \cdot t}. \tag{17-4a}$$

Comparing the frost penetration depths as computed by Neumann and Stefan

$$\xi_N = m_N \cdot \sqrt{t}, \tag{16-12}$$

$$\xi_{St} = 2 \cdot \delta \sqrt{\alpha_1} \cdot \sqrt{t} = m_{St} \cdot \sqrt{t}, \tag{17-4b}$$

it can be seen that both expressions are of similar construction, namely, the frost penetration depth is directly proportional to the square root of time.

The upper limit, δ, of the integral (17-3) is determined by reasoning as follows:

Because the temperature in the frozen zone is a function of two variables—position or x-coordinate and time, i.e., $T_1 = f(x,t)$—the total differential of T_1 is

$$d(T_1) = \frac{\partial T_1}{\partial x} \cdot dx + \frac{\partial T_1}{\partial t} \cdot dt. \tag{17-5}$$

At $x = \xi$, for $T_f = 32°\text{F} = \text{const}$, this differential is zero (see boundary condition, Equation (17-2b):

$$\frac{\partial T_1}{\partial t} + \frac{\partial T_1}{\partial x} \cdot \frac{d\xi}{dt} = 0. \tag{17-6}$$

Substituting $\frac{d\xi}{dt}$ from Equation (17-2c) into Equation (17-6), we obtain

$$\frac{\partial T_1}{\partial t} = -\frac{K_1}{Q_L \cdot \rho_s \cdot w} \cdot \left(\frac{\partial T_1}{\partial x}\right)^2. \tag{17-7}$$

By differentiating Equation (17-3), we have

$$\frac{\partial T_1}{\partial t} = C \cdot (e^{-x^2 \cdot \eta^2}) \cdot \left(\frac{x \cdot \eta}{2 \cdot t}\right) = C \cdot \left(e^{-\frac{x^2}{4 \cdot \alpha_1 \cdot t}}\right) \cdot \left(\frac{x}{4 \cdot t \cdot \sqrt{\alpha_1 \cdot t}}\right). \tag{17-8}$$

$$\frac{\partial T_1}{\partial x} = -C \cdot (e^{-x^2 \eta^2}) \cdot \eta = C \cdot \left(e^{-\frac{x^2}{4 \cdot \alpha_1 \cdot t}}\right) \cdot \left(\frac{1}{2 \cdot \sqrt{\alpha_1 \cdot t}}\right). \tag{17-8a}$$

Because $\delta = x \cdot \eta$, then $x = \xi = \dfrac{\delta}{\eta} = 2 \cdot \delta \cdot \sqrt{\alpha_1 \cdot t}$. (17-4a)

Substitution of Equations (17-4a), (17-8) and (17-8a) into Equation (17-7) gives

$$\left(\frac{\delta}{2 \cdot t}\right) \cdot C \cdot (e^{-\delta^2}) = -\frac{K_1}{Q_L \cdot \rho_s \cdot w} \cdot \eta^2 \cdot C^2 \cdot [e^{-2 \cdot (\delta)^2}], \tag{17-9}$$

and substitution of C from Equation (17-3a) into (17-9) gives

$$\delta \cdot (e^{\delta^2}) \cdot \int_0^{\delta} (e^{-\beta^2}) \cdot d\beta = -\frac{c_1}{2 \cdot Q_L \cdot w} \cdot (T_s - T_f), \tag{17-10}$$

since

$$\alpha_1 = \frac{K_1}{\rho_s \cdot c_1}.$$

Expanding the quantity $(e^{-\beta^2})$ in series and integrating each term of the series separately, it is possible to evaluate the constant δ.

$$\int_0^{\delta} (e^{-\beta^2}) \cdot d\beta = \delta - \frac{\delta^3}{1\,!\,3} + \frac{\delta^5}{2\,!\,5} - \frac{\delta^7}{3\,!\,7} + \ldots \approx \delta \cdot \left(1 - \frac{\delta^2}{3}\right).$$

$$(e^{\delta^2}) = 1 + \delta^2 + \frac{\delta^4}{2} + \frac{\delta^6}{3} + \ldots \approx (1 + \delta^2).$$

$$\delta \cdot (e^{\delta^2}) \cdot \int_0^{\delta} (e^{-\beta^2}) \cdot d\beta =$$

$$= \delta \cdot (1 + \delta^2) \cdot \delta \cdot \left(1 - \frac{\delta^2}{3}\right) \approx \delta^2 \cdot \left(1 + \frac{2}{3} \cdot \delta^2\right). \tag{17-11}$$

Then, by Equation (17-10), the first approximation, δ^2, yields

$$\delta^2 = -\frac{c_1}{2 \cdot Q_L \cdot w} \cdot (T_s - T_f), \tag{17-12}$$

and the frost penetration depth, ξ, is (see Equation (17-4a)).

$$\xi = \sqrt{\frac{2 \cdot c_1}{Q_L \cdot w} \cdot (T_f - T_s) \cdot \alpha_1 \cdot t}. \tag{17-13}$$

It is interesting to observe that if in the Neumann Equation (16-23) we set $T_o = 32°F$, and if we set $m = 2 \cdot \delta \cdot \sqrt{\alpha_1}$, we get the simplified Stefan's solution (Equation 16-10). From this we may conclude that Stefan's solution is merely a special case of Neumann's theory.

The second approximation:

$$(\delta^2) \cdot \left(1 + \frac{2}{3} \cdot \delta^2\right) = -\frac{c_1}{2 \cdot Q_L \cdot w} \cdot (T_s - T_f) \tag{17-14}$$

enables us to calculate δ, and finally ξ.

SPECIAL CASE

When the conditions are such that the temperature gradient in the frozen zone (= ice layer) is linear, the thickness of the ice sheet can be calculated simply as follows:

The amount of heat that flows upward per unit area through the frozen layer (= ice) in time dt is

$$K_1 \cdot \frac{(T_f - T_s)}{\xi} \cdot dt. \tag{17-15}$$

This amount of heat is equal to that released when the thickness of the ice sheet increases by $d\xi$; thus

$$K_1 \cdot \frac{(T_f - T_s)}{\xi} \cdot dt = Q_L \cdot \rho_1 \cdot d\xi. \tag{17-16}$$

Separation of variables gives

$$\xi \cdot d\xi = \frac{K_1}{Q_L \cdot \rho_1} \cdot (T_f - T_s) \cdot dt. \tag{17-17}$$

Integrating this, assuming that the frozen zone (= ice layer) of thickness ξ is zero when time t is zero, we obtain

$$\int_o^\xi \xi \cdot d\xi = \frac{K_1}{Q_L \cdot \rho_1} \cdot (T_f - T_s) \cdot \int_o^t dt,$$

and the frost penetration depth is

$$\xi = \sqrt{\frac{2 \cdot K_1}{Q_L \cdot \rho_1} \cdot (T_f - T_s) \cdot t}, \tag{17-18}$$

or

$$\xi = \sqrt{\frac{2 \cdot c_1 \cdot \alpha_1}{Q_L} \cdot (T_f - T_s) \cdot t}. \tag{17-18a}$$

If the soil possesses a porosity, n, and the soil is saturated corresponding to a moisture content of w, then, instead of Q_L, a quantity of $(n \cdot Q_L)$ is to be used in formulas (17-16) through (17-19). The first derivative of ξ with respect to time, t, gives the rate of the frost penetration:

$$\frac{d\xi}{dt} = \sqrt{\frac{K_1 \cdot (T_f - T_s)}{2 \cdot Q_L \cdot \rho_1}} \cdot \frac{1}{\sqrt{t}}. \tag{17-19}$$

Comparing Equation (17-18a) with Equation (17-13), it can be seen that both equations are equal, if a saturated state ($n \equiv w$) is considered.

Illustrative Problem. The frost penetration depth is to be determined by means of Stefan's first approximation.

Assume: $K_1 = 1.34$ [(B) · (ft)$^{-2}$ · (F)$^{-1}$ · hr^{-1}/ft] for frozen soil,

$Q_L = 144 \left[\frac{\text{B}}{\text{lb}}\right]$,

$w = 0.33$ = saturation moisture content by dry weight,

$\gamma_w = 62.4 \left[\frac{\text{lb}}{\text{ft}^3}\right]$ for water,

$e = 0.50$,

$T_s = 14°\text{F}$,

$T_f = 32°\text{F}$,

$t = 7$ days $= 168$ hr,

$\rho_1 = w \cdot \gamma_w$ = weight of saturation water in soil.

Then, by Equation (17-13) or (17-18) the frost penetration depth, ξ, is

$$\xi = \sqrt{\frac{2K_1}{Q_L \cdot w \cdot \rho_1} \cdot (T_f - T_s) \cdot t} =$$

$$= \sqrt{\frac{(2) \cdot (1.34) \cdot (32 - 14)}{(144) \cdot (0.33) \cdot (62.4)}} \cdot \sqrt{168} = (0.1275) \cdot (12.965) = 1.65 \text{ [ft]}.$$

Here, $m_{St} = 0.127$.

Comparing this result with 1.5 ft, as obtained by means of Neumann's theory, it can be seen that in this example, Stefan's solution gives $\frac{1.65}{1.50} = 1.10$, 10% greater frost penetration depth than that calculated by means of the Neumann theory.

RÉSUMÉ

Neumann's theory is an excellent mathematical treatment of the frost penetration problem.

Neumann's and Stefan's theories are set up for a homogeneous, isotropic, semi-infinite body. Neumann considers not only the frozen part but also the unfrozen part of the soil underneath the frost boundary. The soil moisture present is motionless. This theory takes into account the density of the soil, (ρ), the moisture content of the soil (w) or the porosity (n) or voids ratio (e), the latent heat of fusion of ice (Q_L), the thermal properties of the frozen and unfrozen parts of the soil (K, c, α) and some climatic conditions (T_o, T_s, T_f, T, duration of cold, t). The Neumann theory is of particular value if the thermal properties of the frozen and unfrozen parts of the soil are known.

The whole analysis in the Neumann theory is based on some objectionable assumptions, for example, that

a) the change in density of water when converted into ice is ignored,
b) when $x = 0$, then $T_1 = T_s =$ constant,
c) when $x = \infty$, then $T_2 = T_o$, and
d) the solutions are just particular solutions of the equations.

Nevertheless the Neumann theory deserves credit as an elegant pioneering tool in that it can be adjusted with a greater or lesser degree of accuracy for the practical treatment of the complex frost penetration problem in soil. For example, it is to be noted that a good application of Neumann's theory was made by Berggren (8) in treating the prediction of temperature distribution in frozen soil.

REFERENCES

1. J. Stefan, "Über die Theorie der Eisbildung, insbesondere über die Eisbildung im Polarmeere," vol. XCVIII, no. IIa: *Sitzungsberichte der Mathematisch-Naturwissenschaftlichen Classe der Kaiserlichen Akademie der Wissenschaften,* Wien, 1890, pp. 965–983.
2. S. Tetsu Tamura, "Mathematical Theory of Ice Formation," *Monthly Weather Review and Annual Summary,* Washington, D.C., U.S. Department of Agriculture, Weather Bureau, 1906, vol. 33, February, 1905, pp. 57–59.
3. J. Keränen, "Wärme- und Temperaturverhältnisse der Obersten Bodenschichten," vol. II, *Einführung in der Geophysik,* Berlin, Springer, 1929, pp. 267–273.
4. L. R. Ingersoll, O. J. Zobel and A. C. Ingersoll, *Heat Conduction with Engineering, Geological and Other Applications,* Madison, 1954, University of Wisconsin Press, p. 194.
5. J. Keränen (see Ref. 3), p. 269.
6. J. Stefan, "Probleme der Theorie der Wärmeleitung," vol. XCVIII, no. IIa: *Sitzungsberichte der Mathematisch-Naturwissenschaftlichen Classe der Kaiserlichen Akademie der Wissenschaften,* Wien, 1890, p. 474.
7. A. R. Jumikis, *The Frost Penetration Problem in Highway Engineering,* New Brunswick, N.J., 1955, Rutgers University Press, pp. 88–93.
8. W. P. Berggren, "Prediction of Temperature Distribution in Frozen Soils," *Transactions of the American Geophysical Union,* Pt. 3, 1943, pp. 71–77.

Name Index

Subject Index

For definitions, abbreviations, and symbols, see pages 10–41 and 205–11